NON-RELATIVISTIC QUANTUM MECHANICS

Non-relativistic
QUANTUM
MECHANICS

An introduction

SECOND EDITION

R. M. SILLITTO

NEW YORK

American Elsevier Publishing Company, Inc.

© R. M. Sillitto 1960, 1967
American Elsevier Publishing Company, Inc.
52 Vanderbilt Avenue
New York, New York 10017

First edition published, 1960
Second edition published, 1967

Library of Congress Catalog Card Number 67-30430

First published by Edinburgh University Press
Printed in Great Britain

PREFACE

This book is intended for those honours students in physics who are familiar enough with the development of modern physics to accept, and perhaps welcome, a formal rather than historical approach to quantum mechanics. I have tried to show how the methods which are used when quantum mechanics is applied to particular problems emerge from or exemplify a general formalism, which itself can be inferred from the results of a small number of experiments. And I have tried to do this with the minimum of mathematical sophistication, since the students I have been writing for are not in the main specializing in mathematical physics. This has led to considerable use of matrix methods, which are simple and should be familiar to physics students at this level. Matrix and wave mechanics thus appear at the outset on an equal footing – as indeed they did in 1925 – and we can make use of the one representation or the other as convenient.

The choice of topics for detailed treatment in the later chapters was based on two considerations: firstly that some topics are so important that they must not be omitted from an undergraduate textbook – for instance the hydrogen atom, and the homopolar bond; secondly that some topics seemed to lend themselves very readily to the frankly didactic purpose of the book – thus the Stark effect offers a very manageable example of the application of a perturbation to a degenerate system, and the ground state of the helium atom provides an interesting comparison between the perturbation method and the variation method. This still leaves a good deal of freedom of choice, and I hope that mine will not be thought too eccentric. I have tried to round off the book by returning, in the last chapter, to the topics with which the book begins – the question of the wave and/or particle structure of radiation. This requires some discussion of the quantization of the electro-magnetic field, but I have not ventured into the realm of relativistic quantum mechanics, believing that this cannot at present be treated in a worth-while way in an undergraduate book.

There are two technical points that should be explained here, one of notation and one of typography:

(i) Since most honours-level text-books on electromagnetism now use MKS units – those by Bleaney and Bleaney, Sommerfeld, and Stratton are typical – I have written equations involving electrical and magnetic quantities in the form appropriate for the use of the rationalized MKS system; thus the expression for the *Coulomb potential* contains a factor $1/4\pi\varepsilon_0$, and the *Bohr magneton* is written in terms of fundamental quantities as $\mu_0 e\hbar/2m$. However, for the benefit of those of us who learnt our electromagnetism in terms of Gaussian units I have as far as possible kept intact those groups of factors, such as $4\pi\varepsilon_0$, whose deletion *as a group* will put the equations into 'Gaussian form'.

(ii) The second point concerns the use of surds. The use of the 'bar over' an algebraic expression under a surd involves slow and costly hand-setting, and is unpopular with printers and publishers. On the other hand, in complicated expressions there is ambiguity if the quantities under the surd are not separated from subsequent factors, and a rash of assorted brackets can be confusing. We have therefore, after some discussion, adopted a suggestion made in *The printing of mathematics* (O.U.P., 1954) and enclosed the quantities under the surd between the signs $\sqrt{}$ and $\backslash$, thus: $\sqrt{J(J+1)}\backslash\hbar$. Despite its unfamiliarity this will, I think, be found both unambiguous and legible.

At this point I should acknowledge the energy and skill with which Messrs Robert Cunningham and Sons Ltd. of Alva have tackled the unfamiliar problems encountered in their first use of the 'Monotype' Times Roman four-line mathematical system; and the helpfulness and patience of the staff of the Edinburgh University Press.

I am grateful to Sir Edward Appleton for his interest and encouragement. I am very deeply indebted to Professor N. Kemmer for a number of long and illuminating discussions which materially influenced the course of the transition from draft to final typescript. The residual defects of the text are my own, but some of the great deal I learned in those discussions has found its way on to these pages. I had other helpful discussions on specific points with Dr A. F. Brown, Dr P. S. Farago, Mr A. Nisbet and Dr D. L. Pursey.

Finally it is a pleasure to thank my wife, who helped me by discussing various matters of content and presentation, by sharing the chores of proof-reading and indexing, and in many other ways.

RICHARD M. SILLITTO
The University
Edinburgh
31st *March* 1960

PREFACE TO SECOND EDITION

In plan this edition of *Quantum Mechanics* closely resembles the earlier one, but large sections of the text have been rewritten, a little has been deleted, and there are some substantial additions – particularly to chapters 2, 4, 6, 9, and 11, and in an Appendix. The number of problems has been nearly doubled, and includes many which have been found to stimulate discussion in tutorials.

I am much indebted to my colleagues Dr P. S. Farago and Dr P. J. Kennedy, whose experience in teaching wave and quantum mechanics has influenced the revision of the text, in general and in detail. Dr J. K. Darby read and criticised the draft of three new sections, and Mr J. H. Aitken of the University of Toronto wrote to me on a number of points of detail; to both of them, my thanks.

Mr John McI. Davidson of the Edinburgh University Press has been at all times helpful, and patient with my unscheduled delays. Finally, it is a pleasure again to thank my wife, whose company and help lighten the more tedious tasks and make the others doubly rewarding.

RICHARD M. SILLITTO
The University
Edinburgh
31st *December* 1966

CONTENTS

CHAP.   PAGE

1 GENERAL PRINCIPLES   1

   Fundamental ideas, 1; The principle of superposition, 6; The representation of states and dynamical variables, 12; Products of
   operators; compatible and incompatible variables, 16; Continuous
   distributions of eigenvalues: wave-mechanics, 19; Quantum theory
   and probability, 22. Problems, 23.

2 THE UNCERTAINTY PRINCIPLE AND THE
   COMMUTATION RELATIONS   25

   Uncertainties and uncertainty products, 25; Commutators and
   Poisson brackets, 29; Quantum conditions, 31; Choice of operators,
   34; The time-dependent wave equation, 37; The state-function with
   the minimum uncertainty product, 38. Problems, 39.

3 THE MATRIX TREATMENT OF THE SIMPLE
   HARMONIC OSCILLATOR   41

   Time-dependence of matrix elements, 41; Matrices for H, p and x,
   42; The equation of motion of the simple harmonic oscillator, 47;
   Wave-mechanical state-functions, 49; Expectation values, 50;
   Uncertainty relations for the harmonic oscillator, 52; The oscillator
   in three dimensions; degeneracy, 53; Non-diagonal matrix elements,
   54. Problems, 56.

4 QUANTIZATION OF ANGULAR MOMENTUM   58

   Constants of the motion, 59; The eigenvalues of θ and m_3, 61; The
   half-integral quantum numbers, 65; Electron spin, 67; The spinning
   electron in a magnetic field, 68; The Stern-Gerlach experiment and
   the double Stern-Gerlach experiment, 75; Combination of angular
   momenta: resultant spin of two electrons, 77; Combination of
   orbital and spin angular momenta of a single electron: L-S coupling,
   79; Angular momentum in wave-mechanics, 86; Appendix – the
   angular momentum eigenfunctions, 89. Problems, 91.

5 THE RADIAL FUNCTION, AND THE TOTAL
   ENERGY   93

   General remarks about the radial wave-function, 93; The isotropic
   oscillator, 98; The hydrogen atom, 101; The rectangular potential
   well, 106. Problems, 114.

xi

xii CONTENTS

6 THE PERTURBATION METHOD AND THE
VARIATION METHOD IN QUANTUM STATICS 116

Methods for approximate solution of the eigenvalue equation, 116; The perturbation method, 117; State-functions and energies of the perturbed system, 118; The first-order normal Zeeman effect, 122; The first-order anomalous Zeeman effect, 123; The second-order Zeeman effect, 128; The first-order Stark effect in the hydrogen atom, 130; The second-order Stark effect, 134; The variation method, 136; Atomic polarizability by the variation method, 138. Problems, 141.

7 MANY-ELECTRON ATOMS AND THE HYDROGEN MOLECULE 143

The helium atom, 143; Symmetry and anti-symmetry of state-functions; the exclusion principle, 150; Space-and-spin functions for the helium atom, 153; Energy levels of an electron in a many-electron atom, 154; The periodic system of the elements, 156; State-functions for complex atoms: Hartree's self-consistent field, 159; The hydrogen molecule, 161. Problems, 164.

8 QUANTUM STATISTICS 166

General remarks about indistinguishability, 166; (i) Classical case – the Boltzmann statistics, 168; (ii) 'Symmetric case' – Bose-Einstein statistics, 170; Black-body radiation, 171; Bose-Einstein gas in equilibrium, 173; (iii) 'Anti-symmetric case' – Fermi-Dirac statistics, 175; The electron gas in a metal, 178; The Thomas-Fermi model of the atom, 180. Problems, 182.

9 THE MOTION OF A PARTICLE IN WAVE-MECHANICS 184

Representation of a particle by a wave-packet, 184; Oscillating wave-packet, 186; Motion of a wave-packet in a field of force, 187; Expectation velocity and group velocity of a wave-packet, 189; Probability current density, 192; Penetration of potential barriers, 194; The WKB method, 198; State-functions for a conduction electron in a metal, 203; Effective mass of a conduction electron, 208; Momentum, kinetic energy, and effective mass, 212. Problems, 216.

10 TIME-DEPENDENT PERTURBATIONS: COLLISION THEORY 218

General expression for the transition probability, 218; The cross-section for elastic scattering, 222; Rutherford's law of scattering, 226; Scattering by a spherical potential well, 228; The Born approximation and the classical description, 229; Validity of the Born approximation, 231; The method of partial waves, 233; The partial-wave method for the spherical potential well, 236. Problems, 238.

CHAP.   PAGE

11 TIME-DEPENDENT PERTURBATIONS: SEMI-
CLASSICAL TREATMENT OF RADIATION
PROBLEMS   240

Interaction of atomic electron with electromagnetic radiation, 240;
The dipole approximation, 244; Dipole moments for circularly
polarized radiation, 247; Dipole selection rules, 249; Forbidden
transitions, 256; Optical dispersion, 258. Problems, 261.

12 THE QUANTIZATION OF RADIATION   264

Hamiltonian representation of the classical electromagnetic field,
264; Hamiltonian representation of a quantized wave field, 267;
Interaction of radiation with an atom, 271; The photoelectric effect,
274; The validity of the classical representation of the electromagnetic
field: (i) the radio aerial, 277; (ii) classical wave-theory for optical
interference experiments, 280. Problems, 282.

APPENDIX – THE DENSITY MATRIX   284

Purpose of density matrix techniques, 284; Calculation of expectation values for an ensemble, 000; Trace relations for the density
matrix, 000; Equation of motion for the density matrix, 000; Time-
dependence of the matrix elements of ρ, 000; Entropy, and thermal
equilibrium, 000; Polarization of electron beams, 000; Larmor precession of the electron polarization, 000; Polarization of ensembles of
systems other than electrons, 000; Scattering of light, 000.

BACKGROUND READING AND FURTHER STUDY   310

INDEX   311

CHAPTER ONE

GENERAL PRINCIPLES

Fundamental ideas

By the end of the first decade of this century there was strong evidence that the concepts of classical mechanics were not a satisfactory basis for the description of nature. A number of phenomena – the stability of atoms, the spectral distribution of black-body radiation, the photoelectric effect, optical dispersion, paramagnetism – could not be explained in classical terms. One possible explanation for these failures would have been that the concepts of classical mechanics and classical electrodynamics did not provide a sufficiently comprehensive logical foundation for the discussion of such phenomena. Critical investigations, however, showed that the explanation was not to be found along these lines: the concepts and logical structure of classical physical theory were quite adequate for the tasks of making unambiguous predictions about, say, the spectrum of black-body radiation (Jeans, 1910) or the magnetic susceptibility of matter in bulk (Bohr, 1911; van Leeuwen, 1919), but these predictions were irreconcilable with observation. The next twenty years saw the evolution of a new technique for representing the phenomena of physics, and this technique is called *quantum mechanics*. This new mechanics, which uses concepts different from those of classical physics, and operates with them according to different rules, has been outstandingly successful in the description of phenomena on the atomic and molecular scale, and it is constructed in such a way as to contain classical mechanics as a limiting form, applicable to large-scale systems.

The formulation of quantum mechanics was preceded by attempts to explain the phenomena referred to above by various independent *ad hoc* theories – such as Bohr's orbital atomic model, the hypothesis of light quanta, and Langevin's theory of paramagnetism. One feature which all these *ad hoc* theories had in common was their (at least partial) abandonment, at some vital point, of the classical

1

notion of continuity. In fact, the adoption of the atomic hypothesis about a century before, and the subsequent discovery of the discrete nature of electric charge, marked the beginnings of the abandonment of the idea that physical quantities are always continuously variable. But it was not until the discoveries of the twentieth century forced the realisation that discontinuity and discreteness was a characteristic of most phenomena on the microscopic (i.e. molecular and atomic) scale, that attempts were made to modify the physicist's whole description of nature so as to include discontinuity as one of its necessary elements.

The new modes of description required new modes of thought – as was said earlier, as compared with classical mechanics quantum mechanics uses different concepts and operates with them according to different rules. Any mixing of the classical with the quantal, such as the application of classical modes of thought to quantal concepts, is liable to lead to confusion. Thus, for instance, the introduction of the idea of light quanta in the explanations of the black-body radiation spectrum and of the photoelectric effect suggested the visualization of a beam of light as a stream of corpuscular photons. But this representation, if taken 'literally' (i.e. classically) could not be reconciled with the facts of interference and diffraction. In particular, the experiment of G. I. Taylor on diffraction at very low light intensities (1909), and later more refined interference experiments by Dempster and Batho (1927) and by Janossy and Naray (1957), show that diffraction and interference patterns are produced exactly as predicted by classical wave-optics even when the light intensities are so low that only one photon can be passing through the optical system at any one time. At high light intensities the classical wave-theory therefore predicts the statistical distribution of photons over the screen on which the diffraction or interference pattern is observed, and at low light intensities it predicts the relative probabilities of arrival at the various parts of the screen for individual photons. These predictions are made by superposing wavefunctions which represent, in the classical theory, the portions of the wave-front which travel from the light-source to the screen by the different paths which the geometry of the interferometer (say) allows. *If the beam of light consists of indivisible photons* any one photon must, according to classical ideas, make the journey from source to screen by one or other of the possible light paths, and not by both (or all) of them at once; yet G. I. Taylor's experiment shows that the probability of the arrival of a single photon at a given point on the screen depends on the simultaneous arrangement of *all* the possible light paths. If we try to think in terms of indivisible photons we are thus confronted with the difficulty of explaining why the ultimate location of a photon depends on the paths it does not traverse as much as on the one it does. The discovery of electron diffraction (1927) showed that material particles have wave properties, and behave in a way incompatible with the predictions of classical mechanics, and experiments by G. P. Thomson (1927) and more recently by Fabrikant and others (1949) show that normal electron diffraction patterns are produced by electron beams so weak that only one electron at a time passes through the apparatus. The classical concept of a precisely defined path or trajectory is evidently as inapplicable to electrons as it is to photons – it is in fact inapplicable throughout microphysics.

To resolve the conflicts which result from the apparent necessity for both the wave and particle representations, we have to abandon the precise specification of the 'state of a system' which is used in classical mechanics. According to classical mechanics it is possible in principle to specify the state of a system at a particular instant by giving the instantaneous values of the position and momentum coordinates for all the degrees of freedom of the system. The fact that such a specification may not always be practicable is beside the point. The measurements of the positions and momenta are, it is true, subject to experimental error, but *in principle* experimental uncertainties can be reduced without limit, and the interactions between the observed system and the measuring apparatus can be made negligible or allowed for by exact calculations. According to the ideas of quantum mechanics the situation is very different. Quantum theory starts from the recognition of a discrete structure – a 'graininess' – in nature, which precludes the infinite precision which is implied in the classical specification of a state.

The limitation which this graininess imposes on the precision of measurements can be illustrated in a number of ways. For instance, an observer who wanted to make a precise determination of the position of a small particle which was initially at rest, might illuminate it with light of short wavelength λ, and view the image formed by the scattered light in a microscope with a large numerical aperture. Now each quantum of the short wavelength radiation has the energy hc/λ, which is 'large' – on the appropriate scale – if λ is small.

(h, of course, is Planck's constant, and c is the speed of light.) Since any energy flow has an associated momentum each quantum has a momentum, which is in fact h/λ (see p. 269). The scattering of the light by the particle which is being observed is, on this model, the result of a collision between the particle and the photon, and in this collision there will be a transfer of momentum. How much momentum is transferred cannot be decided precisely; even if the initial direction of motion of the photon was known, all we know about the direction after the collision is that the photon entered the microscope objective, and since the numerical aperture is large this leaves a large uncertainty about the direction. The momentum transferred to the particle is correspondingly uncertain. We conclude that an experiment which measures the position of the particle with high precision can give at the same time only imprecise information about its momentum. If the observer had used light of longer wavelength, and a microscope with a smaller numerical aperture, there would have been less uncertainty about the effect of the measurement on the momentum of the particle, but the position would be determined less precisely because the resolving power of the microscope would be less. If the objective subtends an angle 2θ at the particle, the uncertainty in the determination of position, due to the limited resolving power, is $\lambda/\sin\theta$; the uncertainty in the observer's knowledge of the momentum transfer in the collision, due to the size of the acceptance angle of the objective, is roughly $\sin\theta \cdot h/\lambda$. The product of these uncertainties is $\approx h$.

As another example we could consider an experiment to determine the momentum of a particle whose position was known. Suppose the particle is an atom in an excited state, and the frequency of the radiation it emits as it decays to the ground state is measured. If it is known that the frequency would be v_0 if the atom were at rest, and the frequency is observed to be v, the discrepancy can be explained as a Doppler effect indicating that the atom is moving with speed $v=c(v-v_0)/v_0$. The accurate measurement of a frequency requires a time τ which is long relative to the period $1/v$. In fact, if the measurement extends over a time τ the minimum uncertainty in the frequency determination is $\Delta v \approx 1/\tau$, so the minimum uncertainty in the momentum deduced from this measurement must be $\Delta p = m\Delta v = mc/\tau v_0$. Now the moment at which the atom emits the quantum is uncertain by τ; at the moment of emission the momentum of the atom changes by the momentum of the emitted photon hv/c, so the position of the atom is subsequently uncertain by an amount $\Delta x = \tau \cdot hv/mc$. Then as long as v is not much different from v_0, as will certainly be the case for an atom emitting visible radiation, the irreducible product of the uncertainties in position and momentum is once again $\approx h$.

Dynamical variables whose values cannot be precisely known at the same time are said to be *incompatible*. Arguments like those of the two preceding paragraphs show that the position and momentum of a free particle are incompatible variables. In optical interference experiments the position of a photon and its wavelength are incompatible variables: we can find the wavelength of the light passing through an interferometer only as long as we make no attempt to find out which path a photon traverses. Any modification of the interferometer which enables the detection of a photon in one light path disturbs, in a random and unpredictable way, the phase relations on whose constancy the production of interference depends. For instance, if the mirrors at the ends of the two arms of a Michelson interferometer are so delicately mounted that the reflection of a photon in one path or other is shown by the recoil of the corresponding mirror, the interference pattern must disappear because of the consequent Doppler shift of the frequency of the reflected light in that path, and we cannot determine the wavelength.

It follows that in quantum mechanics the state of a system cannot be specified with the precision to which we are accustomed in classical mechanics, where all variables are assumed to be compatible. The irreducible imprecision in the specification is related to Planck's constant h, which can be regarded as the 'unit of grain size' in quantum mechanical events. The description of the state of a system at a particular instant t_0 is therefore cast in the form of a statement involving probabilities – to say that x is uncertain by $\pm \Delta x$, and that p is uncertain by $\pm \Delta p$, is to assert that there is a distribution-in-x whose breadth, defined in some conventional way, is proportional to Δx, and that there is a distribution-in-p whose conventionally-defined breadth is proportional to Δp; and the fact that it is Planck's constant which measures the minimum value of the product of the statistical parameters Δx and Δp indicates the essentially statistical nature of quantum theory. Since the quantum mechanical specification of the state of a system at an instant t_0 is, in this way, imprecise, it follows that all we can expect to predict about (say) the value of a particular position coordinate at some later time $t_0 + \delta t$ will also be in the form of a statement about probabilities. (If we could not even make statements of that kind, there would be no causality, and therefore no science as we know it.) The typical problem which quantum mechanics enables us to solve is this: If the state of a system is known at some instant, what are the possible results of any subsequent measurement on that system, and what are the probabilities of these several possible results?

The state of a system, in quantum mechanics, is then described by whatever information we need to have about that specific system to enable us to predict, with the aid of general physical laws, the behaviour of that system in future experiments or observations. As we have seen, the predictions we should be able to make are of a statistical kind; this is a fundamental aspect of quantum mechanics, and should not make us suspect that our description is incomplete. The specification of the state is complete, and the state is fully identified, if the information we have about it (whether in the form of data or a state-function) is sufficient to enable us to predict the statistical results of *all conceivable experiments* on the system. In general a prediction about the measurement of some specified dynamical variable will be in the form of a probability distribution over a possible range or set of values of that variable. But we shall find that for certain particular states of a system our theory predicts that the results of certain measurements will be unique, and certain. These are measurements of compatible variables, and they are of particular importance, for the greatest amount of information that we can have about the state of a system is that contained in the statement of the outcome of all those compatible observations which give unique and certain results. A state specified by the values of all possible mutually compatible variables has its properties known with the greatest definiteness that the laws of quantum physics allow; it is called a *pure state*. The state may be represented in a great variety of ways, for example by a set of numbers corresponding to the certain values of the compatible variables, or by a *state-function* from which these values can be deduced by specified mathematical procedures.

The principle of superposition

In the light of the ideas developed so far, we shall now consider, in classical and in quantal terms, the passage of a polarized beam of light through an analyser, and we shall see that it is possible to represent the quantal – that is, the statistical and indeterministic – aspects of this process by means of a formalism which is sufficiently closely related to the classical description to ensure a measure of correspondence between the two descriptions. The analogous experiment with polarized electrons will be discussed later, in chapter 4.

Suppose a horizontally directed beam of light emerges from a Nicol prism with its plane of polarization making an angle θ with the vertical, and then enters a second Nicol prism set to transmit vertically polarized light. The fraction of the incident light which emerges from this second Nicol prism is observed to be $\cos^2\theta$, and the fraction which is stopped by it is $\sin^2\theta$. In terms of classical wave optics we say that the electric vector of the light emerging from the polarizer is inclined at the angle θ to the vertical and has vertical and horizontal components $\mathscr{E}_y = \mathscr{E} \cos \theta$ and $\mathscr{E}_x = \mathscr{E} \sin \theta$ respectively. The vertical component alone is transmitted by the analyser, so the intensity of the transmitted light is to that of the incident light as $(\mathscr{E} \cos \theta)^2 : (\mathscr{E})^2$; hence the fraction transmitted is $\cos^2\theta$. And one other important result is consistent with this explanation – that the light emerging from the analyser is vertically polarized.

Any interpretation of this experiment which we try to construct in terms of photons must lead to the same conclusions. Let the state of polarization of a photon emerging from the polarizer be denoted by π_θ, and let the states of horizontal and vertical polarization be denoted by π_x and π_y. The analyser can now be regarded as an instrument which sorts photons into two classes – those in the state π_x, which it does not transmit, and those in the state π_y, which it does transmit. Then a photon which is incident on the analyser in the state π_θ must have a probability $\cos^2\theta$ of being transmitted, after which it is certainly in the state π_y; and a probability $\sin^2\theta$ of being not transmitted, after which it is certainly in the state π_x – as could be verified by a further analysis of the light reflected sideways out of the Nicol prism. The individual photon is not divided into reflected and transmitted fractions, each fraction behaving in a classically determinate way; rather, the behaviour of each individual photon is indeterminate, only the *probabilities* of its behaving in one or other of two mutually exclusive ways being predictable. And since, according as the photon is transmitted or reflected it could be shown by a subsequent analysis to be certainly in the state π_y or π_x

respectively, it is reasonable to suggest that the state π_θ must always be capable of being represented as some sort of superposition of π_y and π_x, rather analogous to the representation of the electric vector $\mathscr{E}$ as a superposition of components $\mathscr{E}_y$ and $\mathscr{E}_x$.

We shall suppose, tentatively, that this superposition is of the simplest possible kind, which is a *linear superposition*, and recall that in the classical description the field amplitudes superpose linearly. Thus if $\hat{y}$ and $\hat{x}$ are unit vectors in the vertical and horizontal directions we could write

$$\mathscr{E} = \mathscr{E} \cos \theta \hat{y} + \mathscr{E} \sin \theta \hat{x}$$

while the intensities of the light transmitted and reflected by the analyser are $(\mathscr{E} \cos \theta)^2$ and $(\mathscr{E} \sin \theta)^2$. We can maintain a close parallelism between the classical and quantal formalisms at this point if we write the relationship between π_θ, π_y and π_x as

$$\pi_\theta = \cos \theta \cdot \pi_y + \sin \theta \cdot \pi_x.$$

Since the probability that a photon with polarization π_θ will be transmitted with polarization π_y by the analyser is $\cos^2\theta$, and the probability that it is reflected out of the transmitted beam with polarization π_x is $\sin^2\theta$, this case at any rate suggests that it should be the squares of the coefficients in the linear superposition which represent the probabilities of the different outcomes of the measurement. However, if the light incident on the analysing Nicol prism were elliptically polarized, with (in the classical description) components $\mathscr{E}\varepsilon^{i\delta} \cos \theta$ and $\mathscr{E}\varepsilon^{-i\delta} \sin \theta$, the intensities of the vertically and horizontally polarized components, being necessarily real, would be $|\,\mathscr{E}\varepsilon^{i\delta} \cos \theta\,|^2$ and $|\,\mathscr{E}\varepsilon^{-i\delta} \sin \theta\,|^2$. In such a case it might be convenient to write the quantal superposition relation as

$$\pi_{\text{elliptic pol.}} = \varepsilon^{i\delta} \cos \theta\, \pi_y + \varepsilon^{-i\delta} \sin \theta\, \pi_x,$$

and to take the squares of the moduli of the coefficients on the right hand side as the measures of the probabilities of transmission and non-transmission.

We shall now extend the symbolism we have just introduced, to deal with more complicated situations. Let us denote by a set of symbols π_i those states of a system in which the variable p has the corresponding unique values p_i, assuming for the present that the p_i are all different. In relation to the measurement of p, the π_i evidently represent what we have previously called pure states. We want to represent, with the aid of the π_i, a state for which the measurement of p may yield any of the values p_i, with respective probabilities $P(p_i)$. In the light of our discussion of the optical polarization experiment it seems natural to suppose that this general state, which we shall denote by ψ, should be represented by a linear superposition of the π_i, thus:

$$\psi = \sum_i a_i \pi_i \qquad (1.1)$$

where the a_i are related to the probabilities of the various results p_i. In particular, if p_j is a possible result of the measurement, but a_j in the above summation is zero, then the possibility of getting the value p_j is not represented in the summation and the state represented by ψ is then a state for which this result has probability zero. Also, if ψ represents a state in which the measurement of p *certainly* gives the result p_j, this state must be π_j, so (1.1) in this case becomes $\psi = \pi_j$, all the a_i now being zero except for a_j, which is unity. The limiting values 1 and 0 for the coefficients in (1.1) correspond therefore to probabilities of 1 and 0, and it will be consistent with our description of the polarization experiment to suppose that the probability of a measurement of p yielding the result p_i is $|a_i|^2$. Since the sum of the probabilities of all possible p_i must be unity we must have

$$\sum_i |a_i|^2 = 1. \qquad (1.2)$$

Equation (1.1), along with the rules for using and interpreting it – rules which we have only begun to formulate – is called the *principle of superposition of states*. In classical mechanics, too, there is a principle of superposition of states, but its content is entirely different. The contrast is perhaps best brought out if we recall the wording used by Daniel Bernoulli when he stated the classical principle (1755) as the principle of the 'coexistence of small motions'. In classical physics a system whose dynamical properties are represented by a linear differential equation may perform motions represented by the various independent solutions of the differential equation – called in vibration problems the *normal modes of vibration* – and it may also perform more complex motions represented by linear combinations of the independent solutions. These complex motions are set up by exciting simultaneously two or more normal modes, which therefore co-exist. The outcome of any measurement on the system is completely determinate, and will not in general be the same as would be obtained if only one normal mode were excited. The quantum mechanical principle of superposition, on the other hand, deals with the probabilities of getting one or other of a number of *mutually exclusive* results – not 'some combination of $p_1, p_2 \ldots p_n$' but rather 'either p_1 or p_2 or $\ldots p_n$'. The idea of indeterminacy is therefore built into the interpretation of the superposition principle, and is therefore fundamental in the theory which we build up from this starting point.

We can further exemplify the use of the principle of superposition by considering a two-beam interference experiment. In an ideally simple electron interference experiment it might be arranged that electrons emitted from a source could travel to a fluorescent screen through an apparatus which allowed them two alternative paths, e.g. the electron-optical analogue of the Fresnel biprism experiment, first performed by Möllenstedt and Düker (1956). Since we cannot be certain by which path any electron travels to the screen to produce interference – and indeed the experiments of Taylor, Fabrikant *et al.*, etc., show that the question is not meaningful – we must represent what is known about the state of motion of the electron by a superposition of state symbols representing the two alternatives, say

$$\psi = a_1 \psi_1 + a_2 \psi_2.$$

If the functions represented by these symbols are to enable us to predict the interference pattern they must be wave-functions similar to those encountered in classical interference optics, where the square of the modulus of the (possibly complex) amplitude represents the intensity of the wave. In this specific application the intensity of the electron beam in either path must be proportional to the probability of observing an electron there, in conformity with our postulate that the squares of the coefficients in the statement of the superposition principle represent the probabilities that the corresponding values of the quantity p will be the result of a measurement made on a system in the state ψ.

Now let us suppose that a very large number of systems are all in a state ψ, which is represented through (1.1) as a superposition of the states which correspond to all possible results of the measurement of p. (For instance, the 'systems' might be the atoms in an atomic beam, and the p_i might be the components of their angular momenta along the direction of a magnetic field.) Then the $|a_i|^2$

taken all together represent the distribution-in-p of the results of the measurement of p for all the systems; conversely, if p is measured for every system the frequencies of the various results determine the $| a_i |^2$ (but not the associated phases). All the statistical parameters of the distribution are definite, and may be inferred from the results of the measurements: for instance, if the probabilities $| a_i |^2$ of the various p_i are found we can compute the mean and mean-square values of p as

$$\bar{p} = \sum_i | a_i |^2 p_i, \quad \overline{p^2} = \sum_i | a_i |^2 p_i{}^2. \tag{1.3}$$

If the word 'measurement' in the preceding paragraph is understood to mean a sorting or selection process, all those systems for which the result of the measurement is p_i are thereafter certainly in the state π_i, and a repetition of the measurement on all such systems will again give the result p_i. For example, in the Stern-Gerlach experiment a beam of silver atoms was separated into two beams travelling in slightly different directions, all the atoms in one beam having their magnetic moments pointing upwards (say) and those in the other beam having their magnetic moments pointing downwards. The repeatability of this process shows in the fact that if either of these separated beams were passed through a second analysing field parallel to the first, the direction of the magnetic moments would not change. In general, though, the state of a quantum mechanical system is changed in an unpredictable way when the system interacts with any macroscopic apparatus; as we saw earlier, the making of a measurement may change the amount or nature of our knowledge of the state of the system. Referring again to the Stern-Gerlach experiment, if the atoms in either of the separated beams are made to register their presence by interacting with a macroscopic detector, such as a particle counter, this interaction destroys the 'purity' of the state and randomizes the directions of the magnetic moments. (Such questions are discussed generally in Landau and Lifshitz: *Quantum Mechanics*, Pergamon Press, 1958, chapter 1, section 7, and more fully by H. S. Green in *Nuovo Cimento*, 1958, **9**, p. 880 *et seq.*)

Throughout the greater part of this book we shall be concerned with systems in pure states, states, that is, which can be specified by the values of all mutually compatible variables, and can be represented by a state-function. Frequently, however, it is necessary to predict the behaviour in a prescribed experimental situation of an assembly of systems whose state is not as well defined as this – for example, an unpolarized light beam, or an atomic beam in which the energies and total angular momenta of the atoms are all the same but the directions of their magnetic moments are randomly distributed. One method of dealing with such a case is to represent the *impure* or *mixed* state as an *incoherent superposition* of pure states, a superposition, that is, which differs from (1.1) in that the phases of the coefficients are regarded as random variables, so that the calculation of the average value (say) of a variable p involves an extra process of averaging over the phases. An alternative method, which is proving very powerful, is to represent the 'impure state' by a *density matrix*; a brief introduction to this technique is given in an Appendix, pp. 284-309.

The representation of states and dynamical variables

Equation (1.1), expressing the superposition principle, resembles the expression for a vector ψ in terms of its components. If the π_i were a set of orthogonal unit vectors in an n-dimensional space, and the a_i were the lengths of the components of ψ along the various π_i, (1.2) would then assert that ψ also is a unit vector – and implies that it must be the direction, rather than the standardized length, of this vector that characterizes the state. Now the π_i, by definition, represent states in each of which the variable p has a unique and definite value, which for the present we assume to be different for each state. According to the superposition principle any state for which the measurement of p may yield any one of a number of values must be able to be represented as a sum of the corresponding π_i with amplitudes a_i. A state for which this measurement can give only one result, say p_j, must be simply the state π_j. It follows that there is no way of writing π_j as a superposition of the other π_i. For this to be true π_j must be linearly independent of all the other π_i, and this argument can be applied in turn to each of the π_i, to show that the unit vectors representing states for which the variable p has different values must all be linearly independent.

In the previous section we saw that the effect of performing a measurement on a system was often, though not invariably, to change the state of the system. Now let α and β be two n-dimensional vectors and let P symbolize the operation of transforming α into β; whatever the nature of this operation may be, whether rotation, translation, extension or contraction, or any combination of these, we can symbolize the process by writing

$$P\alpha = \beta. \tag{1.4}$$

Then if, in addition, the operator denoted by P is such that, for any two vectors like α and β, say ψ and ϕ, and for any constant a,

$$P(\psi + \phi) = P\psi + P\phi$$

and $\qquad\qquad P(a\psi) = a \cdot P\psi,$

P is said to be a *linear operator*; the components of β in (1.4) are then linearly related to the components of α, so that the ith component of β can be expressed as

$$\beta_i = \sum_j P_{ij}\,\alpha_j \tag{1.5}$$

where the P_{ij} are independent of α and β and can be written as a matrix array. For such an operator there may be certain vectors $\pi_i{}'$ such that

$$P\,\pi_i{}' = p_i{}'\,\pi_i{}' \tag{1.6}$$

where the $p_i{}'$ are numbers which may be complex. We see then that the effect of operating on a vector with a linear operator is in general to transform it into a different vector, but that there are special vectors – vectors specially related to the operator, that is – for which the effect of the operator is simply to multiply the vector by a (possibly complex) number. These special vectors, defined by (1.6), are called the *eigenvectors* of the operator, and the numbers $p_i{}'$ are called the *eigenvalues* of the operator.

It might be useful, then, to try to associate an operator P with a dynamical variable p of the system whose state is represented by the vector ψ. The eigenvectors of the operator might be associated with the states in which p has unique and definite values, and the corresponding eigenvalues of P might appropriately be associated with the corresponding values of p. It would, however, be undesirable to use a *complex* eigenvalue to represent the single result of a measurement, since a complex number requires two real numbers for its specification. It will avoid this difficulty if we decide to confine our attention to those linear operators which have real eigenvalues. Such operators are called *Hermitian*, or *self-adjoint*.

We shall adopt the convention that P^* denotes the *adjoint* or *complex transpose* of P; then if P is Hermitian $P^* = P$. If P is represented by a matrix we shall write the complex conjugate of the element P_{ij} as $\overline{P}_{ij}$, so if P is Hermitian $P_{ji} = \overline{P}_{ij}$. The vector ψ will be written as a column vector, and its complex transpose ψ^* is then a row vector. The scalar product of two vectors will be $\psi^* \phi$ or $\phi^* \psi$. Clearly $(\psi^* \phi)^* = \phi^* \psi$. The scalar product of a vector with itself is the square of its modulus: $\psi^* \psi = |\psi|^2$. If the scalar product of two non-zero vectors is zero they are said to be orthogonal.

An important property of the eigenvectors of an Hermitian linear operator is their orthogonality: to be precise, if π_i' and π_j' are eigenvectors of the Hermitian operator P, and the corresponding eigenvalues p_i' and p_j' are not equal, then

$$\pi_i'^* \pi_j' = 0.$$

This we shall now prove.

From (1.6),
$$P \pi_i' = p_i' \pi_i'$$
$$P \pi_j' = p_j' \pi_j'.$$

Multiplying the second of these from the left by $\pi_i'^*$ gives

$$\pi_i'^* P \pi_j' = p_j' \pi_i'^* \pi_j'.$$

Taking the complex transpose of the first – remembering that P is Hermitian and p_i' is real – and multiplying from the right by π_j' gives

$$\pi_i'^* P \pi_j' = p_i' \pi_i'^* \pi_j'.$$

Comparing, we see that

$$p_i' \pi_i'^* \pi_j' = p_j' \pi_i'^* \pi_j'$$

and since $p_i' \neq p_j'$ this means that

$$\pi_i'^* \pi_j' = 0.$$

Eigenvectors corresponding to *equal* eigenvalues are not necessarily orthogonal, but we shall see in chapter 6 that the set of eigenvectors belonging to identical eigenvalues can be formed into an equally numerous set of independent orthogonal linear combinations. The occurrence of two or more eigenvectors with the same eigenvalue is called *degeneracy* and the number of eigenvectors belonging to the same eigenvalue is called the *degree of degeneracy*. We shall accept without proof the well known result that the totality of the orthogonal and orthogonalized eigenvectors of a Hermitian operator forms a *complete* set, so that *any* arbitrary vector in the same n-dimensional space can be represented by a linear superposition of these eigenvectors. The orthogonal eigenvectors of a Hermitian operator are clearly linearly independent, and henceforth, unless the contrary is stated we shall assume that the vectors π_i which appear on the right hand side of (1.1) are not merely linearly independent unit vectors, but are in fact orthogonal.

Now let us consider any state-vector ψ, which is expressed in terms of its components (or projections) along the directions of the orthogonal unit vectors π_i' which are the eigenvectors of P. Forming the scalar product of ψ with $P\psi$ we see that

$$\psi^* P\psi = \sum_i \overline{a_i}\, \pi_i'^* \; P \sum_j a_j \pi_j'$$

$$= \sum_i \overline{a_i}\, \pi_i'^* \sum_j a_j p_j' \pi_j'$$

$$\therefore \quad \psi^* P\psi = \sum_i |a_i|^2 p_i', \tag{1.7}$$

since $\qquad \pi_i'^* \pi_j' = 0 \quad$ if $\; j \neq i$
and $\qquad \pi_i'^* \pi_i' = 1 \quad$ for all i.

We note that the right-hand side of (1.7), which involves the eigenvalues of the operator P, resembles the expression in (1.3) for the mean value of the observable p in a system whose state is represented by ψ.

The resemblances between, on the one hand, the very slender formalism we have associated with the superposition principle and our related ideas about measurement, and on the other hand, the formalism associated with linear operators, can be linked firmly together if we make the following assumptions:

(1) Each dynamical variable of a system can be represented by a Hermitian linear operator.

(2) The eigenvalues of P, which we shall now denote by p_i, are the possible results of the measurement of the dynamical variable represented by the operator P.

(3) When the state of a system is represented by a state-function or state-vector ψ, the probability that a measurement of p will give the result p_i is proportional to $|a_i|^2$ where

$$\psi = \sum_i a_i \pi_i$$

the π_i being now the eigenfunctions of P so that $P\pi_i = p_i\pi_i$.

From this it follows that when a system is in the state ψ the mean or *expectation value* of the variable represented by the operator P is

$$\bar{p} = \sum_i \left| a_i \right|^2 p_i = \psi^* P \psi. \qquad (1.8)$$

These assumptions are to be justified by the results which stem from them, by the extent to which they lead to predictions which agree with experiment. They cannot be justified *a priori*. The discussion with which we have introduced them has been aimed at showing that they have some plausibility, but the underlying and often implicit assumptions of classical physics certainly appear more plausible because the ideas they embody are more familiar. These classical assumptions – that we may make a very simple and direct association between observables and algebraic quantities, that observables vary smoothly and continuously, and above all that physical systems are unaffected by being observed – seem so natural that they are seldom stated as the starting points of classical mechanics. But because they lead to predictions which are, in vital respects, irreconcilable with observation, they have to be abandoned. The attempt to build into the foundations of a new system of mechanics the idea that indeterminacy is inseparable from observation at the molecular and atomic level leads to the new assumptions set out above. Whether a satisfactory system of mechanics can be built on this foundation depends on whether it is possible to choose operators which are so related that they can be associated with the variables which occur in mechanics, and which have eigenvalues corresponding numerically with the possible results of measurements. Such a choice does indeed prove to be possible, and the success of the formalism which emerges is a pragmatic justification of the assumptions from which it sets out.

The remainder of this chapter will deal with some formal consequences of these assumptions, and the next chapter will see the formalism developed up to the point at which we can begin to use it to predict the behaviour of real physical systems.

Products of operators; compatible and incompatible variables

If X and Y are a pair of Hermitian (or non-Hermitian) linear operators they do not in general commute. (See, for example, problems 2 to 5 on page 24.) This means that if we operate on a vector or function ψ with Y, the result of this operation being symbolized by $Y\psi$, and then operate on $Y\psi$ with X to produce the result symbolized by $X(Y\psi)=XY\psi$, what we get is not in general (i.e. for arbitrary ψ) the same as we get by operating with X and Y in the reverse order; thus

$$XY\psi \neq YX\psi \quad \text{where } \psi \text{ is any vector}$$

$$\therefore \quad (XY-YX)\psi \neq 0$$

which is often written

$$XY-YX \neq 0. \tag{1.9}$$

The algebra of these operators is therefore said to be non-commutative. This has a physical interpretation which derives from our earlier remark that the state of a system is in general changed by the making of a measurement. The measurement of y on a system which is initially in the state ψ may change the state of the system – $Y\psi$ is not the same as ψ unless a very special relation exists between Y and ψ – so that a subsequent measurement of x is not made on the system in the state ψ, but in the state $Y\psi$. Consequently, predictions about the probable outcome of the measurements of y have to be made in terms of the parameters of the state ψ, while predictions about the probable outcome of the subsequent measurement of x have to be made in terms of the parameters of the state $Y\psi$. If the order of the measurements is reversed, predictions about the probable outcome of the measurement of x have to be made in terms of the parameters of the state ψ, while the outcome of the measurement of y has to be predicted in terms of the parameters of the state $X\psi$. In the one case we are concerned with the states $Y\psi$ and ψ, in the other case with ψ and $X\psi$. Looking at the matter like this we can see little reason to suppose that the results will be the same in both cases, and (1.9) implies that they will not.

States may exist, however, which are simultaneously eigenstates of two operators (see problem 3, p. 24). Suppose that π is an eigenstate of X with eigenvalue x and an eigenstate of Y with eigenvalue y. Then

$$(XY)\pi = X(y\pi) = yX\pi = yx\pi$$

$$\text{and} \quad (YX)\pi = Y(x\pi) = xY\pi = xy\pi$$

$$\therefore \quad XY\pi = YX\pi \quad \text{(since } x \text{ and } y \text{ are numbers)}$$

$$\therefore \quad (XY-YX)\pi = 0.$$

If this is true *for any* ψ, X and Y are said to commute.

In quantum mechanics the occurrence of simultaneous eigen-states is extremely important. For example, the classification of atomic energy states according to the values of the energy, total angular momentum, and magnetic moment, shows that there must be state-functions which are simultaneously eigenfunctions of the three corresponding operators (see chapter 4). Two important theorems about commuting operators and simultaneous eigenstates will now be established.

Theorem 1. Let X and Y be two operators which commute, i.e.

$$(XY - YX)\psi = 0 \quad \text{for all } \psi.$$

> Then their simultaneous eigenvectors form a complete set.

(We have previously accepted (p. 14), as a well known mathematical result, the completeness of the set of eigenvectors of a Hermitian operator. The completeness of the set of simultaneous eigenvectors of two such operators will be shown because simultaneous eigenstates are of such interest in physical problems, and it might seem, without such explicit demonstration, that the simultaneous eigenvectors might be only a restricted selection from a complete set.)

Let η_i be an eigenvector of Y with eigenvalue y_i. Expand η_i in terms of the eigenvectors ξ_j of X – which must be possible since the ξ_j must constitute a complete set. We write this expansion as

$$\eta_i = \sum_j a_j(\eta_i) \cdot \xi_j \qquad \text{(cf. (1.1))}.$$

Then, because η_i is an eigenvector of Y,

$$(Y - y_i)\, \eta_i = 0$$

$$\therefore \ \sum_j a_j(\eta_i) \cdot (Y - y_i)\, \xi_j = 0. \qquad (1.10)$$

Now $\quad X(Y - y_i)\, \xi_j = (Y - y_i)X\, \xi_j \quad$ (since X and Y commute)

$$= (Y - y_i)x_j\, \xi_j \quad \text{(since } \xi_j \text{ is an eigenvector of } X)$$

therefore $(Y - y_i)\xi_j$ is an eigenvector of X with eigenvalue x_j. Hence the equation (1.10) asserts that a sum of linearly independent vectors is zero, which can be true only if every term in the summation vanishes independently. Hence, for all the ξ_j which appear in this summation, $(Y - y_i)\, \xi_j = 0$, so all these ξ_j are eigenvectors of Y as well as of X. Thus all the η_i can be expressed as superpositions of simultaneous eigenvectors of X and Y; since the η_i are themselves a complete set it follows that these simultaneous eigenvectors of X and Y are a complete set.

Theorem 2. Conversely, if two operators X and Y are such that any vector can be represented as a linear superposition of their simultaneous eigenvectors, the operators commute.

Let the simultaneous eigenvectors be denoted by $(\pi_{xy})_i$. Then by hypothesis we can write

$$\psi = \sum_i a_i \cdot (\pi_{xy})_i \quad \text{for any } \psi$$

$$\therefore \quad (XY - YX)\psi = \sum_i a_i \cdot (XY - YX) \cdot (\pi_{xy})_i.$$

Since every term in the summation vanishes we have $(XY - YX)\psi = 0$ *for any ψ*, so X and Y commute.

If a pair of quantum mechanical operators commute the corresponding physical observables are compatible, for their simultaneous eigenstates are states in which the values of both variables can be known precisely at one time. Variables whose operators do not commute are incompatible. The identification of a set of compatible variables, whose values may subsequently be used to specify a pure state, may be effected by identifying an appropriate set of corresponding commuting operators. Frequently this will correspond to the problem in classical dynamics of identifying the constants of the motion – the quantities which are conserved. For closed systems, whose energy is conserved, the constants of the motion will be represented by operators which commute with the total-energy operator, and conversely any variable whose operator commutes with the total-energy operator is a constant of the motion. This conclusion will be arrived at more formally in chapter 3, and applied to find the constants of the motion of a particle in a central field of force in chapter 4.

Continuous distributions of eigenvalues: wave-mechanics

The foregoing discussion has assumed that the eigenvalues of the operators are discrete. If a variable is continuously distributed –

like the energy of a free electron, or the position coordinate – it must be represented by an operator whose eigenvalues form a continuum, and the representation of the operator by a matrix is then impracticable. In such a case we may make use of differential operators. Such operators are linear, and the real eigenvalues λ for which such a differential equation as

$$\frac{d\psi}{dx} = \lambda\psi$$

has solutions extend continuously from $-\infty$ to $+\infty$; the eigenfunction belonging to the eigenvalue λ is $\varepsilon^{\lambda x}$. It sometimes happens that the imposition of suitable boundary conditions (arising from physical considerations) restricts the spectrum of eigenvalues of a differential equation to discrete values: the wave-equation for the vibrations of a string stretched between stationary supports has solutions only for modes of vibration in which the wavelenth is any integral sub-multiple of twice the distance between the supports. Hence it appears that the use of differential operators may enable us to deal either with discrete or with continuously distributed eigenvalues. The branch of quantum mechanics which deals with the representation of states by continuous functions, and of observables by continuous variables and differential operators, is called *wave-mechanics*.

Suppose that an observable x has its values continuously distributed, so that the eigenvalues of the corresponding operator X form a continuum. As before we associate unit vectors with the pure states in which the values of x are unique and definite: let ε_x and $\varepsilon_{x'}$ denote the pure states in which the variable has the values x and x', respectively. These unit vectors are to be orthogonal, so that $\varepsilon_x{}^*\varepsilon_{x'} = \delta(x-x')$, where $\delta(x-x')$ is the Dirac delta function; $\delta(x-x')$ is zero except when $x = x'$, when it becomes infinite in such a way that

$$\int_{-\infty}^{+\infty} \delta(x-x')\, dx' = 1.$$

Any vector ψ will have its components along the directions of the various ε_x represented by the corresponding values of the function $\psi(x)$, which is a function of the continuous variable x. The probability that an observation of x will give a result between x and $x + \delta x$ is then

$$p(x)\, \delta x \propto |\psi(x)|^2\, \delta x, \tag{1.11}$$

and if we adjust the scale of $\psi(x)$ so that

$$\int_{-\infty}^{+\infty} |\psi(x)|^2 \, dx = 1 \qquad \text{(cf. eqn. (1.2))}$$

we can write

$$p(x) \, \delta x = |\psi(x)|^2 \, \delta x. \qquad (1.12)$$

The vector ψ, whose components now form a continuum, is written as a superposition of its components:

$$\psi = \int_{-\infty}^{+\infty} \psi(x) \, \varepsilon_x \, dx, \qquad \text{(cf. eqn. (1.1))}$$

and its scalar product with itself, i.e. the square of its length, is

$$\iint_{-\infty}^{+\infty} \psi^*(x) \, \varepsilon_x^* \, \psi(x') \, \varepsilon_{x'} \, dx dx'$$

$$= \iint_{-\infty}^{+\infty} \psi^*(x) \, \psi(x') \, \delta(x-x') \, dx dx'$$

$$= \int_{-\infty}^{+\infty} \psi^*(x) \, \psi(x) \, dx = \int_{-\infty}^{+\infty} |\psi(x)|^2 \, dx.$$

Thus the step leading from (1.11) to (1.12) shows that $|\psi(x)|^2 \, \delta x$ can be interpreted as a probability if ψ is a unit vector, i.e. $\psi(x)$ is normalized to unity.

In a similar way the scalar product of two vectors ϕ and ψ is

$$\phi^*\psi = \int_{-\infty}^{+\infty} \phi^*(x) \, \psi(x) \, dx.$$

If this is zero, the vectors – or states – ϕ and ψ are said to be orthogonal.

The expectation value of any variable p for the state ψ is, by analogy with (1.8),

$$(\bar{p})_\psi = \int_{-\infty}^{+\infty} \psi^*(x) \, p(x) \, \psi(x) \, dx$$

where we must remember that $p(x)$ may be an operator.

The normalization of $\psi(x)$ between $-\infty$ and $+\infty$ is not always possible. In chapter 5 for instance we shall solve the eigenvalue equation which determines the energy eigenvalues and the corresponding eigenfunctions for the hydrogen atom: we shall find that when the total energy of the atom is negative there are bound states with discrete energies, whereas the eigenvalue equation has other solutions representing unbound states for *all* $E>0$. The eigenfunctions of this continuous spectrum can not be normalized in the way we have supposed, and this is always true of eigenfunctions which belong to a continuous spectrum. In such cases it is possible to construct 'eigendifferentials'

$$\int_E^{E+\Delta E} \psi(x,E)\, dE = \psi(x,E,\Delta E)$$

which can be normalized, and which have the following orthogonality property: all eigendifferentials are orthogonal to eigenfunctions belonging to the discrete spectrum, and eigendifferentials are orthogonal to one another as long as the energy ranges in which they are defined do not overlap.

An alternative method of handling the eigenfunctions of a continuous spectrum, which will be used in chapter 10 and subsequently, is to imagine the system under consideration confined in a box of very large but finite volume; then if the box is large enough those eigenvalues which were discrete before the enclosure are scarcely affected, while those which were continuously distributed are now discrete but very closely spaced. It is always possible, therefore, to contrive to deal with normalizable functions, but as long as we are content to calculate only relative probabilities normalization may be unnecessary.

The functions $\psi(x)$ are the wave-functions introduced by Schrödinger (1925). Although in some relatively simple processes these functions can be pictured as waves in three-dimensional space, this 'model' is not generally valid; the ψ-function represents the statistical character of the predictions we can make about measurements on atomic and molecular systems rather than the distribution of a 'real' wave in space.

Quantum theory and probability

It must always be remembered, and the approach in this chapter has been intended to emphasize, that quantum mechanics is a theory about measurement; and whenever the measurements we are concerned with are carried out on a system which is 'small' – we still have to make precise our meaning of this relative term, but Planck's constant is certainly going to determine the scale, in some way – our theory will predict an unavoidable statistical spread or uncertainty in the results of the measurements. If the new mechanics contains classical mechanics as a limiting case – as it will be designed to do – the indeterminacy which is built into its foundations at the quantum mechanical level will, in the classical limit, become negligible – not non-existent, but negligible.

Classical physics also makes use of statistical and probabilistic ideas, but it does so in a way entirely different from quantum theory. Classical statistical mechanics – or the kinetic theory of gases, to take a more limited example – uses statistical methods partly because it would not be *practicable* to construct the more detailed particle-by-particle description whose *possibility in principle* it does not call in question; and partly because that more detailed description is not relevant in detail to the measurements which are actually made on assemblies of molecules. Statistics and probability are used in classical physics as a matter of convenience – of expediency, even – but they are used in quantum mechanics because the study of microphysics has developed the conviction, in most physicists, that *nature is like that.* According to classical ideas a fast-moving atom or electron, whose direction of travel is known if it has passed through a pair of very small apertures placed some distance apart, will travel on in that same direction after emerging from the second aperture, unless it experiences an interaction which changes its direction. According to quantum theory a diffraction process occurs at the second, as at any, aperture; the fact that the particle has passed through both apertures *does not prescribe its subsequent direction of travel,* but locates only the central peak of a probability distribution-in-angle whose spread is the greater the narrower is the aperture. Arguments based on probability must be used to predict the behaviour of *single* electrons, atoms, or molecules, no matter what their previous history, because such entities behave neither like the particles nor like the waves of classical physics, but in accordance with laws of a kind which are new and unfamiliar (although at times the classical notions of 'wave' and 'particle' provide deceptively familiar metaphors). These laws are the subject-matter of quantum mechanics.

Problems

(1) α and β are unit vectors. (i) Show that the vectors $\alpha + \beta$ and $\alpha - \beta$ are orthogonal. (ii) Find expressions in terms of α and β

for a vector perpendicular to α, and for a vector perpendicular to β.

(2) **i, j, k** are unit vectors along the directions of the x, y, z axes respectively. Operators P and Q are defined by the relations:

$$P\mathbf{i} = \mathbf{j}, \quad P\mathbf{j} = -\mathbf{i}, \quad P\mathbf{k} = \mathbf{k};$$
$$Q\mathbf{i} = -\mathbf{k}, \quad Q\mathbf{j} = \mathbf{j}, \quad Q\mathbf{k} = \mathbf{i}.$$

Interpret the effect of these operators in geometrical terms. Show that P and Q do not commute.

Construct 3×3 matrices to represent P and Q, and find their eigenvalues and eigenvectors.

(3) $s_1 = \begin{bmatrix} 0 & 1 \\ 1 & 0 \end{bmatrix}$, $s_2 = \begin{bmatrix} 0 & -i \\ i & 0 \end{bmatrix}$, $s_3 = \begin{bmatrix} 1 & 0 \\ 0 & -1 \end{bmatrix}$, $s_4 = \begin{bmatrix} 1 & 0 \\ 0 & 1 \end{bmatrix}$.

Find the eigenvalues and eigenvectors of each of these Hermitian matrices. Which pairs of them commute? and what are the simultaneous eigenvectors of each commuting pair?

(4) Taking x as an ordinary algebraic variable, find whether x and $\dfrac{d}{dx}$ commute.

Hint: evaluate $\left(\dfrac{d}{dx}x - x\dfrac{d}{dx}\right)f(x)$ where $f(x)$ is any differentiable function of x.

(5) Do $\dfrac{\partial}{\partial x}$ and $\dfrac{\partial}{\partial y}$ commute?

(6) A matrix S is said to be unitary if $S^*S = I$, where I is a unit matrix. Show that if X is a Hermitian matrix $S^{-1}XS$ is also Hermitian.

Then show that if X and Y are both Hermitian, X and Y must commute if $S^{-1}XS$ and $S^{-1}YS$ are both diagonal.

(7) In wave-mechanics the adjoint $A^\dagger$ of an operator A is defined by the statement that, for any pair of well-behaved orthonormal functions $\psi(x)$ and $\phi(x)$,

$$\int_{-\infty}^{+\infty} \psi^*(x)A\phi(x)dx = \int_{-\infty}^{+\infty} (A^\dagger\psi(x))^*\phi(x)dx.$$

Show that the operator $i\dfrac{d}{dx}$ is self-adjoint (or Hermitian), i.e., that

$$\int_{-\infty}^{+\infty} \psi^*(x)i\frac{d}{dx}\phi(x)dx = \int_{-\infty}^{+\infty} \left(i\frac{d}{dx}\psi(x)\right)^*\phi(x)dx.$$

CHAPTER TWO

THE UNCERTAINTY PRINCIPLE AND THE COMMUTATION RELATIONS

Uncertainties and uncertainty products

We now have to develop the formalism outlined in the last chapter so that it may be used for quantitative discussion. In this chapter we shall apply it in a discussion of the uncertainty principle, in the course of which we shall introduce Planck's constant to fix the scale of the events which quantum mechanics must be used to describe.

Suppose that a state is represented by a state-vector ψ which is an eigenvector of the operator P, so that if a measurement of the variable p is carried out on a system in the state ψ the result of the measurement is certainly p_i. This is symbolized by the equation

$$P\psi = p_i\psi. \tag{2.1}$$

Then if we write the expectation value of p for the state ψ as $\langle p \rangle_\psi$ we know that

$$\langle p \rangle_\psi = \psi^* P \psi = p_i$$

and similarly $\qquad \langle p^2 \rangle_\psi = \psi^* P^2 \psi = \psi^* P P \psi = p_i{}^2.$

Now the mean-square deviation, or variance, of p is in general

$$(\Delta p)^2 = \langle (p - \langle p \rangle)^2 \rangle = \langle p^2 \rangle - \langle p \rangle^2 \tag{2.2}$$

so when ψ is an eigenvector of P, $(\Delta p)^2$ is zero. This is not a new conclusion, but simply a reminder of the meaning we assigned to an eigenstate of an operator – that it is a state for which a measurement of the corresponding observable certainly yields a definite, sharp value.

If ψ is also an eigenvector of another operator Q, corresponding to the observable q, the variance in q, $(\Delta q)^2$, is also zero. It follows that if a system is in a state which is an eigenstate of the two observables p and q the variances in p and q vanish simultaneously. More generally, if P and Q are commuting operators, in which case p and q are compatible variables, *there are states* for which the variances of p and q are both zero. It is important to notice that even when P and Q commute the variances in p and q do not vanish for any arbitrary ψ; on the other hand when P and Q commute they have simultaneous eigenstates, and these are the states for which p and q both have zero variance. (See problem 1 on p. 39.)

$(\Delta p)^2$ and its square root, Δp, are important measures of the breadth of the distribution-in-p for the state ψ. In statistics Δp is called the *standard deviation* in p, but in quantum mechanics it is usually called the *uncertainty* in p. Since $(\Delta p)^2$ can be determined from measurements it is an observable, and there is a corresponding operator which can be written as $(P-\langle p \rangle I)^2$ where I is the unit or identical operator. I has the properties that $I\psi = \psi$, $\psi^* I = \psi^*$ for any ψ, and $IP = PI = P$ for any P. Using these properties we can check that $(P-\langle p \rangle I)^2$ is indeed a variance operator, for

$$\psi^*(P-\langle p \rangle I)^2 \psi = \psi^*(P^2 - \langle p \rangle (PI + IP) + \langle p \rangle^2 I^2)\psi$$

$$= \psi^*(P^2 - 2\langle p \rangle P + \langle p \rangle^2)\psi$$

$$= \langle p^2 \rangle - 2\langle p \rangle \langle p \rangle + \langle p \rangle^2$$

$$= \langle p^2 \rangle - \langle p \rangle^2$$

$$\therefore \quad \psi^*(P-\langle p \rangle I)^2 \psi = \langle p^2 \rangle - \langle p \rangle^2 = (\Delta p)^2 \qquad \text{(cf. (2.2)).}$$

We may note that $(P-\langle p \rangle I)$ is Hermitian, and is the operator corresponding to the deviation of the observable p from its mean value $\langle p \rangle$. The use of the operator $(P-\langle p \rangle I)$ in a calculation, instead of P, therefore implies the adoption of $\langle p \rangle$ as a new origin-of-p – a 'shifting of the zero', in fact. It will be convenient in what follows to denote the operator, representing the variable p referred to its mean value $\langle p \rangle$ as origin, by P_0, and to attach the zero subscript to other operators for the same purpose.

Suppose P and Q are the operators corresponding to the observables p and q. Then, for a system in the state represented by ψ, the variances in p and q are

$$(\Delta p)^2 = \psi^*(P-\langle p \rangle I)^2 \psi = \psi^* P_0^2 \psi, \qquad (2.3\text{a})$$

$$(\Delta q)^2 = \psi^*(Q-\langle q \rangle I)^2 \psi = \psi^* Q_0^2 \psi. \qquad (2.3\text{b})$$

We saw in chapter 1 that, according as p and q are or are not compatible, the operator $(PQ-QP)$ is equal to zero, or is non-zero. And we have seen in this chapter that the compatibility of p and q is a precondition for the simultaneous vanishing of $(\Delta p)^2$ and $(\Delta q)^2$. We shall now show that for any pair of variables p and q the least possible value of the product $(\Delta p)^2 \cdot (\Delta q)^2$ can be found using the operator $(PQ-QP)$. In this section we shall carry the argument as far as we can without introducing any assumptions additional to those made in chapter 1. This is done partly to explore the consequences of these assumptions and show how far-reaching they are, and partly because the conclusion we can reach – that for any given pair of variables there is a definite lower limit to the product of their variances – exemplifies in a significant way the assertion in chapter 1 that the idea of indeterminacy is built into the foundations of quantum theory through the interpretation of the superposition principle.

We have related the compatibility or otherwise of the variables p and q to the vanishing or otherwise of the operator $(PQ-QP)$, which is called the commutator of P and Q, and will be abbreviated as $[P, Q]$. Now $(PQ-QP)$ is not Hermitian, for $(PQ-QP)^* = (Q^*P^* - P^*Q^*) = (QP - PQ) = -(PQ-QP)$. On the other hand, $i(PQ-QP)$ is Hermitian (and therefore more 'suitable' for quantum mechanical purposes) because it follows from the above that $(i(PQ-QP))^* = -i(PQ-QP)^* = i(PQ-QP)$. (See also problem 2 on p. 39.) Next we show that the commutator of $P_0 = (P-\langle p \rangle I)$ and $Q_0 = (Q-\langle q \rangle I)$ is the same as the commutator of P and Q. Remembering that $\langle p \rangle$ and $\langle q \rangle$ are numbers, and recalling the properties of the unit operator, we can see that

$$[P_0, Q_0] = (P-\langle p \rangle I)(Q-\langle q \rangle I) - (Q-\langle q \rangle I)(P-\langle p \rangle I)$$

$$= PQ - P\langle q \rangle - \langle p \rangle Q + \langle p \rangle \langle q \rangle - QP + Q\langle p \rangle$$

$$+ \langle q \rangle P - \langle q \rangle \langle p \rangle$$

$$= PQ - QP$$

$$\therefore [P_0, Q_0] = [P, Q].$$

The importance of this step is that it expresses the commutator of P and Q in terms of the operators which we need in the expressions (2.3) for the variances.

If we write $P_0\psi = \alpha$, $Q_0\psi = \beta$, where α and β are vectors, equations (2.3) become

$$(\Delta p)^2 = \alpha^*\alpha = |\alpha|^2 \qquad (2.3c)$$

$$(\Delta q)^2 = \beta^*\beta = |\beta|^2 \qquad (2.3d)$$

so $\qquad (\Delta p)^2 . (\Delta q)^2 = |\alpha|^2 . |\beta|^2.$

Now the product of the squares of the lengths of the vectors α and β must be either equal to or greater than the squared modulus of their scalar product (see problem 3 on p. 39), i.e.

$$|\alpha|^2 . |\beta|^2 \geqq |\alpha^*\beta|^2, \qquad (2.4)$$

and the equality sign applies only if the vectors are parallel (in which case $\alpha = k\beta$ where k is a constant). Hence

$$(\Delta p)^2 . (\Delta q)^2 \geqq |\alpha^*\beta|^2$$

$$\geqq |(P_0\psi)^*Q_0\psi|^2$$

$$\geqq (\psi^*P_0Q_0\psi)(\psi^*Q_0P_0\psi).$$

If we now write $\quad \psi^*P_0Q_0\psi = x - iy$

it follows that $\quad \psi^*Q_0P_0\psi = x + iy$

from which $\qquad x = \tfrac{1}{2}\psi^*(P_0Q_0 + Q_0P_0)\psi \qquad (2.5a)$

and $\qquad y = \tfrac{i}{2}\psi^*(P_0Q_0 - Q_0P_0)\psi. \qquad (2.5b)$

Evidently $2y/i$ is the expectation value of the commutator of P_0 and Q_0, which is the same as that of P and Q. We make use of this in the following way:

$$(\psi^*P_0Q_0\psi)(\psi^*Q_0P_0\psi) = (x - iy)(x + iy)$$

$$= x^2 + y^2$$

$$\geqq y^2 \qquad (2.6)$$

(the sign of equality applying only if $x = 0$)

so $\qquad (\Delta p)^2 . (\Delta q)^2 \geqq (\psi^*P_0Q_0\psi)(\psi^*Q_0P_0\psi) \geqq y^2$

$$\therefore \quad (\Delta p)^2 . (\Delta q)^2 \geqq \tfrac{1}{4}\langle i[P, Q]\rangle^2. \qquad (2.7)$$

From (2.7) we have, finally,

$$\Delta p . \Delta q \geqq \tfrac{1}{2}\langle i[P, Q]\rangle. \qquad (2.8)$$

(We note for future discussion, on pp. 38-39, that the equality sign applies in (2.8) only if two conditions are satisfied simultaneously. One is that the vectors $\alpha = P_0\psi$ and $\beta = Q_0\psi$ which appear in (2.3) are related through $\alpha = k\beta$, where k is a constant; and the other is that the quantity x defined in (2.5a) vanishes.)

(2.8) is the most general statement of the *uncertainty principle*, and it shows the direct link between, on the one hand, the incompatibility of certain pairs of variables, and on the other hand the mathematical property of non-commutability of certain pairs of operators.

The continuation of our argument to the point at which we can make quantitative statements about physical systems requires a method of obtaining an explicit expression for the commutator of any pair of variables. This step is necessarily something of a leap in the dark. It is here that the distinction between classical and quantum mechanics crystallizes and that we should expect the appearance of Planck's constant. The only positive guidance we have comes from the successes of classical physics in an immense domain, and the conclusion that classical mechanics should emerge as a limiting case of the formalism of quantum mechanics. Thus we should expect, in quantum mechanics, to have to deal with representations of the quantities we know in classical mechanics – energy, linear and angular momentum, position, and so on – and we should expect them to have the same functional relationships with one another as they do in classical mechanics. In particular we might expect that the functions which play such an important role in analytical dynamics, like the Hamiltonian and the Lagrangian, will also be of particular importance in quantum theory.

Commutators and Poisson brackets

One method of inferring the expressions for the commutators relies on an analogy between the quantum mechanical commutator and one of the invariant functions of classical mechanics, the Poisson bracket.

The Poisson bracket plays a useful part in the discussion of constants of the motion in classical mechanics; it is treated in many texts on classical mechanics, for example in chapter 9 of Leech's monograph, *Classical Mechanics* (Methuen, 1958). The Poisson bracket of any two functions of the position and momentum coordinates is defined as

$$\{\xi, \eta\} = \sum_i \left(\frac{\partial \xi}{\partial p_i} \cdot \frac{\partial \eta}{\partial q_i} - \frac{\partial \xi}{\partial q_i} \cdot \frac{\partial \eta}{\partial p_i} \right)$$

where the summation is over all degrees of freedom.

The following properties of Poisson brackets are easy to verify:

$$\{\xi, \eta\} = -\{\eta, \xi\} \tag{2.9a}$$

$$\{\xi, c\} = 0 \quad \text{where } c \text{ is a constant} \tag{2.9b}$$

$$\{\xi_1 + \xi_2, \eta\} = \{\xi_1, \eta\} + \{\xi_2, \eta\} \tag{2.9c}$$

$$\{\xi_1 \xi_2, \eta\} = \xi_1 \{\xi_2, \eta\} + \{\xi_1, \eta\} \xi_2 \tag{2.9d}$$

$$\{\xi, \eta_1 \eta_2\} = \eta_1 \{\xi, \eta_2\} + \{\xi, \eta_1\} \eta_2 \tag{2.9e}$$

$$\frac{dF}{dt} = \frac{\partial F}{\partial t} + \{H, F\} \tag{2.9f}$$

where F is any function of the position and momentum coordinates and of the time, and H is the Hamiltonian; this result follows from an application of Hamilton's canonical equations. (See also problem (4) on p. 39.)

The relations (a) to (e) above apply also to commutators; e.g. if we start from the commutator analogue of the l.h.s. of (d), we can proceed as follows:

$$[\xi_1 \xi_2, \eta] = (\xi_1 \xi_2 \eta - \eta \xi_1 \xi_2)$$
$$= \xi_1 \xi_2 \eta - \xi_1 \eta \xi_2 + \xi_1 \eta \xi_2 - \eta \xi_1 \xi_2$$
$$= \xi_1 (\xi_2 \eta - \eta \xi_2) + (\xi_1 \eta - \eta \xi_1) \xi_2$$
$$= \xi_1 [\xi_2, \eta] + [\xi_1, \eta] \xi_2.$$

There is therefore a formal similarity between the properties of Poisson brackets and of commutators, and we make use of this in order to make an informed guess at the value of $\langle i[P, Q] \rangle$ in the uncertainty relation, equation (2.8). Let us expand the Poisson bracket $\{\xi_1 \xi_2, \eta_1 \eta_2\}$ while retaining as far as possible the order of the factors. We can do this in two different ways, according as we use (2.9d) to break up the product $\xi_1 \xi_2$ before or after we apply (2.9e) to break up the product $\eta_1 \eta_2$:

(i) $\{\xi_1 \xi_2, \eta_1 \eta_2\} = \xi_1 \{\xi_2, \eta_1 \eta_2\} + \{\xi_1, \eta_1 \eta_2\} \xi_2$

$\qquad = \xi_1 \eta_1 \{\xi_2, \eta_2\} + \xi_1 \{\xi_2, \eta_1\} \eta_2 + \eta_1 \{\xi_1, \eta_2\} \xi_2 + \{\xi_1, \eta_1\} \eta_2 \xi_2$

(ii) $\{\xi_1\xi_2, \eta_1\eta_2\} = \eta_1\{\xi_1\xi_2, \eta_2\}+\{\xi_1\xi_2, \eta_1\}\eta_2$

       $= \eta_1\xi_1\{\xi_2, \eta_2\}+\eta_1\{\xi_1, \eta_2\}\xi_2+\xi_1\{\xi_2, \eta_1\}\eta_2+\{\xi_1, \eta_1\}\xi_2\eta_2.$

If we equate these two expansions we find

$$\xi_1\eta_1\{\xi_2, \eta_2+\{\xi_1, \eta_1\}\eta_2\xi_2 = \eta_1\xi_1\{\xi_2, \eta_2\}+\{\xi_1, \eta_1\}\xi_2\eta_2$$

$$\therefore \quad (\xi_1\eta_1-\eta_1\xi_1)\{\xi_2, \eta_2\} = \{\xi_1, \eta_1\}(\xi_2\eta_2-\eta_2\xi_2)$$

and this can be true for *any* four functions ξ_1, ξ_2, η_1, η_2, only if
$i(\xi_1\eta_1-\eta_1\xi_1)=\hbar\{\xi_1, \eta_1\}$ and $i(\xi_2\eta_2-\eta_2\xi_2)=\hbar\{\xi_2, \eta_2\}$ (2.10a)
where $\hbar$ has to satisfy these conditions:

(i) $\hbar$ must commute with $\{\xi_1, \eta_1\}$ whatever the form of ξ_1 and η_1; and

(ii) $\hbar$ must be independent of ξ_1, ξ_2, η_1, η_2.
      $\hbar$ must therefore be simply a number.

(iii)   *$\hbar$ must be real,* since if ξ_1 and η_1 are real observables $\{\xi_1, \eta_1\}$ is real, and the form $i(\xi_1\eta_1-\eta_1\xi_1)$ is Hermitian.

(iv)   *$\hbar$ must have the dimensions of action,* from comparison of (2.10a) with the definition of the Poisson bracket.

Since Planck's constant h is a real universal constant with the dimensions of action this seems to provide the opportunity for us to introduce Planck's constant into the theory, by assuming that $\hbar$=constant × h. It turns out that we get agreement with experiment if we take $\hbar=h/2\pi$, and we thus arrive at the most general statement of the quantum conditions for any problem:

Quantum conditions

The commutator of the *operators* ξ, η is equal to $h/2\pi i$ times the Poisson bracket of the *variables* ξ, η, i.e.

$$i(\xi\eta-\eta\xi) = \hbar\{\xi, \eta\}. \qquad (2.10b)$$

The numerical magnitude of $\hbar$ is $1\cdot054\times 10^{-27}$ erg sec or $1\cdot054\times 10^{-34}$ joule sec. If the quantity of action transferred in any process is *very large* compared with $\hbar$, (2.10b) may reasonably be approximated by $\xi\eta-\eta\xi=0$, which means that we may use ordinary commuting algebraic variables for all ξ and η; we are *then* in the domain of classical mechanics.

For any pair of canonically conjugate variables, such as the position and momentum variables associated with any one degree of freedom, the Poisson bracket is unity; the quantum mechanical commutator is then

$$pq - qp = \hbar/i. \tag{2.11}$$

In this case, then, $i(pq - qp) = \hbar$, and for the state represented by any (normalized) state-vector ψ,

$$\tfrac{1}{2}\langle i(pq - qp)\rangle = \tfrac{1}{2}\psi^* i(pq - qp)\psi = \hbar/2\psi^*\psi = \hbar/2$$

so (2.8) becomes

$$\Delta p \, \Delta q \geqq \hbar/2. \tag{2.12}$$

This is the most familiar form of the uncertainty principle, defining the maximum precision attainable in our simultaneous knowledge of the values of the conjugate variables p and q, and (2.12) is the precise statement to which we were able only to approximate after the discussions of hypothetical experiments, on pp. 4 and 5. On the other hand, there is no limit – in principle – to the precision with which we can know the simultaneous values of the position and momentum associated with *different* degrees of freedom, for $\{p_r, q_s\} = 0$ unless $r = s$; more generally, then, when p and q represent momentum and position coordinates (2.11) can be written as $p_r q_s - q_s p_r = \delta_{rs}\hbar/i$, where δ_{rs} is the Kronecker delta symbol. Again, for a particle moving in a field-free space the kinetic energy is

$$T = (p_1{}^2 + p_2{}^2 + p_3{}^2)/2m$$

and $\qquad \{T, p_i\} = 0, \{T, q_i\} = \dot{q}_i \neq 0 \quad$ in general,

so we may have precise knowledge of the simultaneous values of the kinetic energy and any momentum component, but not of the kinetic energy and a position coordinate. Considerations such as these provide a formal 'justification' for the statement made on p. 3 – and given there as a generalization from experimental evidence – that the classical concept of a trajectory is inapplicable throughout microphysics.

A problem arises in the evaluation of commutators of *functions* of the position and momentum coordinates, because the classical method of evaluating Poisson brackets by partial differentiation may not sufficiently conserve the order of factors. For instance, the

Poisson bracket of the squares of the conjugate variables p and q is

$$\{p^2, q^2\} = \frac{\partial p^2}{\partial p} \cdot \frac{\partial q^2}{\partial q} - \frac{\partial p^2}{\partial q} \cdot \frac{\partial q^2}{\partial p}$$

$$= 4pq$$

from which we should expect that

$$[p^2, q^2] = -4i\hbar pq.$$

On the other hand, if we use Poisson bracket algebra to express $\{p^2, q^2\}$ in terms of $\{p, q\}$, and then use eqn. (2.11), we find

$$\{p^2, q^2\} = p\{p, q^2\} + \{p, q^2\}p$$

$$= pq\{p, q\} + p\{p, q\}q + q\{p, q\}p + \{p, q\}qp$$

$$= pq + pq + qp + qp \quad (\text{since } \{p, q\} = 1)$$

$$= 2pq + 2qp$$

$$= 4pq - 2(pq - qp)$$

from which

$$[p^2, q^2] = -i\hbar(4pq - 2[p, q])$$

$$= -i\hbar(4pq + 2i\hbar)$$

$$= -4i\hbar pq + 2\hbar^2.$$

Finally, if we use (2.11) in a direct evaluation of $[p^2, q^2]$ we find

$$[p^2, q^2] = p^2q^2 - q^2p^2$$

$$= p(pq)q - q(qp)p$$

$$= p(qp - i\hbar)q - q(pq + i\hbar)p$$

$$= pqpq - i\hbar pq - qpqp - i\hbar qp$$

$$= pqpq - i\hbar pq - (pq + i\hbar)(pq + i\hbar) - i\hbar(pq + i\hbar)$$

$$= pqpq - i\hbar pq - pqpq - 2i\hbar pq + \hbar^2 - i\hbar pq + \hbar^2$$

$$\therefore \quad [p^2, q^2] = -4i\hbar pq + 2\hbar^2.$$

In this case, then, the use of partial differentiation to evaluate the Poisson bracket leads to a result which differs by a term in $\hbar^2$ from that given by algebraic methods which pay full regard to the non-commutative character of p and q; when such discrepancies arise it is the results of the latter methods that must be used.

Choice of operators

The next problem is to decide how to choose operators to represent the various dynamical variables which are used in the description of physical systems. We shall require that these operators are functionally related as the corresponding classical variables; our choice is further circumscribed by the obligation to satisfy the appropriate commutation relations, and by the rules of linear algebra. Altogether these do not define a unique choice of operators, and taste and expediency play a part too. It can be shown that the representation of a dynamical variable by an operator is unique only when what is called the 'basis of the representation' is chosen. Nevertheless many representations are possible; thus, as was suggested in chapter 1, we may represent dynamical variables by matrices, or by differential operators, these alternatives arising from different choices of the 'basis'. The basis is effectively a set of coordinate axes in n-dimensional space. When the coordinate system has been chosen there is one and only one operator for each dynamical variable. We also have to be able to choose operators to represent functions of variables, e.g. $\frac{1}{2}mv^2$. It can be shown that if the operator P represents the variable p with eigenvalues p_i, $f(p)$ is represented by the operator $f(P)$ with eigenvalues $f(p_i)$, subject to certain qualifications concerning the possibility of forming the operator $f(P)$. For instance, P^{-1} can exist only if P does not have zero as one of its eigenvalues; $P^{\frac{1}{2}}$ does not exist if P has any negative eigenvalues. These results will not be proved here, but they are discussed in larger works, like Dirac's *Principles of Quantum Mechanics* (Oxford, 1958).

Historically two different categories of suitable operators were discovered before the general formalism showed their alternative validity. These were the matrix operators discovered by Heisenberg, and the differential operators discovered by Schrödinger. The matrix method will be illustrated in the next two chapters, in the problem of the one-dimensional simple harmonic oscillator and the quantization of angular momentum. The use of differential operators is usually more convenient, for in non-relativistic quantum mechanics there is a simple recipe for the setting up of the great majority of problems, based on the non-commutative property of the operators x and $\frac{d}{dx}$. According to the result of problem (4) on p. 24,

$$\left(\frac{d}{dx}x - x\frac{d}{dx}\right)f(x) = f(x).$$

Hence, symbolically,

$$\frac{d}{dx}x - x\frac{d}{dx} = 1$$

and

$$\left(\frac{\hbar}{i}\frac{d}{dx}x - x\frac{\hbar}{i}\frac{d}{dx}\right) = \frac{\hbar}{i}.$$

This is the same as the commutation relation (2.11) satisfied by a pair of conjugate variables, and suggests that we might associate variables and operators thus:

$$p_x \to \frac{\hbar}{i}\frac{d}{dx}, \ x \to x.$$

Then, for instance, the Hamiltonian for a particle moving along the x-axis where its potential energy is $V(x)$, is

$$H = T + V = \frac{p_x^2}{2m} + V(x)$$

and would be represented by the operator

$$H \to -\frac{\hbar^2}{2m}\frac{d^2}{dx^2} + V(x).$$

The functions $\psi(x)$ which are eigenfunctions of this operator, and therefore represent states in which the energy is sharply defined, are found by solving the eigenvalue equation

$$-\frac{\hbar^2}{2m}\frac{d^2}{dx^2}\psi(x) + V(x)\,\psi(x) = E\,\psi(x). \tag{2.13}$$

By itself this equation, which was introduced by Schrödinger, does not define a discrete set of eigenvalues, as our knowledge of spectroscopy, say, might lead us to expect. The discreteness of the eigenvalues usually follows from the imposition of boundary conditions, such as the requirement that $\psi(x)$ shall vanish at ∞, or at certain limiting values of $+x$ and $-x$. In terms of the interpretation of $|\psi(x)|^2$ as a probability density, introduced near the end of chapter 1, this implies that we are dealing with a 'bound' or 'confined' system, as an atomic electron is bound by electrostatic forces to the nucleus, or as the electrons in a metal are confined by the surfaces of the sample.

An alternative differential operator representation would be

$$p_x \rightarrow p, \ x \rightarrow i\hbar \frac{d}{dp}$$

for these operators also satisfy the commutation relation (2.11). In many cases this representation is not so convenient, for example in problems in which the potential energy involves high powers or inverse powers of x; in the problem of the one-dimensional simple harmonic oscillator, on the other hand, the Hamiltonian is symmetric in p and x:

$$H = \frac{1}{2m}p^2 + \tfrac{1}{2}m\omega^2 x^2 \tag{2.14}$$

and the eigenvalues of H may be found by solving either of the equations:

(i) $\qquad -\dfrac{\hbar^2}{2m}\dfrac{d^2\psi(x)}{dx^2} + \tfrac{1}{2}m\omega^2 x^2\psi(x) = E\,\psi(x)$

$\hspace{11cm}$ (2.15)

(ii) $\qquad \dfrac{p^2}{2m}\,\phi(p) - \dfrac{m\omega^2\hbar^2}{2}\dfrac{d^2\phi(p)}{dp^2} = E\,\phi(p)$

The two types of eigenfunction $\psi(x)$ and $\phi(p)$ will in this rather exceptional case be identical in form, though their immediate physical significance is different. $|\psi(x)|^2\,\delta x$ represents the probability that the oscillator's *position* coordinate is in a range of length δx in the neighbourhood of x, while $|\phi(p)|^2\,\delta p$ represents the probability that its *momentum* is in a range δp in the neighbourhood of p. It should be remembered, however, that (1.8) implies that either of these types of state function contains information, not only about the variable on which it depends explicitly, but also about all other dynamical variables which can be expressed in terms of that variable.

The time-dependent wave equation

Problems will arise later in which we have to deal with super-positions of state-functions belonging to different energies (chapter 9), in which case equation (2.13) is not appropriate, since it contains the energy E as a parameter; or in which the energy and state of the system described by the state-function are time-dependent – as, for instance, when the oscillatory electromagnetic field of a light wave falls on an atom (chapter 11) – in which case again (2.13) is not appropriate, and a more general equation is required in which time appears as an independent variable. A more general equation cannot be *derived* from a less general one; what we shall do is try to *infer* from (2.13) and our general ideas about variables and operators a plausible form for a time-dependent equation akin to (2.13), and leave it to be tested by the comparison of the predictions we can make from it with the results of observation. Although in non-relativistic mechanics the time appears on quite a different footing from the space-coordinates, it is convenient to look for guidance to the formalism of relativistic mechanics. The position and momentum 4-vectors are (x_1, x_2, x_3, ict) and $(p_1, p_2, p_3, iE/c)$, and we shall assume that the fourth position and momentum coordinates are conjugate in the same way as the first three. By analogy with the operator substitutions

$$p_r \rightarrow \frac{\hbar}{i} \frac{\partial}{\partial x_r} \qquad (r = 1, 2, 3)$$

we shall put

$$\frac{iE}{c} \rightarrow \frac{\hbar}{i} \frac{\partial}{\partial(ict)}$$

$$\therefore \quad E \rightarrow i\hbar \frac{\partial}{\partial t}.$$

If the energy is not explicitly dependent on time we may then write

$$E\Psi = i\hbar \frac{\partial \Psi}{\partial t}$$

as

$$H(p, q)\Psi = i\hbar \frac{\partial \Psi}{\partial t}. \tag{2.16}$$

In this 'equation of motion', from which the time-variation of the state-function may be derived, we have written the state-function as Ψ rather than ψ to remind us that we are now dealing with a function of the position coordinates and the time, i.e. $\Psi = \Psi(q, t)$. It is easy to verify (see problem (5) on p. 40) that Ψ can be written as a product of space-dependent and time-dependent factors, $\Psi(q, t) = \psi(q)\varepsilon^{-iEt/\hbar}$. State-functions of this type and containing different values of the energy parameter E may be superposed to represent states in which the energy is not sharp – see, for example, the discussion of the oscillating wave packet, on pp. 186 and 187.

The state-function with the minimum uncertainty product

We are now in a position to refer back to the derivation of the uncertainty relation (2.8) and enquire what are the consequences of imposing the conditions that must be satisfied if the equality sign, rather than the inequality, is to be used in this equation. We have seen that there are in fact two conditions, relating to equations (2.4) and (2.6). The first condition, from (2.4), is that $\alpha = k\beta$ or $P_0\psi = kQ_0\psi$ where k is a constant; the second condition, from (2.6), is that

$$\psi^*(P_0Q_0 + Q_0P_0)\psi = 0$$
$$\therefore \quad \psi^*P_0Q_0\psi + \psi^*Q_0P_0\psi = 0.$$

Putting

$$P_0\psi = kQ_0\psi \text{ and } \psi^*P_0 = \psi^*Q_0\bar{k}$$

gives

$$\psi^*Q_0Q_0\psi(\bar{k}+k) = 0$$

which is true only if k is a pure imaginary, say ic, where c is real. Then $P_0\psi = kQ_0\psi = icQ_0\psi$ can be written as a differential equation, by setting

$$P_0 = \frac{\hbar}{i}\frac{d}{dx} - \langle p \rangle, \quad Q_0 = x - \langle x \rangle.$$

This gives

$$\frac{\hbar}{i}\frac{d\psi}{dx} - \langle p \rangle \psi = ic(x - \langle x \rangle)\psi$$

or

$$\frac{d\psi}{dx} = \left(-\frac{c}{\hbar}(x - \langle x \rangle) + \frac{i}{\hbar}\langle p \rangle\right)\psi$$

or

$$\psi(x) = N \exp\left(-\frac{c}{2\hbar}(x - \langle x \rangle)^2 + \frac{i}{\hbar}\langle p \rangle x\right)$$
$$= N \varepsilon^{-c(x-\langle x \rangle)^2/2\hbar} \varepsilon^{ipx/\hbar}.$$

The first factor here is like a Gaussian error function; in error theory this function is commonly written, in normalized form,

$$\frac{1}{\sqrt{2\pi}\,\sigma}\,\varepsilon^{-(x-\bar{x})^2/2\sigma^2}$$

where $\bar{x}$ replaces $\langle x \rangle$ and σ is the standard deviation. Now the function $\psi(x)$ which we have determined does not represent a probability distribution, but $|\psi(x)|^2$ does; thus comparing

$$|\psi(x)|^2 = N^2\,\varepsilon^{-c(x-\langle x\rangle)^2/\hbar}$$

with the Gaussian function we see that

$$\frac{c}{\hbar} = \frac{1}{2\sigma^2} = \frac{1}{2(\Delta x)^2}$$

and

$$N^2 = \frac{1}{\sqrt{2\pi}\,\sigma} = \frac{1}{\sqrt{2\pi}\,\Delta x}$$

so that

$$\psi(x) = \frac{1}{(2\pi(\Delta x)^2)^{\frac{1}{4}}}\,\varepsilon^{\frac{-(x-\langle x\rangle)^2}{4(\Delta x)^2}+\frac{i\langle p\rangle x}{\hbar}}. \tag{2.17}$$

Thus the minimum value of the uncertainty product is obtained only for a function of this Gaussian type. We shall see in the next chapter that the ground state of the simple harmonic oscillator is represented by a state-function of this kind.

Problems

(1) The operators s_3 and s_4 of problem (3) on p. 24 commute. Calculate $(\Delta s_3)^2$ and $(\Delta s_4)^2$ for the states represented by each of the column vectors

$$\begin{bmatrix} 1 \\ 0 \end{bmatrix}, \quad \begin{bmatrix} 0 \\ 1 \end{bmatrix}, \quad \frac{1}{\sqrt{2}}\begin{bmatrix} 1 \\ 1 \end{bmatrix}, \quad \frac{1}{\sqrt{2}}\begin{bmatrix} 1 \\ -1 \end{bmatrix}.$$

(2) For the operators s_2 and s_3 of problem (3) on p. 24 show that $s_2 s_3 - s_3 s_2$ is not Hermitian, but that $i(s_2 s_3 - s_3 s_2)$ is Hermitian.

(3) Verify eqn. (2.4).

(The vectors α and β define a plane. Relative to orthogonal axes in this plane α and β may be written in terms of their components as $(\alpha_1 \varepsilon^{i\theta_1}, \alpha_2 \varepsilon^{i\theta_2})$ and $(\beta_1 \varepsilon^{i\phi_1}, \beta_2 \varepsilon^{i\phi_2})$.)

(4) Show that in Poisson bracket form Hamilton's canonical equations can be written

$$\dot{q}_i + \{q_i, H\} = \dot{p}_i + \{p_i, H\} = 0.$$

(5) Show, from the eigenvalue equation $E\Psi = i\hbar \dfrac{\partial \Psi}{\partial t}$ that $\Psi(x, y, z; t)$ $= \psi(x, y, z)\varepsilon^{-i\omega t}$ is an eigenfunction of the energy operator, and find the corresponding eigenvalue.

(6) Using the representation
$$x \rightarrow x, \quad p_x \rightarrow \frac{\hbar}{i} \frac{d}{dx}$$
set up the Schrödinger equation $H\psi = E\psi$ for a particle of mass m confined between perfectly reflecting walls; find the eigenfunctions $\psi(x)$ and the eigenvalues of the operator H. Show that the energy of the lowest state is consistent with the uncertainty principle.

$$\left(\text{Take the potential energy as } \begin{cases} V(x) = 0 \text{ for } |x| \leqq a \\ V(x) = \infty \text{ for } |x| > a \end{cases} \right)$$

(7) When considering the motion of a particle in a central field of force we may treat the angular and radial motions separately. The obvious choice for the radial coordinate is $r = (x^2 + y^2 + z^2)^{\frac{1}{2}}$. Classically the radial momentum can be taken to be

$$p_r' = \frac{1}{r}(\mathbf{r} \cdot \mathbf{p}) \quad or \quad (\mathbf{p} \cdot \mathbf{r})\frac{1}{r},$$

where $\mathbf{p}$ is the vector whose components are (p_x, p_y, p_z). However, neither of these is a suitable form for the momentum conjugate to r in quantum mechanics, since the conjugate momentum operator must (i) be Hermitian, and (ii) satisfy with r a commutation relation of the form (2.11), and either of the p_r' defined above satisfies only one of these conditions.

Investigate whether the suggested forms for p_r' are Hermitian or not, and by evaluating the Poisson brackets $\{p_r', r\}$ for each of these forms find whether they satisfy the requisite commutation relation. (The relations $\{p_x, r\} = \dfrac{x}{r}$, etc. and $\left\{ p_x, \dfrac{1}{r} \right\} = -\dfrac{x}{r^3}$,

etc. will be found useful.)

Hence, or otherwise, show that

$$p_r = \frac{1}{2}\left[\frac{1}{r}(\mathbf{r} \cdot \mathbf{p}) + (\mathbf{p} \cdot \mathbf{r})\frac{1}{r} \right] = \frac{1}{r}(\mathbf{r} \cdot \mathbf{p} - i\hbar)$$

is a suitable operator for the radial momentum, since it satisfies both the conditions (i) and (ii) above.

CHAPTER THREE

THE MATRIX TREATMENT OF THE SIMPLE HARMONIC OSCILLATOR

The first problem to which matrix mechanics was applied was that of predicting the energy levels and spectrum of a simple harmonic oscillator. We have already remarked that the Hamiltonian of such an oscillator has a particularly symmetrical form, and this makes the algebraic manipulations particularly simple.

Time-dependence of matrix elements

We first recall equation (2.9f), for the time-derivative of any function F which depends explicitly on a set of canonical momentum and position coordinates and on time, i.e. $F = F(\mathbf{p}, \mathbf{q}; t)$. We have

$$\frac{dF}{dt} = \frac{\partial F}{\partial t} + \{H, F\}$$

where H, the Hamiltonian, depends only on the momentum and position coordinates. The first term on the right, the partial derivative, takes care of the explicit dependence of F on t, while the Poisson brackets of F with H represents the contribution to $\dfrac{dF}{dt}$ of the time dependence of the other dynamical variables on which F depends. In the event that F is not explicitly dependent on time this becomes

$$\frac{dF}{dt} = \{H, F\} = \frac{i}{\hbar} (HF - FH). \qquad (3.1)$$

It follows that if F commutes with H, $\dot{F}$ is zero and F is a constant of the motion. (In this chapter the 'dot notation' is used for the *total* derivative.)

In a matrix representation in which H is a diagonal matrix (and in which the basis of the coordinate system is the set of eigenvectors of H) the elements of the time derivative of any matrix F are, from (3.1),

41

$$\dot{F}_{rs} = \frac{i}{\hbar}\,(HF - FH)_{rs}$$

$$= \frac{i}{\hbar}\,(H_r F_{rs} - F_{rs} H_s)$$

$$\therefore \quad \dot{F}_{rs} = \frac{i}{\hbar}\,(H_r - H_s)F_{rs} = i\omega_{rs}F_{rs}. \tag{3.2}$$

Here we have made the substitution $\omega_{rs} = (H_r - H_s)/\hbar$, which looks like the Bohr frequency condition; we cannot yet say that it *is* the Bohr frequency condition, because so far we have no physical interpretation of this relationship. Integrating (3.2) with respect to time we get

$$F_{rs}(t) = F_{rs}(0)\,\varepsilon^{i\omega_{rs}t}$$

and if F is Hermitian $\tag{3.3}$

$$F_{sr}(t) = F_{sr}(0)\,\varepsilon^{-i\omega_{rs}t}.$$

In this representation, then, the matrix elements of the operator representing any dynamical variable contain time factors $\varepsilon^{\pm i\omega_{rs}t}$. Only a diagonal matrix has none of these time-dependent factors; when H, which is a constant of the motion, is represented by a diagonal matrix, all other constants of the motion will be represented by diagonal matrices since they commute with H. (This point was referred to in chapter 1, on p. 19, and the result of problem 6 on p. 24 is relevant here.)

Equation (3.1) or the more general equation

$$\frac{dF}{dt} = \frac{\partial F}{\partial t} + \frac{i}{\hbar}\,(HF - FH), \tag{3.1'}$$

is Heisenberg's equation of motion for the dynamical variable F. It is worth noting that, whereas wave-mechanics furnishes an equation for the time-variation of the (unobservable) state-function (equation (2.16)), the corresponding equation in matrix mechanics is concerned with the time-variation of the matrices which represent dynamical variables.

Matrices for H, p and x

We now attempt to construct a matrix representation in which the Hamiltonian of the one-dimensional simple harmonic oscillator is a diagonal matrix, and in which the matrices representing the momentum and position variables on which H depends through (2.14) satisfy the commutation relation (2.11).

It will save labour if we replace the variables p and x by new variables P and Q which are defined by

$$P^2 = p^2/m, \quad Q^2 = m\omega^2 x^2.$$

The Hamiltonian is then

$$H = \tfrac{1}{2}(P^2 + Q^2) \tag{3.4}$$

and P and Q, each of which has dimensions [energy]$^{\frac{1}{2}}$, satisfy the commutation relation

$$i(PQ - QP) = \hbar\omega. \tag{3.5}$$

If P and Q were commuting variables we could write $P^2 + Q^2 = (P+iQ)(P-iQ)$, but this is not the case here. Instead, using (3.5) we see that

$$(P+iQ)(P-iQ) = P^2 + Q^2 - i(PQ - QP) = P^2 + Q^2 - \hbar\omega$$

$$(P-iQ)(P+iQ) = P^2 + Q^2 + i(PQ - QP) = P^2 + Q^2 + \hbar\omega$$

It will be convenient to denote the non-Hermitian operator $(P+iQ)/\sqrt{2}$ by R; then since P and Q are Hermitian it follows that $(P-iQ)/\sqrt{2} = R^*$. Then we have, from the two equations above, along with (3.4):

$$H = \tfrac{1}{2}(P^2 + Q^2) = RR^* + \hbar\omega/2$$

$$= R^*R - \hbar\omega/2. \tag{3.6}$$

Now, if ψ_n is an eigenfunction of H belonging to the eigenvalue E_n, so that $H\psi_n = E_n\psi_n$, it follows that

$$HR\psi_n = (RR^* + \hbar\omega/2)R\psi_n$$

$$= RR^*R\psi_n + (\hbar\omega/2)R\psi_n$$

$$= R(H + \hbar\omega/2)\psi_n + R(\hbar\omega/2)\psi_n$$

$$= R(H + \hbar\omega)\psi_n$$

$$= R(E_n + \hbar\omega)\psi_n$$

$$\therefore \quad HR\psi_n = (E_n + \hbar\omega)R\psi_n$$

so $R\psi_n$ is an eigenfunction of H with eigenvalue $E_n + \hbar\omega$. It follows, by induction, that

$$HR^s\psi_n = (E_n + s\hbar\omega)R^s\psi_n \qquad (3.7a)$$

i.e., $R^s\psi_n$ is an eigenfunction of H with eigenvalue $E_n + s\hbar\omega$.

In an exactly analogous way it can be shown that

$$HR^*\psi_n = (E_n - \hbar\omega)R^*\psi_n$$

and hence that

$$H(R^*)^s\psi_n = (E_n - s\hbar\omega)(R^*)^s\psi_n \qquad (3.7b)$$

i.e., $(R^*)^s\psi_n$ is an eigenfunction of H with eigenvalue $E_n - s\hbar\omega$. Evidently there is a ladder of uniformly spaced eigenvalues, the height of each step being $\hbar\omega$, and if we know the eigenfunction corresponding to any one of these we can find all the other eigenfunctions by repeated application of the shifting operators R and R^*.

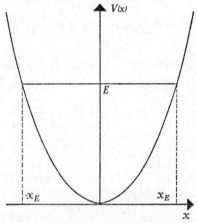

FIG. 3.1. The potential function $V = \frac{1}{2}m\omega^2 x^2$ for the simple harmonic oscillator. According to classical mechanics a particle with total energy E would oscillate with (angular) frequency ω between the limits x_E and $-x_E$.

Inspection of the potential well for the harmonic oscillator (Fig. 3.1) suggests that there should be no upper limit to the eigenvalue adder, but that there must be a lower limit. The existence of the lower limit can also be shown algebraically. For if A is any Hermitian matrix the diagonal elements of A^2 are of the form

$$[A^2]_{rr} = \sum_s A_{rs}A_{sr}$$

$$= \sum_s |A_{rs}|^2$$

$$\geqq 0.$$

Hence the diagonal elements of the matrices of P^2, Q^2 and H cannot be negative, so the eigenvalues of H – the allowed energies – cannot be negative.

Now let ψ_0 be the eigenfunction belonging to the lowest eigenvalue E_0, which must be the energy of the ground state of the oscillator.

Then

$$R^*\psi_0 = 0, \tag{3.8}$$

for $R^*\psi_0$ would represent a state of lower energy, and there is no such state.

Also

$$\tfrac{1}{2}(P^2+Q^2)\psi_0 = E_0\psi_0$$

$$\therefore \quad \{RR^*+\hbar\omega/2\}\psi_0 = E_0\psi_0$$

$$\therefore \quad R(R^*\psi_0)+\tfrac{1}{2}\hbar\omega\psi_0 = E_0\psi_0.$$

From (3.8) the first term on the left vanishes, and so

$$E_o = \tfrac{1}{2}\hbar\omega \tag{3.9a}$$

which is the ground-state energy for the one-dimensional oscillator. It follows that the energy of the nth excited state is

$$E_n = (n+\tfrac{1}{2})\hbar\omega. \tag{3.9b}$$

These values of E_0 and E_n are also the elements of the diagonal matrix of H.

We now want to find the matrix elements of the shifting operators R and R^*.

From (3.4) and (3.6),

$$RR^* = H-\hbar\omega/2$$

and

$$R^*R = H+\hbar\omega/2$$

$$\therefore \quad R^*(H-\hbar\omega/2) = (H+\hbar\omega/2)R^*.$$

Equating the rsth element of each side

$$R_{rs}^*(H_s - \hbar\omega/2) = (H_r + \hbar\omega/2)R_{rs}^*$$
$$\therefore \quad R_{rs}^*(H_r - H_s + \hbar\omega) = 0.$$

This means that $R_{rs}^* = 0$ unless $H_r - H_s = -\hbar\omega$, i.e. unless H_r and H_s are neighbouring elements of H, in which case $s = r+1$. In the same way we could show that $R_{rs} = 0$ unless $s = r-1$.

The matrices of R and R^* must therefore look like:

R $\qquad\qquad\qquad\qquad$ R^*

Here the dots represent elements which are zero, the crosses represent non-zero elements, and the matrices are drawn without boundaries at the right and the bottom because they extend to infinity in these directions.

We can now write

$$RR^* = H - \hbar\omega/2$$

in terms of elements as

$$R_{r,\,r-1}\,R_{r-1,\,r}^* = H_r - \hbar\omega/2$$
$$= r\hbar\omega \quad \text{(using (3.9b))}$$
$$\therefore \quad |R_{r,\,r-1}|^2 = |R_{r-1,\,r}^*|^2 = r\hbar\omega$$
$$\therefore \quad 2^{\frac{1}{2}}R_{r,\,r-1} = (P+iQ)_{r,\,r-1} = (2r\hbar\omega)^{\frac{1}{2}}\,\varepsilon^{-i\gamma}\,\varepsilon^{i\omega t} \tag{3.10a}$$
$$\text{and} \quad 2^{\frac{1}{2}}R_{r-1,\,r}^* = (P-iQ)_{r-1,\,r} = (2r\hbar\omega)^{\frac{1}{2}}\,\varepsilon^{i\gamma}\,\varepsilon^{-i\omega t} \tag{3.10b}$$

These are the only non-vanishing elements of the matrices for

$(P \pm iQ)$. From them we can go on to find the matrices for P and Q. Dropping the indeterminate and unobservable phase factors $\varepsilon^{\pm i\gamma}$ we can write

$$P_{r,r-1} = \tfrac{1}{2}\{(P+iQ)_{r,r-1} + (P-iQ)_{r,r-1}\}$$

$$\therefore P_{r,r-1} = \tfrac{1}{2}(P+iQ)_{r,r-1} = \left(\frac{r\hbar\omega}{2}\right)^{\frac{1}{2}} \varepsilon^{i\omega t}$$

$$\text{and} \quad P_{r-1,r} = \tfrac{1}{2}(P-iQ)_{r-1,r} = \left(\frac{r\hbar\omega}{2}\right)^{\frac{1}{2}} \varepsilon^{-i\omega t} \tag{3.11}$$

and in the same way

$$Q_{r,r-1} = \frac{1}{2i}(P+iQ)_{r,r-1} = \frac{1}{i}\left(\frac{r\hbar\omega}{2}\right)^{\frac{1}{2}} \varepsilon^{i\omega t}$$

$$\text{and} \quad Q_{r-1,r} = -\frac{1}{2i}(P-iQ)_{r-1,r} = -\frac{1}{i}\left(\frac{r\hbar\omega}{2}\right)^{\frac{1}{2}} \varepsilon^{-i\omega t}. \tag{3.12}$$

The matrices for p and x are simply those for P and Q multiplied by $m^{\frac{1}{2}}$ and $(m^{\frac{1}{2}}\omega)^{-1}$ respectively, i.e.

$$p_{r,r-1} = \left(\frac{rm\hbar\omega}{2}\right)^{\frac{1}{2}} \varepsilon^{i\omega t}$$

$$p_{r-1,r} = \left(\frac{rm\hbar\omega}{2}\right)^{\frac{1}{2}} \varepsilon^{-i\omega t} \tag{3.11'}$$

$$x_{r,r-1} = \frac{1}{i}\left(\frac{r\hbar}{2m\omega}\right)^{\frac{1}{2}} \varepsilon^{i\omega t}$$

$$x_{r-1,r} = -\frac{1}{i}\left(\frac{r\hbar}{2m\omega}\right)^{\frac{1}{2}} \varepsilon^{-i\omega t}. \tag{3.12'}$$

The equation of motion of the simple harmonic oscillator

Having now obtained the matrices for H, p and x, we can, by two successive applications of eqn. (3.1), find the matrix for $\ddot{x}$, thus:

$$\dot{x} = \frac{i}{\hbar}(Hx - xH),$$

$$\ddot{x} = \frac{i}{\hbar}(H\dot{x} - \dot{x}H).$$

From the first of these the rsth element of the matrix for $\dot{x}$ is

$$\dot{x}_{rs} = \frac{i}{\hbar}(Hx - xH)_{rs}$$

$$= \frac{i}{\hbar}(H_r x_{rs} - x_{rs} H_s)$$

$$= \frac{i(H_r - H_s)}{\hbar} x_{rs}$$

$$= i\omega_{rs} x_{rs}.$$

It follows that $\dot{x}_{rs}$, like x_{rs}, vanishes unless $r = s \pm 1$, and that

$$\omega_{r,\, r-1} = \omega = -\omega_{r-1,\, r}.$$

Thus
$$\dot{x}_{r,\, r-1} = i\omega x_{r,\, r-1} = p_{r,\, r-1}/m,$$

$$\dot{x}_{r-1,\, r} = -i\omega x_{r-1,\, r} = p_{r-1,\, r}/m,$$
$$\text{(using (3.11') and (3.12'))}$$

so the matrices for p and x satisfy the relation $p = m\dot{x}$ as we should expect. Applying equation (3.1) a second time, the rsth element of the matrix for $\ddot{x}$ must be

$$\ddot{x}_{rs} = \frac{i}{\hbar}(H_r \dot{x}_{rs} - \dot{x}_{rs} H_s)$$

$$= \frac{i(H_r - H_s)}{\hbar} \dot{x}_{rs}$$

$$= i\omega_{rs} \dot{x}_{rs}.$$

Again, $\ddot{x}_{rs}$, like $\dot{x}_{rs}$, must vanish unless $r = s \pm 1$, so that

$$\ddot{x}_{r,\, r-1} = i\omega(i\omega x_{r,\, r-1}) = -\omega^2 x_{r,\, r-1}$$

$$\ddot{x}_{r-1,\, r} = -i\omega(-i\omega x_{r-1,\, r}) = -\omega^2 x_{r-1,\, r}.$$

Thus the matrices for $\ddot{x}$ and x satisfy an equation of motion,

$$\ddot{x} = -\omega^2 x,$$

which has the same appearance as that for the corresponding variables in the classical treatment of the simple harmonic oscillator. We shall make use of this equation in chapter 4, when we consider the precession of the magnetic moment of an electron in a magnetic field (pp. 71-75).

Wave-mechanical state-functions

The eigenfunctions of the Hamiltonian operator in the wave-mechanical representation can be found if we put the shifting operators into differential form by the substitutions

$$Q \rightarrow Q, \quad P \rightarrow \frac{\hbar\omega}{i} \frac{d}{dQ},$$

which satisfy the commutation relation (3.5). Then eqn. (3.8) can be rewritten as

$$\frac{\hbar\omega}{i} \frac{d\psi_0}{dQ} - iQ\psi_0 = 0$$

whose solution is the wave-mechanical representation of the ground state:

$$\psi_0 = C_0 \, \varepsilon^{-Q^2/2\hbar\omega} = C_0 \, \varepsilon^{-m\omega x^2/2\hbar}. \tag{3.13}$$

For the nth excited state

$$\psi_n = (P+iQ)^n \psi_0$$

$$= \left(\frac{1}{i}\right)^n C_n \left\{ \hbar\omega\frac{d}{dQ} - Q \right\}^n \psi_0. \tag{3.14}$$

An alternative method of finding the wave-mechanical state-functions is to substitute the differential operators in the eigenvalue equation for the Hamiltonian

$$H\psi = E\psi$$

and so form the Schrödinger equation. This is solved by a series expansion of ψ, as is done for the three-dimensional oscillator in the second section of chapter 5. The method used here obviates the solution of a second-order differential equation by using information about the properties of the solutions which has been obtained by algebraic manipulation.

The energy eigenfunctions are of the form $\psi_n = H_n(x)\varepsilon^{-\alpha x^2/2}$, where $H_n(x)$ is a polynomial containing only even or odd powers of x according as n is even or odd (see problem 3, p. 57). It was explained in chapter 1 that wave-mechanical state-functions are superpositions – in fact continuous distributions – of position eigenfunctions. It is easy to see that the Hamiltonian for the oscillator does not commute with x, and any energy eigenfunction is represented by a distribution-in-x whose range extends from $-\infty$ to $+\infty$. If the oscillator is observed and the value of the coordinate is determined rather precisely, the information so acquired can be represented by a distribution-in-x which is considerably more localized than a *single* energy eigenfunction. It must however be possible to represent this localized distribution-in-x by a suitably constructed *superposition* of energy eigenfunctions, implying that a localized configuration must be one in which the energy is not sharp. (Problem 6 on p. 57, and the discussion of the *Oscillating wave-packet* in chapter 9, both have a bearing on this point.)

Expectation values

When a system is in the state represented by ψ, the expectation value of a variable or function, say f, represented by the operator F, is $\langle f \rangle_\psi = \psi^* F \psi$. If ψ is a column vector with elements a_i (and ψ^*, therefore, a row vector with elements $\bar{a}_i$), and if F is a Hermitian matrix with elements f_{ij}, matrix multiplication gives us the expression

$$\langle f \rangle_\psi = \sum_i \sum_j \bar{a}_i f_{ij} a_j.$$

(This is a more general form than we had for $\langle p \rangle$ in equation (1.8). There we assumed the eigenfunctions and eigenvalues of P to be known, and expressed ψ as a linear superposition of those eigenfunctions. Here, on the other hand, no such intimate relationship is assumed between the operator F and the components of ψ.) Now, in the representation in which the Hamiltonian matrix H is diagonal, any eigenstate of H, say ψ_n, is represented by a vector of whose elements all but one vanish, and that one, a_n say, has modulus unity if the vector is normalized. The above expression for $\langle f \rangle_\psi$ then simplifies and can be written

$$\langle f \rangle_n = |a_n|^2 f_{nn} = f_{nn}. \tag{3.15}$$

This means that when the simple harmonic oscillator is in a state ψ_n in which the energy is sharp, the expectation value of any dynamical variable such as p or x is the nth diagonal element of the matrix which represents that variable. As we saw on p. 47 the matrices of p and x – or P and Q – have zeros all the way down the diagonal, so for every eigenstate of the energy the expectation or mean values of the displacement x and momentum p are zero. In classical mechanics too the mean values of the displacement and momentum of a harmonic oscillator are zero. By matrix multiplication we find that the matrix for x^2 is

$$x^2 = \begin{vmatrix} x_{01}x_{10} & 0 & x_{01}x_{12} & 0 & 0 \\ 0 & x_{10}x_{01}+x_{12}x_{21} & 0 & x_{12}x_{23} & 0 \\ x_{21}x_{10} & 0 & x_{21}x_{12}+x_{23}x_{32} & 0 & x_{23}x_{34} \\ 0 & x_{32}x_{21} & 0 & x_{32}x_{23}+x_{34}x_{43} & 0 \\ 0 & 0 & x_{43}x_{32} & 0 & x_{43}x_{34}+x_{45}x_{54} \end{vmatrix}$$

$$= \frac{\hbar}{2m\omega} \begin{vmatrix} 1 & 0 & \sqrt{2}\,\varepsilon^{-2i\omega t} & 0 & 0 \\ 0 & 3 & 0 & \sqrt{2.3}\,\varepsilon^{-2i\omega t} & 0 \\ \sqrt{2}\,\varepsilon^{2i\omega t} & 0 & 5 & 0 & \sqrt{3.4}\,\varepsilon^{-2i\omega t} \\ 0 & \sqrt{2.3}\,\varepsilon^{2i\omega t} & 0 & 7 & 0 \\ 0 & 0 & \sqrt{3.4}\,\varepsilon^{2i\omega t} & 0 & 9 \end{vmatrix}$$

so that
$$\langle x^2 \rangle_n = (2n+1)\frac{\hbar}{2m\omega}.$$

Now $\langle x \rangle_n$ is zero, so the uncertainty in x is equal to $\langle x^2 \rangle_n^{\frac{1}{2}}$ and we see that it increases as the energy increases.

The potential energy in the nth excited state is

$$\langle V \rangle_n = \tfrac{1}{2}m\omega^2 \langle x^2 \rangle_n = \tfrac{1}{2}m\omega^2 \cdot 2(n+\tfrac{1}{2})\frac{\hbar}{2m\omega}$$

$$= \tfrac{1}{2}(n+\tfrac{1}{2})\hbar\omega = \tfrac{1}{2}E_n.$$

The expectation value of kinetic energy is

$$\langle T \rangle_n = \frac{1}{2m}\langle p^2 \rangle_n = \frac{1}{2m}\langle (m\dot{x})^2 \rangle_n = \frac{1}{2m}\langle (im\omega x)^2 \rangle_n$$

$$\therefore \langle T \rangle_n = \frac{m\omega^2}{2}\langle x^2 \rangle_n = \langle V \rangle_n = \tfrac{1}{2}E_n.$$

Thus the expectation values of the potential and kinetic energies are equal, and are each equal to half the total energy. These results are true also in classical mechanics, but there a more precise statement is possible: that the sum of the instantaneous kinetic and potential energies is equal to the total energy. That statement is not verifiable according to quantum mechanics since p^2 and x^2 do not commute, so their instantaneous values cannot both be measured at the same time.

Uncertainty relations for the harmonic oscillator

At this point it is interesting to look at the uncertainty relation $\Delta p \Delta x \geq \hbar/2$ in its specific application to the oscillator. From (2.3)

$$\Delta p = \{\langle p^2 \rangle - \langle p \rangle^2\}^{\frac{1}{2}}$$

$$\Delta x = \{\langle x^2 \rangle - \langle x \rangle^2\}^{\frac{1}{2}}.$$

We have found that

$$\langle p^2 \rangle_n = \frac{m\omega}{2}(2n+1)\, \hbar$$

$$\langle p \rangle_n = 0$$

$$\langle x^2 \rangle_n = \frac{1}{2m\omega}(2n+1)\, \hbar$$

$$\langle x \rangle_n = 0$$

$$\therefore \ (\Delta p \Delta x)_n = (\langle p^2 \rangle_n \langle x^2 \rangle_n)^{\frac{1}{2}} = (n+\tfrac{1}{2})\hbar.$$

Thus the uncertainties, or spreads, in p and x increase as $n^{\frac{1}{2}}$ for large values of n, and their product increases as the energy. For the ground state

$$(\Delta p \Delta x)_0 = \frac{\hbar}{2}$$

which is the minimum value allowed by the general argument of chapter 2, and it will be noted that the wave-mechanical ground-state function for the oscillator, eqn. (3.13), is a special case of the Gaussian one found at (2.17), which gives the uncertainty product its minimum value. For the excited states of the oscillator the uncertainty product has larger values, and the wave-functions found from (3.14) are not Gaussian. (See problem 3, p. 57.)

The oscillator in three dimensions; degeneracy

The extension of the foregoing discussion to the three-dimensional oscillator is now simple. The Hamiltonian is

$$H = \frac{1}{2m}(p_1{}^2 + p_2{}^2 + p_3{}^2) + k_1 x_1{}^2 + k_2 x_2{}^2 + k_3 x_3{}^2$$

where $k_1 = k_2 = k_3$ if the oscillator is isotropic. Since x_1, p_1 commute with x_2, p_2, x_3, p_3, and similarly for the other pairs, this can be written in three separate equations

$$H_1 = \frac{1}{2m}p_1{}^2 + k_1 x_1{}^2$$

$$H_2 = \frac{1}{2m}p_2{}^2 + k_2 x_2{}^2$$

$$H_3 = \frac{1}{2m}p_3{}^2 + k_3 x_3{}^2$$

subject to the condition $H_1 + H_2 + H_3 = H$, so the total energy is

$$E_1 + E_2 + E_3 = E.$$

The E_1, E_2 and E_3 are the energies for each of the independent degrees of freedom. If we write $k_i = \frac{1}{2}m\omega_i{}^2$,

$$E = (n_1 + \tfrac{1}{2})\hbar\omega_1 + (n_2 + \tfrac{1}{2})\hbar\omega_2 + (n_3 + \tfrac{1}{2})\hbar\omega_3.$$

When the oscillator is isotropic $\omega_1 = \omega_2 = \omega_3$ and

$$E_{123} = (n_1 + n_2 + n_3 + \tfrac{3}{2})\hbar\omega.$$

The ground-state energy is then $\tfrac{3}{2}\hbar\omega$, i.e. $\tfrac{1}{2}\hbar\omega$ for each degree of freedom.

A given energy can occur in a number of ways. If we write

$$E_N = (N + \tfrac{3}{2})\hbar\omega \quad \text{with} \quad N = n_1 + n_2 + n_3 \qquad (3.16)$$

there are as many configurations of the system giving this energy as there are groups of three non-negative integers which sum to N, i.e. $\tfrac{1}{2}(N+1)(N+2)$. The existence of different combinations of state-functions having the same energy is called *degeneracy*; the number of such combinations is called the degree of degeneracy. Degeneracy is generally associated with symmetry. For example, the first excited state of the isotropic oscillator, with $N=1$, may arise in three ways, the three sets of values of (n_1, n_2, n_3) being $(1, 0, 0)$, $(0, 1, 0)$, and

(0, 0, 1). But any of the three configurations represented by the corresponding combination of state functions can be transformed into the others by 90° rotations of the cartesian coordinate axes. If however the oscillator is made anisotropic by putting $k_1 = k$, $k_2 = k_3 = k'$, the states corresponding to the sets of quantum numbers (0, 1, 0) and (0, 0, 1) have the same energy and can be transformed into one another by a 90° rotation about the x-axis, but the energy for the set (1, 0, 0) is different. The degree of degeneracy has therefore been reduced, and the remaining degeneracy would be eliminated by making $k_1 \neq k_2 \neq k_3$.

Non-diagonal matrix elements

It is natural to wonder what, if any, physical significance can be attached to the non-diagonal elements of the matrices we construct. A diagonal element of a matrix represents the expectation value of the corresponding dynamical variable when the system is in one of the basic states relative to which the matrix is defined. A non-diagonal element, on the other hand, is not associated with a single state, but rather with a pair of states. We can show this by an argument similar to that which led to equation (3.15). Let ψ_m and ψ_n be two normalized eigenvectors of the Hamiltonian, the only non-vanishing element of ψ_m being a_n, and the only non-vanishing element of ψ_n being b_n, with $|a_m|^2 = 1$, $|b_n|^2 = 1$. Then, with the matrix F represented as before,

$$\psi_m{}^* F \psi_n = \bar{a}_m f_{mn} b_n = f_{mn} \varepsilon^{i\alpha}$$

(where α is the difference of the phase angles associated with the complex amplitudes a_m and b_n, and will often turn out to be unobservable). Thus the off-diagonal matrix element f_{mn} is associated with the states ψ_m and ψ_n, and (3.3) shows that f_{mn} will depend on time through a factor like $\varepsilon^{i(E_m - E_n)t/\hbar} = \varepsilon^{i\omega_{mn}t}$. It will appear in chapter 11 that any off-diagonal element is related to the probability of a transition between the states m and n with which it is associated, and that the corresponding frequency ω_{mn} is that of the radiation which may accompany the transition.

The only non-zero elements in the x-matrix for the simpleharmonic oscillator are, as we have seen, of the type $x_{n,\,n-1}$ or $x_{n-1,\,n}$, and this implies that the only transitions which such an oscillator can make are between neighbouring states; and the occurrence of the same frequency ω in all these matrix elements shows that the possible transitions, indicated by arrows on the energy-level diagram of Fig. 3.2, all give rise to radiation of one frequency. A highly excited state will decay by a cascade of single steps, and the spectrum of the radiation will exhibit a single line. This is substantially true of the molecular vibration spectrum in the near infra-red. The occurrence of weak lines at other frequencies is attributed

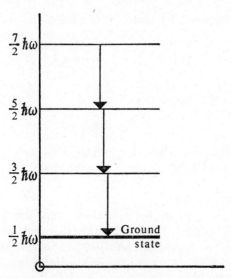

FIG. 3.2. The energy eigenvalues of the harmonic oscillator form a regular 'ladder'. Electric dipole transitions occur between neighbouring states.

to anharmonicity of the molecular oscillator: the potential is not simply $\propto x^2$, but contains higher powers of x which give rise to additional frequencies in the spectrum. These correspond to the upper harmonic frequencies which occur in the analogous classical problem.

If the wave-mechanical expressions for the state-functions and coordinate operators are used the matrix elements can be computed according to the prescription

$$[f(p,x)]_{mn} = \int \psi_m^* f\left(\frac{\hbar}{i}\frac{d}{dx}, x\right)\psi_n dx$$

so, for instance, the expectation values of x and x^2 for the ground state of the oscillator are obtained by integrating

QM E

$$| C_0 |^2 \int_{-\infty}^{+\infty} x\, \varepsilon^{-m\omega x^2/\hbar}\, dx$$

which vanishes because the integrand is odd, and

$$| C_0 |^2 \int_{-\infty}^{+\infty} x^2\, \varepsilon^{-m\omega x^2/\hbar}\, dx$$

which is integrated by parts. Normalizing the wave function by setting

$$\int_{-\infty}^{+\infty} \varepsilon^{-m\omega x^2/\hbar}\, dx = | C_0 |^{-2}$$

this gives, as we should expect,

$$\langle x^2 \rangle_0 = \hbar/2m\omega.$$

The non-diagonal elements are evaluated similarly; the integrations for the non-vanishing elements may be simplified by using (3.14) and (3.5).

The earlier forms of quantum theory, due mainly to Bohr and Sommerfeld, predicted integral rather than half-integral quantum numbers for the harmonic oscillator, and so gave the ground-state energy as zero. These earlier theories could not predict expectation values, transition probabilities or spectral intensities. The separate but almost simultaneous developments of matrix mechanics and wave-mechanics, by Heisenberg and Schrödinger respectively, both succeeded in these respects, though it was not at once obvious that these two theories, superficially so very different, were fundamentally equivalent. The close connection between them was first shown by Schrödinger, and the more general treatment was developed subsequently by Pauli, Dirac, von Neumann and others.

Problems

(1) If F is a variable not explicitly dependent on t, show that in any eigenstate of the energy the average value (or expectation value) of $\dot{F}$ is zero.

(2) Given that $p^2 = p_1^2 + p_2^2 + p_3^2$, $r^2 = q_1^2 + q_2^2 + q_3^2$, $V(r) \propto r^n$, apply the result of problem 1 to the variable $F = p_1 q_1 + p_2 q_2 + p_3 q_3$ for a system whose Hamiltonian is $H = p^2/2m + V(r)$, and show

that for the sth eigenstate of the Hamiltonian $2\langle T\rangle_s = n\langle V(r)\rangle_s$. This important result is known as the *virial theorem*. Check its predictions for the energy eigenstates of the harmonic oscillator.

(3) From (3.13) and (3.14) find the energy eigenfunctions of a few of the excited states of the harmonic oscillator. Note that these can be written as $H_n(x)\varepsilon^{-\alpha x^2/2}$, where $H_n(x)$ is either an odd or an even polynomial in x. Show that for the nth excited state this polynomial has n zeroes.

Show also that the state-functions have points of inflexion at those values of x at which a classical particle oscillating in the same potential well with the same energy would have zero velocity.

Hence sketch the state-functions and the probability distributions.

(4) If the functions found in problem 3 are written as $H_n(\xi)\varepsilon^{-\xi^2/2}$, they satisfy the relation

$$\psi_{n+1} = -i\left(\frac{d}{d\xi}-\xi\right)\psi_n; \text{ cf. (3.7) and (3.14)}.$$

Justify this, and hence show that

$$H_{n+1}(\xi) = 2\xi\,H_n(\xi) - H_n'(\xi).$$

Using the other shifting operator relation show that

$$H_n'(\xi) = 2n\,H_{n-1}(\xi).$$

(5) Using the results of problem (4), and remembering that the eigenfunctions for different n must be orthogonal, show that the 'electric dipole matrix' element

$$ex_{mn} = \int_{-\infty}^{+\infty} \psi_m^*(x)\,ex\,\psi_n(x)\,dx$$

vanishes unless $m=n\pm1$. (Here e is the magnitude of an oscillating electric charge.)

(6) Show that the mean value of x or p need not be zero for a state which is a superposition of two or more adjacent eigenstates of the harmonic oscillator.

(7) Find the uncertainty relation for the kinetic energy and potential energy of a one-dimensional simple harmonic oscillator.

(Caution: the discussion on pp. 32–34 is relevant.)

CHAPTER FOUR

QUANTIZATION OF ANGULAR MOMENTUM

The classification of molecular, atomic and nuclear states according to their angular momenta is one of the main tasks of spectroscopy; the first classification of the spectral series of atomic hydrogen according to principal quantum numbers proved less useful in the case of more complex systems where several such series may overlap, and the fine details of line structure, which are the clue to regularities in complex spectra, are found to depend on the angular momentum properties of the initial and final states between which radiative transitions occur. Further it is in terms of these properties that selection rules are formulated stating that transitions between certain types of states do not occur, or occur only in very exceptional circumstances.

The earlier quantum theories predicted that θ, the square of the angular momentum – which is of course proportional to the rotational kinetic energy – would have values

$$\theta = n^2\hbar^2 \qquad \text{where } n = 1, 2, 3 \ldots \text{etc.} \quad (4.1)$$

This did not agree with experimental results about the rotational spectra of molecules, where the separations of neighbouring rotational levels were found to be in the proportions

$$1 : 2 : 3 : 4 : 5 \ldots$$

rather than

$$3 : 5 : 7 : 9 : 11 \ldots$$

as would be the case if the above expression (4.1) were correct. One of the first successes of the new quantum mechanics, in Schrödinger's treatment of the Kepler problem, was the replacement of (4.1) by the relation

$$\theta = l(l+1)\hbar^2 \qquad \text{where } l = 0, 1, 2 \ldots \text{etc.} \quad (4.2)$$

First we shall discuss the properties of angular momentum in a central field of force; this introduces the quantization of angular

QUANTIZATION OF ANGULAR MOMENTUM 59

momentum through those commutation relations which are analogous to the classical laws of conservation of rotational energy and
angular momentum. Subsequently we shall show how the same
quantum numbers are used in the description of the motion of an
electron in certain non-central fields.

Constants of the motion

A central field of force is one which can be represented by a
potential which is a function of distance from a fixed point. We
shall write it as $V(r^2)$ where $r^2 = x_1{}^2 + x_2{}^2 + x_3{}^2$. The Hamiltonian
can then be written as

$$H = \frac{1}{2m}(p_1{}^2 + p_2{}^2 + p_3{}^2) + V(x_1{}^2 + x_2{}^2 + x_3{}^2).$$

We shall now show that for such a Hamiltonian the components of
angular momentum about the three coordinate axes, say m_1, m_2, m_3,
commute with H and are therefore constants of the motion; from
this it follows at once that the square of the total angular momentum,
$\theta = m_1{}^2 + m_2{}^2 + m_3{}^2$, commutes with H and so is a constant of the
motion.

Writing the angular momentum $\mathbf{m} = \mathbf{r} \wedge \mathbf{p}$ in component form we get

$$m_1 = x_2 p_3 - x_3 p_2$$
$$m_2 = x_3 p_1 - x_1 p_3$$
$$m_3 = x_1 p_2 - x_2 p_1.$$

The Poisson bracket of any one of these with any position or
momentum coordinate is easily found, e.g.

$$\{m_3, x_1\} = \{x_1 p_2 - x_2 p_1, x_1\}$$
$$= \{x_1 p_2, x_1\} - \{x_2 p_1, x_1\}$$
$$= x_1\{p_2, x_1\} + \{x_1, x_1\}p_2 - x_2\{p_1, x_1\} - \{x_2, x_1\}p_1$$
$$\therefore \{m_3, x_1\} = -x_2.$$

There are six such results involving m_3:

$$\{m_3, x_1\} = -x_2 \qquad \{m_3, p_1\} = -p_2$$
$$\{m_3, x_2\} = x_1 \qquad \{m_3, p_2\} = p_1 \qquad (4.3)$$
$$\{m_3, x_3\} = 0 \qquad \{m_3, p_3\} = 0$$

Further

$$\{m_3, m_1\} = \{m_3, x_2 p_3 - x_3 p_2\}$$

$$= x_2\{m_3, p_3\} + \{m_3, x_2\}p_3 - x_3\{m_3, p_2\} - \{m_3, x_3\}p_2$$

$$= x_1 p_3 - x_3 p_1$$

$$\therefore \ \{m_3, m_1\} = -m_2,$$

and the set of such results is

$$\{m_3, m_1\} = -m_2$$

$$\{m_1, m_2\} = -m_3 \qquad\qquad (4.4)$$

$$\{m_2, m_3\} = -m_1$$

along with $\qquad\qquad \{m_i, m_i\} = 0 \quad$ for any i.

We shall adopt (4.4) as definitions of the operators m_1, m_2, m_3, and by implication of θ.

The Hamiltonian is a function of p^2 and r^2, i.e. of $p_1{}^2 + p_2{}^2 + p_3{}^2$ and of $x_1{}^2 + x_2{}^2 + x_3{}^2$. Now, using (4.3),

$$\{m_3, r^2\} = x_1\{m_3, x_1\} + \{m_3, x_1\}x_1$$

$$+ x_2\{m_3, x_2\} + \{m_3, x_2\}x_2$$

$$+ x_3\{m_3, x_3\} + \{m_3, x_3\}x_3$$

$$= -x_1 x_2 - x_2 x_1 + x_2 x_1 + x_1 x_2$$

$$\therefore \ \{m_3, r^2\} = 0 \qquad\qquad (4.5a)$$

and similarly for m_1 and m_2.
In the same way

$$\{m_3, p^2\} = \{m_1, p^2\} = \{m_2, p^2\} = 0. \qquad (4.5b)$$

The angular momentum components therefore commute with the variables on which H depends. If H is expanded as a power series in these variables the commutator of any of the m's with H vanishes term by term. This proves that m_1, m_2 and m_3 are constants of the motion, and therefore that $\theta = m_1{}^2 + m_2{}^2 + m_3{}^2$ is a constant of the motion.

We shall next show that θ commutes with any of the m's, e.g. with m_3:

$$\{m_3, \theta\} = \{m_3, m_1{}^2 + m_2{}^2 + m_3{}^2\}$$
$$= m_1\{m_3, m_1\} + \{m_3, m_1\}m_1$$
$$+ m_2\{m_3, m_2\} + \{m_3, m_2\}m_2$$
$$+ m_3\{m_3, m_3\} + \{m_3, m_3\}m_3$$
$$= -m_1 m_2 - m_2 m_1 + m_2 m_1 + m_1 m_2$$
$$\therefore \quad \{m_3, \theta\} = 0$$

and by symmetry

$$\{m_1, \theta\} = \{m_2, \theta\} = 0.$$

It follows that H, θ and *any one* of m_1, m_2 or m_3 have simultaneous eigenstates, and may be known with precision simultaneously. Since the m's do not commute in pairs no two of them may be known precisely at the same time. It is conventional to choose the coordinate axes so that m_3 is the component whose value is sharp.

The eigenvalues of θ and m_3

To find the eigenvalues of θ and m_3 it will be most convenient to work in a matrix representation in which the matrices of θ and m_3 are diagonal. The unit coordinate vectors on which this representation is based – called the *basis of the representation* – represent the simultaneous eigenstates of H, θ and m_3. Suppose that f is any function of the m's. Then it must commute with θ:

$$\theta f - f\theta = 0$$

or, in terms of a typical element,

$$(\theta f - f\theta)_{rs} = \theta_r f_{rs} - f_{rs}\theta_s = 0$$
$$\therefore \quad f_{rs}(\theta_r - \theta_s) = 0$$
$$\therefore \quad f_{rs} = 0 \quad \text{unless} \quad \theta_r = \theta_s. \tag{4.6}$$

This means that the matrix of any function of the m's does not have any non-zero elements referring to pairs of states with different values of θ.

We now define two non-Hermitian operators

$$N = m_1 + im_2$$
$$N^* = m_1 - im_2$$

both of which commute with H and θ.

Then

$$\{m_3, N\} = \{m_3, m_1 + im_2\}$$
$$= -m_2 + im_1$$
$$= iN.$$

Hence

$$i(m_3N - Nm_3) = i\hbar N$$

or $\qquad m_3N - Nm_3 = \hbar N \qquad\qquad$ (4.7a)

and similarly

$$m_3N^* - N^*m_3 = -\hbar N^*. \qquad\qquad (4.7b)$$

Further

$$\{N, N^*\} = \{m_1 + im_2, m_1 - im_2\}$$
$$= \{m_1, m_1\} + \{m_2, m_2\} + i\{m_2, m_1\} - i\{m_1, m_2\}$$
$$= 2im_3$$
$$\therefore \quad NN^* - N^*N = 2\hbar m_3. \qquad\qquad (4.8a)$$

Let ψ be a simultaneous eigenvector of H, θ, m_3 with eigenvalues α, λ, μ respectively.

$$m_3\psi = \mu\psi$$

and $\qquad Nm_3\psi = \mu N\psi.$

Using (4.7a) this becomes

$$(m_3N - \hbar N)\psi = \mu N\psi$$
$$\therefore \quad m_3N\psi = (\mu + \hbar)N\psi$$

so that if $\quad \psi$ is an eigenfunction of m_3 with eigenvalue μ,

then $\qquad N\psi$ is an eigenfunction of m_3 with eigenvalue $\mu + \hbar$

and $\qquad N^p\psi$ is an eigenfunction of m_3 with eigenvalue $\mu + p\hbar$.

In a similar way we could show that

if $\qquad \psi$ is an eigenfunction of m_3 with eigenvalue μ,

then $(N^*)^q\psi$ is an eigenfunction of m_3 with eigenvalue $\mu - q\hbar$.

Further, the definitions of N^* and N along with (4.6) show that $N^p\psi$ and $(N^*)^q\psi$ belong to the same eigenvalues α and λ as does ψ. There is then a ladder of eigenvalues for the operator m_3, and we want to know whether the ladder is limited in length. To find this we expand the operator N^*N as

$$N^*N = (m_1 - im_2)(m_1 + im_2)$$

$$= m_1{}^2 + m_2{}^2 + i(m_1 m_2 - m_2 m_1)$$

$$= (m_1{}^2 + m_2{}^2 + m_3{}^2) - m_3{}^2 - \hbar m_3 \qquad \text{(using (4.4))}$$

$$\therefore \quad N^*N = \theta - m_3{}^2 - \hbar m_3. \qquad (4.8b)$$

Since the matrices of θ, m_3 and therefore of $m_3{}^2$ are diagonal it follows that an eigenfunction of θ and m_3 with eigenvalues λ and μ must be an eigenfunction of N^*N with eigenvalue $\lambda - \mu^2 - \hbar\mu$. The typical (diagonal) element of N^*N is of the form

$$(N^*N)_{rr} = \sum_s (m_1 - im_2)_{rs}(m_1 + im_2)_{sr}$$

$$= \sum_s |(m_1 + im_2)_{sr}|^2 \geq 0$$

$$\therefore \quad \lambda - \mu^2 - \hbar\mu \geq 0$$

$$\therefore \quad \lambda \geq \mu(\mu + \hbar).$$

For any given λ, then, the greatest value of μ is limited. If μ' is the maximum value, and ψ' is the corresponding eigenfunction,

$$N\psi' = 0$$

$$\therefore \quad N^*N\psi' = 0 = (\lambda - \mu'^2 - \mu'\hbar)\psi'$$

$$\therefore \qquad \lambda = \mu'(\mu' + \hbar). \qquad (4.9a)$$

From (4.8a) and (4.8b) the eigenvalues of NN^* are $\lambda - \mu^2 + \mu\hbar$, and for any λ there must be a lowest value of μ, say μ'' fixed by

$$\lambda = \mu''(\mu'' - \hbar). \qquad (4.9b)$$

Together, (4.9a) and (4.9b) show that $\mu'' = -\mu'$, so that the eigenvalues of μ lie symmetrically about zero.

Further, we recall that the successive eigenvalues of m_3 differ by $\hbar$. Completing the squares in (4.9a) and (4.9b),

$$\lambda + \frac{\hbar^2}{4} = \left(\mu' + \frac{\hbar}{2}\right)^2$$

$$\lambda + \frac{\hbar^2}{4} = \left(\mu'' - \frac{\hbar}{2}\right)^2$$

so μ ranges, in steps of $\hbar$, from

$$\left(\lambda+\frac{\hbar^2}{4}\right)^{\frac{1}{2}} - \frac{\hbar}{2} \quad \text{to} \quad -\left(\lambda+\frac{\hbar^2}{4}\right)^{\frac{1}{2}} + \frac{\hbar}{2}.$$

The total range is therefore

$$2\left(\lambda+\frac{\hbar^2}{4}\right)^{\frac{1}{2}} - \hbar = 2l\hbar \quad \text{(say)}$$

where $2l$ is an integer.
Then

$$\left(\lambda+\frac{\hbar^2}{4}\right)^{\frac{1}{2}} = (l+\tfrac{1}{2})\hbar$$

$$\therefore \ \lambda+\frac{\hbar^2}{4} = l(l+1)\hbar^2 + \frac{\hbar^2}{4}$$

or $\qquad\qquad \lambda = l(l+1)\hbar^2.$ (4.10)

The eigenvalues of θ, the square of the total angular momentum, are therefore $l(l+1)\hbar^2$ where l is half an integer, e.g. $0, \tfrac{1}{2}, 1, \tfrac{3}{2} \ldots$ etc.

Finally

$$\left(\mu'+\frac{\hbar}{2}\right)^2 = \lambda+\frac{\hbar^2}{4} = (l+\tfrac{1}{2})^2\hbar^2$$

$$\therefore \ \mu' = l\hbar$$

and $\quad \mu'' = -l\hbar$

$$\therefore \ -l\hbar \leqq \mu \leqq +l\hbar,$$

or, putting

$$\mu = m\hbar,$$

we get

$$-l \leqq m \leqq +l.$$ (4.11)

The commutation relations between H, θ and m_1, m_2 and m_3 along with equations (4.10) and (4.11) are the most important results that we need concerning angular motion; we shall not usually, for instance, need to be explicit about the elements of the matrices for m_1 and m_2, though they may if required be found with the aid of eqn. (4A.2) of the appendix to this chapter (p. 89).

If we want to know the rotational energy and momentum of a top which is constrained to rotate about an axis fixed in direction the preceding argument is simplified because for such a top θ must be equal to $m_3{}^2$, and $m_3 = m\hbar$, so the rotational kinetic energy is

$$E_\theta = \frac{\theta}{2I} = \frac{m^2\hbar^2}{2I} \qquad \text{(cf. (4.1))}$$

(I is the moment of inertia).

If however the top has three rotational degrees of freedom the argument of the preceding pages applies in full so that

$$E_\theta = \frac{\theta}{2I} = \frac{l(l+1)\hbar^2}{2I} \qquad \text{(cf. (4.2))}$$

and $m_3 = m\hbar$ with $|m| \leq l$.

The half-integral quantum numbers

The surprising result of this argument, which is at variance with the conclusion from wave-mechanics (see pp. 86-89), is the prediction of half-integral values for l and m, as well as integral values. We recall that the wave-mechanical operators are written throughout explicitly in terms of the space-coordinates x_1, x_2, x_3. In the matrix treatment only the commutation relations for the angular momentum operators, eqns. (4.3) and (4.4), were derived using expressions involving space-coordinates; once these commutation relations had been derived no further reference to spatial dependence was made.

If we express m_3 in terms of wave-mechanical operators we get

$$m_3 = x_1 p_2 - x_2 p_1$$

$$= \frac{\hbar}{i}\left(x\frac{\partial}{\partial y} - y\frac{\partial}{\partial x}\right).$$

To transform to polar coordinates we set

$$x = r\sin\theta\cos\phi$$
$$y = r\sin\theta\sin\phi$$
$$z = r\cos\theta$$

and

$$x\frac{\partial\psi}{\partial y} - y\frac{\partial\psi}{\partial x} = \frac{\partial\psi}{\partial\phi}$$

$$\therefore\ m_3 \rightarrow \frac{\hbar}{i}\frac{\partial}{\partial\phi}.$$

At once we see that m_3 and ϕ are canonically conjugate, i.e. that

$i(m_3\phi - \phi m_3) = \hbar$. Thus nothing can be known about the ϕ-co-ordinate of a system which is in an eigenstate of m_3; the probability density derived from the state-function will then not depend on ϕ, and will depict an axially symmetric distribution. The eigenfunctions of the operator m_3 are found from

$$m_3 \Phi = \mu \Phi$$

$$\therefore \; \frac{\hbar}{i} \frac{\partial \Phi}{\partial \phi} = \mu \Phi$$

$$\therefore \; \Phi = \Phi_0 \, \varepsilon^{i\mu\phi/\hbar}. \qquad (4.12)$$

This solution is valid for all μ, but since ϕ is a cyclic coordinate the solution will be single valued only if

$$\varepsilon^{i\mu\phi/\hbar} = \varepsilon^{i\mu(\phi + 2\pi)/\hbar}$$

which requires that $\mu = \pm m\hbar$ where m is any positive or negative integer or zero. The restriction to integral values of m, which through (4.9a) and (4.9b) involves a similar restriction on l, first entered wave-mechanics through the requirement that the state-function should be a single-valued function of the space-coordinates. (See e.g. Schrödinger, *Collected papers on wave-mechanics*, Blackie, 1928, p. 3.) In fact this requirement is unnecessarily stringent. There is no logical reason why quantities which are not measurable should be single-valued, and the amplitude of the wave-function is certainly not measurable. Only measurable quantities, such as pro-bability densities and expectation values of dynamical variables, need to be single-valued. In wave-mechanics the angular momentum eigen-functions for half-integral quantum numbers are excluded because the half-integral values of l give solutions representing states in which a 'source of probability' is located at one pole of the sphere (at $\theta = 0$ or π) and there is a sink at the other pole, so that there is a probability current from one pole to the other.† Such solutions are not physically admissible, and may be termed 'ill behaved'.

An angular momentum which does not originate from a motion in space and is not described by space-coordinates need not be so restricted, and its quantum numbers might be half-integral. The treatment given here shows us no reason for believing in the existence of such a quantity, but enables us to consider the properties that such an angular momentum would have. There is experimental

† The concept of *probability current* is introduced and discussed in chapter 9.

evidence that the electron, proton, and certain other fundamental particles possess an angular momentum of $\hbar/2$, quite apart from any angular momentum which they may acquire by virtue of their motion. This intrinsic angular momentum, which is as much a property of the particle as its charge or mass, is called *spin*.

Electron spin

The explanation of the origin of electron spin, and of its magnitude, requires a relativistic treatment which would be beyond the scope of this book. However, a formal representation of the experimentally established properties of spin is possible on the basis of the work of this chapter, and historically a discussion of this type was given by Pauli before Dirac's relativistic theory of the electron was published. We shall give a brief account of this formal treatment, partly because it is the simplest illustration of the matrix representation of angular momentum, and partly because the discussion of some of the consequences of the exclusion principle in chapter 7 will involve the use of spin functions.

The experimental evidence for the occurrence of an angular momentum variable with just two eigenvalues came first from the doublet structure of certain spectral lines – such as the visible lines in the spectrum of sodium – and from the atomic beam experiment of Stern and Gerlach. An angular momentum quantum number s will correspond to a multiplicity $2s+1$; hence if the multiplicity is 2, s must be $\frac{1}{2}$. This angular momentum is attributed, not to a motion of the electron, but to an internal degree of freedom. We associate with it a non-spatial coordinate called the spin-coordinate. The term *intrinsic spin* is sometimes used to emphasize that this is a property of the particle itself and not of its motion. The spin operator will commute with all operators which can be expressed as functions of space-coordinates, and state-functions will therefore be separable into a space-factor and a spin-factor.

Since $s=\frac{1}{2}$, the z-component of the spin will have eigenvalues $+\frac{1}{2}$ and $-\frac{1}{2}$, and its matrix will be the very simple one,

$$s_3 = \hbar \begin{bmatrix} \frac{1}{2} & 0 \\ 0 & -\frac{1}{2} \end{bmatrix} = \frac{\hbar}{2} \begin{bmatrix} 1 & 0 \\ 0 & -1 \end{bmatrix}. \tag{4.13a}$$

The matrices for s_1 and s_2 are found from the commutation relations
$$i(s_1 s_2 - s_2 s_1) = -\hbar s_3$$
$$i(s_3 s_1 - s_1 s_3) = -\hbar s_2.$$

The matrices are indeterminate to the extent of arbitrary phase factors, and the relations above lead to

$$(s_1)_{11} = (s_1)_{22} = (s_2)_{11} = (s_2)_{22} = 0,$$
$$(s_1)_{12} = i(s_2)_{12},$$
and
$$|(s_1)_{12}|^2 = 1.$$

The conventional choice of components for these matrices gives

$$s_1 = \frac{\hbar}{2}\begin{bmatrix} 0 & 1 \\ 1 & 0 \end{bmatrix}, \quad s_2 = \frac{\hbar}{2}\begin{bmatrix} 0 & -i \\ i & 0 \end{bmatrix}. \tag{4.13b}$$

(Alternatively the elements of s_1 and s_2 can be found from eqn. (4A.2) on page 90.)

It is easy to verify that

$$s_1{}^2 + s_2{}^2 + s_3{}^2 = \frac{3\hbar^2}{4}\begin{bmatrix} 1 & 0 \\ 0 & 1 \end{bmatrix}$$

so that the eigenvalues of the operator representing the square of the spin angular momentum are

$$\frac{3\hbar^2}{4} = \tfrac{1}{2}(\tfrac{1}{2}+1)\hbar^2.$$

If we write α for the state-function of an electron for which $s_3 = \tfrac{1}{2}$ and β for the state-function of an electron for which $s_3 = -\tfrac{1}{2}$, the vector representation of these will be

$$\alpha = \begin{bmatrix} 1 \\ 0 \end{bmatrix}, \quad \beta = \begin{bmatrix} 0 \\ 1 \end{bmatrix}.$$

These are eigenvectors of the operator s_3 but not of s_1 and s_2. Indeed, we see that

$$s_1\alpha = \frac{\hbar}{2}\beta, \quad s_2\alpha = i\frac{\hbar}{2}\beta, \quad s_3\alpha = \frac{\hbar}{2}\alpha,$$

$$s_1\beta = \frac{\hbar}{2}\alpha, \quad s_2\beta = -i\frac{\hbar}{2}\alpha, \quad s_3\beta = -\frac{\hbar}{2}\beta. \tag{4.14}$$

The spinning electron in a magnetic field

As an example of the usefulness of this formalism, we can calculate the energy of a spinning electron in a magnetic field $\mathscr{H}$. Let the field have components $\mathscr{H}_1$, $\mathscr{H}_2$ and $\mathscr{H}_3$, and suppose the spin has associated with it a magnetic moment with components μ_1, μ_2, μ_3, which are related to the spin components through

$$\mu_i = s_i \, k \, \frac{\mu_0 e}{m}. \tag{4.15}$$

Here μ_0 is the magnetic constant of free space, and k is a dimensionless constant to be determined by comparison with experiment; the factor $\mu_0 e/m$ converts the dimensions from those of angular momentum to those of magnetic moment. (The Bohr magneton in these units is $\mu_0 e\hbar/2m$.)

The eigenvalue equation for the energy is

$$\frac{k\mu_0 e}{m} (s_1 \mathscr{H}_1 + s_2 \mathscr{H}_2 + s_3 \mathscr{H}_3)\psi = E\psi.$$

Now ψ must be expressible as a superposition of α and β, say $\psi = a\alpha + b\beta$, so that we we can write

$$\frac{k\mu_0 e}{m}\{s_1 \mathscr{H}_1(a\alpha + b\beta) + s_2 \mathscr{H}_2(a\alpha + b\beta) + s_3 \mathscr{H}_3(a\alpha + b\beta)\} = E(a\alpha + b\beta).$$

Using the equations (4.14) this becomes

$$\frac{k\mu_0 e}{m}\frac{\hbar}{2}\{\mathscr{H}_1(a\beta + b\alpha) + i\mathscr{H}_2(a\beta - b\alpha) + \mathscr{H}_3(a\alpha - b\beta)\} = E(a\alpha + b\beta).$$

Multiplying through by α^* and remembering that α and β are orthogonal we get

$$\frac{k\mu_0 e\hbar}{2m}(\mathscr{H}_1 b - i\mathscr{H}_2 b + \mathscr{H}_3 a) = Ea \tag{4.16a}$$

and similarly, after multiplying through by β^* we get

$$\frac{k\mu_0 e\hbar}{2m}(\mathscr{H}_1 a + i\mathscr{H}_2 a - \mathscr{H}_3 b) = Eb. \tag{4.16b}$$

These equations have non-zero solutions for a and b if

$$\begin{vmatrix} \mu\mathscr{H}_3 - E & \mu(\mathscr{H}_1 - i\mathscr{H}_2) \\ \mu(\mathscr{H}_1 + i\mathscr{H}_2) & -(\mu\mathscr{H}_3 + E) \end{vmatrix} = 0$$

where

$$\mu = \frac{k\mu_0 e\hbar}{2m}.$$

This gives

$$\mu(\mathscr{H}_1{}^2 + \mathscr{H}_2{}^2 + \mathscr{H}_3{}^2) = E^2$$

$$\therefore \quad E = \pm \mu \mathscr{H}.$$

The two energies correspond to different eigenvectors, whose components (a_+, b_+) and (a_-, b_-) have to be found.

If we write (4.16a) as $\mu(\mathscr{H}_1 - i\mathscr{H}_2)b_+ = (E - \mu\mathscr{H}_3)a_+$ and put $E = +\mu\mathscr{H}$ we get $(\mathscr{H}_1 - i\mathscr{H}_2)b_+ = (\mathscr{H} - \mathscr{H}_3)a_+$ and so

$$\frac{a_+}{b_+} = \frac{\mathscr{H}_1 - i\mathscr{H}_2}{\mathscr{H} - \mathscr{H}_3}$$

and

$$\frac{|a_+|^2}{|b_+|^2} = \frac{\mathscr{H}_1{}^2 + \mathscr{H}_2{}^2}{(\mathscr{H} - \mathscr{H}_3)^2}.$$

If $\mathscr{H}$ makes the angle θ with the z-axis, $\mathscr{H}_3 = \mathscr{H} \cos \theta$ and $\mathscr{H}_1{}^2 + \mathscr{H}_2{}^2 = \mathscr{H}^2 \sin^2 \theta$
so

$$\frac{|a_+|^2}{|b_+|^2} = \frac{\sin^2 \theta}{(1 - \cos\theta)^2} = \frac{\cos^2 \theta/2}{\sin^2 \theta/2}.$$

The relative phases of a_+ and b_+ need not concern us; they depend on the polar angle ϕ; a_+ and b_+ are both real if $\mathscr{H}$ is in the x-z-plane, and we may assume this to be the case. Then the eigenvector belonging to the energy E_+ is

$$\begin{bmatrix} \cos\dfrac{\theta}{2} \\[2mm] \sin\dfrac{\theta}{2} \end{bmatrix}$$

and the state-function is

$$\psi_+ = \left(\cos\frac{\theta}{2}\right)\alpha + \left(\sin\frac{\theta}{2}\right)\beta. \tag{4.17a}$$

In the same way the state-function corresponding to the energy E_- is

$$\psi_- = \left(\sin\frac{\theta}{2}\right)\alpha - \left(\cos\frac{\theta}{2}\right)\beta. \tag{4.17b}$$

The squares of the coefficients of α and β in these expansions represent the probabilities of finding the spin directed along the z-axis in the positive or negative directions; it should be noted that for either energy there is a finite probability of finding the spin pointing either way except when $\theta = 0$ or π. This means that if $\mathscr{H}$ is directed along the z-axis the two states of energy E_+ and E_- are 'unmixed' in the sense that one is the state α with $s_3 = \hbar/2$ and the other is the state β with $s_3 = -\hbar/2$.

Thus if electrons are passed through a region of space in which there is a homogeneous magnetic field $\mathscr{H}$, and if the direction of $\mathscr{H}$ coincides with the positive z-direction, the interaction between the spin magnetic moment and the magnetic field so aligns the spin axes that the electrons are either in the state α with energy $\mu\mathscr{H}$, or in the state β with energy $-\mu\mathscr{H}$. We say briefly that the spins are aligned parallel or antiparallel to the magnetic field. Anticipating a conclusion whose justification is given in the next section, we write the energy difference $2\mu\mathscr{H}$ between the states α and β as $\mu_0\mathscr{H}e\hbar/m$. Now it follows from (3.3) that matrix elements which couple the states α and β, as the off-diagonal elements of the matrices s_1 and s_2 in (4.13b) do in the case when no magnetic field is present, must in the case we are now considering contain factors like $\varepsilon^{\pm i\omega_L t}$ where $\omega_L = \mu\mathscr{H}e/m$. The matrices

$$s_1' = \frac{\hbar}{2}\begin{bmatrix} 0 & \varepsilon^{i\omega_L t} \\ \varepsilon^{-i\omega_L t} & 0 \end{bmatrix}, \quad s_2' = \frac{\hbar}{2}\begin{bmatrix} 0 & -i\varepsilon^{i\omega_L t} \\ i\varepsilon^{-i\omega_L t} & 0 \end{bmatrix}, \qquad (4.18a)$$

$$s_3 = \frac{\hbar}{2}\begin{bmatrix} 1 & 0 \\ 0 & -1 \end{bmatrix}$$

clearly satisfy the requirement of (3.3) and can easily be shown (see problem (5) on p. 91) to satisfy the commutation relations (4.4), to have eigenvalues $\pm\hbar/2$, and to lead to

$$s_1'^2 + s_2'^2 + s_3'^2 = \frac{3\hbar^2}{4}\begin{bmatrix} 1 & 0 \\ 0 & 1 \end{bmatrix}. \qquad (4.18b)$$

These matrices therefore represent the components of the spin angular momentum vector in the presence of a magnetic field directed along the z-axis.

Since the magnitude of the total angular momentum is $\hbar\sqrt{3}/2$, while its z-component is only $\hbar/2$, it might appear that the angular momentum vector, and therefore the magnetic moment, must make an angle of $54\cdot7°$ with the z-axis – since $\cos 54\cdot7° = 1/\sqrt{3}$. Classically the magnetic moment would then experience a torque which would cause it to precess about the z-axis. We can investigate the quantum dynamics of this with the aid of the equation of motion (3.1). We note first that the matrix of the Hamiltonian for the interaction of the electron's magnetic moment with the magnetic field – which we have assumed to be in the z-direction – is

$$H = \mu \mathscr{H} \begin{bmatrix} 1 & 0 \\ 0 & -1 \end{bmatrix} = \frac{\mu_0 \mathscr{H} e}{m} \cdot \frac{\hbar}{2} \begin{bmatrix} 1 & 0 \\ 0 & -1 \end{bmatrix} = \frac{\mu_0 \mathscr{H} e}{m} s_3.$$

Then, using (3.1), we find that the rate of change of the z-component of the spin is

$$\dot{s}_3 = \frac{i}{\hbar}(H s_3 - s_3 H) = \frac{i\mu_0 \mathscr{H} e}{\hbar m}(s_3 s_3 - s_3 s_3)$$

$$\therefore \quad \dot{s}_3 = 0,$$

which simply confirms that s_3 is a constant of the motion, as we already knew from the form of the matrix for s_3 in (4.18a). New results emerge, however, if we investigate the time-variation of $s_1{}'$ and $s_2{}'$. Thus,

$$\dot{s}_1{}' = \frac{i}{\hbar}\frac{\mu_0 \mathscr{H} e}{m}(s_3 s_1{}' - s_1{}' s_3) = -\frac{\mu_0 \mathscr{H} e}{m} s_2{}' = -\omega_L s_2{}'$$

whence

$$\ddot{s}_1{}' = -\frac{i}{\hbar}\left(\frac{\mu_0 \mathscr{H} e}{m}\right)^2 (s_3 s_2{}' - s_2{}' s_3) = -\left(\frac{\mu_0 \mathscr{H} e}{m}\right)^2 s_1{}' = -\omega_L{}^2 s_1{}';$$

and similarly,

$$\ddot{s}_2{}' = -\omega_L{}^2 s_2{}'.$$

Thus $s_1{}'$ and $s_2{}'$ vary simple harmonically with angular frequency $\omega_L = \mu_0 e \mathscr{H}/m$ (cf. chapter 2, p. 48); the sum of their squares, however, remains constant, for

$$s_1{}'^2 + s_2{}'^2 = \tfrac{3}{4}\hbar^2 - s_3{}^2 = \tfrac{1}{2}\hbar^2.$$

This is just what we should expect from the picture (see Fig. 4.1) of an angular momentum vector of length $\hbar\sqrt{3}/2$, aligned at an angle $54 \cdot 7°$ to the z-axis, rotating about the z-axis with precessional frequency ω_L. For the length of the projection of this vector on the x-y plane should, from this picture, be $\hbar\sqrt{3}/2 \times \sin 54 \cdot 7° = \hbar/\sqrt{2}$, whose square is $\hbar^2/2$ – the same as our calculated value for $s_1{}'^2 + s_2{}'^2$.

But the picture suggests that we can assign precise values simultaneously to all three components of an angular momentum, and since we know from the commutation relations (4.4) that this is not possible we see that there is a danger of reading out of such pictorial representations more than is quantum-mechanically admissible.

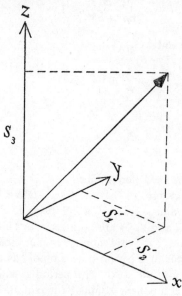

FIG. 4.1

With s_1', s_2' and s_3 defined as in (4.18a), for any state represented by

$$\frac{1}{\{aa^*+bb^*\}^{\frac{1}{2}}}\begin{bmatrix} a \\ b \end{bmatrix}$$

we have

$$\langle s_1' \rangle = \frac{1}{aa^*+bb^*} \cdot \frac{\hbar}{2}[a^*\; b^*]\begin{bmatrix} 0 & \varepsilon^{i\omega_L t} \\ \varepsilon^{-i\omega_L t} & 0 \end{bmatrix}\begin{bmatrix} a \\ b \end{bmatrix}$$

$$= \frac{1}{aa^*+bb^*} \cdot \frac{\hbar}{2}(a^*b\, \varepsilon^{i\omega_L t}+ab^*\, \varepsilon^{-i\omega_L t}).$$

We can write

$$a^*b = |ab|\, \varepsilon^{i\delta},\quad ab^* = |ab|\, \varepsilon^{-i\delta},$$

so

$$\langle s_1' \rangle = \frac{2\,|\,ab\,|}{aa^* + bb^*} \cdot \frac{\hbar}{2} \cos(\omega_L t + \delta)$$

where

$$\frac{2\,|\,ab\,|}{aa^* + bb^*} \leqq 1.$$

By a similar argument

$$\langle s_2' \rangle = \frac{2\,|ab|}{aa^* + bb^*} \cdot \frac{\hbar}{2} \sin(\omega_L t + \delta).$$

Finally,

$$\langle s_3 \rangle = \frac{aa^* - bb^*}{aa^* + bb^*} \cdot \frac{\hbar}{2},$$

as it would be if no field were applied.

If either a or b is zero, so that the given state is an eigenfunction of s_3 with eigenvalue $-\hbar/2$ or $+\hbar/2$ respectively, $|\,ab\,|=0$ and consequently $\langle s_1' \rangle$ and $\langle s_2' \rangle$ are both zero; but if a and b are both *non*-zero $\langle s_1' \rangle$ and $\langle s_2' \rangle$ are non-zero and oscillate simple-harmonically, a quarter of a period out of phase, as if the spin-vector were precessing about the z-axis with period $2\pi/\omega_L$. The amplitude of the precessing component attains its maximum value only when there is complete uncertainty with regard to the value of the z-component, i.e., when $|\,a\,| = |\,b\,| = 1/\sqrt{2}$.

The precession can be discussed in another way. If a vector has cartesian components (s_1', s_2', s_3), its projection on a datum line whose direction is specified by the polar angles θ and ϕ is

$$s_{\theta,\phi} = s_1' \sin\theta \cos\phi + s_2' \sin\theta \sin\phi + s_3 \cos\theta.$$

The particular polar angles $\pi/2$, $\omega_L t$ specify a datum line which rotates in the x-y plane ($\theta = \pi/2$) with angular velocity ω_L (since then $\phi = \omega_L t$). Then if we write s^+ for $s_{\theta,\phi}$ in this special case, the above expression for $s_{\theta,\phi}$ becomes

$$s^+ = s_1' \cos\omega_L t + s_2' \sin\omega_L t$$

and the corresponding operator, representing the projection of the spin on this line, is

$$s^+ = \frac{\hbar}{2} \begin{bmatrix} 0 & \cos \omega_L t \, \varepsilon^{i\omega_L t} \\ \cos \omega_L t \, \varepsilon^{-i\omega_L t} & 0 \end{bmatrix} + \frac{\hbar}{2} \begin{bmatrix} 0 & -i \sin \omega_L t \, \varepsilon^{i\omega_L t} \\ i \sin \omega_L t \, \varepsilon^{-i\omega_L t} & 0 \end{bmatrix}$$

$$= \frac{\hbar}{2} \begin{bmatrix} 0 & (\cos \omega_L t - i \sin \omega_L t) \, \varepsilon^{i\omega_L t} \\ (\cos \omega_L t + i \sin \omega_L t) \, \varepsilon^{-i\omega_L t} & 0 \end{bmatrix}$$

$$\therefore \quad s^+ = \frac{\hbar}{2} \begin{bmatrix} 0 & 1 \\ 1 & 0 \end{bmatrix}.$$

The states

$$\frac{1}{\sqrt{2}} \begin{bmatrix} 1 \\ \pm 1 \end{bmatrix}$$

are readily seen to be eigenstates of s^+, with eigenvalues $\pm \hbar/2$ respectively. These are both states in which the z-component of the spin, represented by the operator s_3, is completely indefinite, but in which the spin has a well-defined component rotating in the x-y plane with angular velocity ω_L. Since *any* spin state represented by

$$\frac{1}{\{aa^* + bb^*\}^{\frac{1}{2}}} \begin{bmatrix} a \\ b \end{bmatrix}$$

can be represented by a linear superposition of the two eigenstates of s^+, then the general state

$$\frac{1}{\{aa^* + bb^*\}^{\frac{1}{2}}} \begin{bmatrix} a \\ b \end{bmatrix}$$

must also be a state in which the component of the spin in the x-y plane rotates with the angular velocity ω_L.

The Stern-Gerlach experiment and the double Stern-Gerlach experiment

In the experiment of Stern and Gerlach (1922) a beam of silver atoms, whose magnetic moment is due to the spin of a single electron in a state of zero orbital angular momentum, is passed through an inhomogeneous magnetic field. The magnetic energy of each atom at a point where the field strength is $\mathscr{H}$ is $\pm \mu \mathscr{H}$, and since $\mathscr{H}$ is not uniform each atom experiences a force

$$-\frac{\partial}{\partial z}(\pm \mu \mathscr{H}) = \mp \mu \frac{\partial \mathscr{H}}{\partial z}.$$

Accordingly the beam is split into two components, one deviated slightly in the positive z-direction, the other in the negative z-direction. In one of these components all the atoms have $s_3 = \hbar/2$, and in the other all the atoms have $s_3 = -\hbar/2$. This is represented in the diagram (Fig. 4.2) by attaching to the separated beam components arrows which point upwards and downwards, as though the spin axes were aligned in these directions.

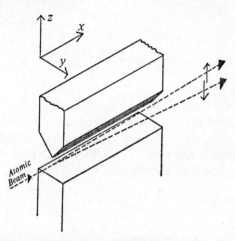

FIG. 4.2.   Schematic arrangement of the Stern-Gerlach experiment.

In the sense of chapter 1 this experiment constitutes a measurement of the magnetic moment associated with the electron spin, and measurements of the angular separation of the two beams have shown that in eqn. (4.15), which relates the spin angular momentum and the spin magnetic moment, the constant k must be 1. (In the corresponding relation between orbital angular momentum and magnetic moment k is $\frac{1}{2}$.) The magnetic moment associated with the spin angular momentum $\hbar/2$ is therefore *one* Bohr magneton.

What would happen now if one of the separated beams produced in a Stern-Gerlach type of experiment were passed through a second inhomogeneous field $\mathscr{H}'$ inclined at an angle θ to the first field? With the direction of $\mathscr{H}'$ we can associate spin eigenfunctions ξ and η (say) which are the eigenfunctions for electrons whose energies in the magnetic field are $\mu\mathscr{H}'$ and $-\mu\mathscr{H}'$ respectively, and whose spin axes are parallel and antiparallel respectively to the direction of $\mathscr{H}'$. We can express the spin function α of an electron whose spin axis is parallel to the first field $\mathscr{H}$ as a superposition of the functions ξ and η, by a relation (cf. eqns. (4.17))

$$\alpha = \left(\cos\frac{\theta}{2}\right)\xi - \left(\sin\frac{\theta}{2}\right)\eta.$$

The proposed experiment is a measurement of the magnetic moment of the electron spin – more precisely it finds the answer to the question: 'Is the magnetic moment along or against the direction of $\mathscr{H}'$?' The above expression shows that the probabilities of the two possible results are $\cos^2\theta/2$ and $\sin^2\theta/2$. If the field $\mathscr{H}'$ is perpendicular to $\mathscr{H}$, so that $\theta = \pi/2$, there is a maximum indeterminacy about the outcome of the experiment, for the two possible results are equally probable. The beam emerging from the second magnetic field will then be split into two equally intense components. A beam of electrons or atoms whose spin axes are completely aligned in the z-direction is thus shown to have a complete indeterminacy in the orientation of the spin components along a direction perpendicular to the z-axis. This is what we should expect from the non-commutability of s_3 and s_1 or s_2, or more generally of m_3 and m_1 or m_2. Experimentally it results from the precession of the electron magnetic moments about the field direction. If the beam spends enough time in the field to be resolved into separate components the differing rates of precession in different regions of the inhomogeneous field produce a complete disorder of the spin components perpendicular to the field. (See problem 9, p. 92.)

Combination of angular momenta: resultant spin of two electrons

We shall now use the formalism of the earlier sections of this chapter to derive some results for the combination of the spin angular momenta of two electrons, and we shall see how these results may be visualized in terms of the two allowed alignments – parallel or antiparallel – of the spins of the electrons.

We shall denote the matrices of (4.13) by

$$\sigma_x = \begin{bmatrix} 0 & 1 \\ 1 & 0 \end{bmatrix}, \quad \sigma_y = \begin{bmatrix} 0 & -i \\ i & 0 \end{bmatrix}, \quad \sigma_z = \begin{bmatrix} 1 & 0 \\ 0 & -1 \end{bmatrix},$$

which satisfy the relations

$$\sigma_x{}^2 = \sigma_y{}^2 = \sigma_z{}^2 = 1$$

$$\sigma_x\sigma_y = i\sigma_z, \quad \sigma_y\sigma_z = i\sigma_x, \quad \sigma_z\sigma_x = i\sigma_y. \tag{4.19}$$

Now suppose we have two particles, each with spin $\frac{1}{2}$. The spin angular momentum of the system of the two particles has components

$$S_x = s_x(1) + s_x(2) = \tfrac{1}{2}\sigma_x(1) + \tfrac{1}{2}\sigma_x(2)$$

and

$$S_y = \tfrac{1}{2}\sigma_y(1) + \tfrac{1}{2}\sigma_y(2)$$

$$S_z = \tfrac{1}{2}\sigma_z(1) + \tfrac{1}{2}\sigma_z(2).$$

The spin operators for the different particles must commute with each other and must separately obey the rules (4.18). It follows that

$$
\begin{aligned}
S^2 &= S_x^2 + S_y^2 + S_z^2 \\
&= \tfrac{1}{4}(\sigma_x^2(1) + \sigma_y^2(1) + \sigma_z^2(1)) + \tfrac{1}{4}(\sigma_x^2(2) + \sigma_y^2(2) + \sigma_z^2(2)) \\
&\quad + \tfrac{1}{2}(\sigma_x(1)\sigma_x(2) + \sigma_y(1)\sigma_y(2) + \sigma_z(1)\sigma_z(2)) \\
&= S^2(1) + S^2(2) + \tfrac{1}{2}\sigma(1) \cdot \sigma(2) \\
&= \tfrac{3}{4} + \tfrac{3}{4} + \tfrac{1}{2}\sigma(1) \cdot \sigma(2) \\
\therefore \quad S^2 &= \tfrac{1}{2}(3 + \sigma(1) \cdot \sigma(2)).
\end{aligned}
$$

Further

$$
\begin{aligned}
S^4 &= \tfrac{1}{4}(3 + \sigma(1) \cdot \sigma(2))^2 \\
&= \tfrac{1}{4}(9 + 6\sigma(1) \cdot \sigma(2) + (\sigma(1) \cdot \sigma(2))^2) \\
&= \tfrac{1}{4}(9 + 6\sigma(1) \cdot \sigma(2) + (\sigma_x(1)\sigma_x(2) + \sigma_y(1)\sigma_y(2) + \sigma_z(1)\sigma_z(2))^2) \\
&= \tfrac{1}{4}(9 + 6\sigma(1) \cdot \sigma(2) + \sigma_x^2(1)\sigma_x^2(2) + \sigma_y^2(1)\sigma_y^2(2) + \sigma_z^2(1)\sigma_z^2(2) \\
&\qquad + \sigma_x(1)\sigma_y(1)\sigma_x(2)\sigma_y(2) + \sigma_y(1)\sigma_x(1)\sigma_y(2)\sigma_x(2) \\
&\qquad + \ldots \text{ terms in } y \text{ and } z \\
&\qquad + \ldots \text{ terms in } z \text{ and } x) \\
&= \tfrac{1}{4}(9 + 6\sigma(1) \cdot \sigma(2) + 1 + 1 + 1 \\
&\qquad - \sigma_z(1)\sigma_z(2) - \sigma_z(1)\sigma_z(2) \\
&\qquad - \ldots \text{ terms in } x \\
&\qquad - \ldots \text{ terms in } y) \\
&= \tfrac{1}{4}(9 + 6\sigma(1) \cdot \sigma(2) + 3 - 2\sigma(1) \cdot \sigma(2)) \\
&= \tfrac{1}{4}(12 + 4\sigma(1) \cdot \sigma(2)) \\
\therefore \quad S^4 &= 2S^2 \\
\therefore \quad S^2(S^2 - 2) &= 0 \\
\therefore \quad S^2 &= 0 \text{ or } S^2 = 2.
\end{aligned}
$$

The values of S^2 represent the square of the total angular momentum resulting from the combination of the spins of the two electrons. By analogy with (4.10) and (4.11) we introduce quantum numbers J_s and M_s such that $S^2 = J_s(J_s+1)\hbar^2$, and $-J_s \leq M_s \leq J_s$. Then when $S^2 = 0$ we must have $J_s = 0$, $M_s = 0$, and when $S^2 = 2$ we must have $J_s = 1$, $M_s = -1$, 0 or $+1$.

In the first case the individual electron spins are pictured as being oppositely directed and having zero resultant, while in the second case we picture the spins of the two electrons as being parallel and having resultant unity (in units of $\hbar$); then if a weak magnetic field is applied to define the z-direction, the possible (observable) values of the z-component of the resultant spin are $-\hbar$, 0 and $+\hbar$. Because of their different multiplicities the configuration with $S^2 = 0$ is called a *singlet* configuration, and that with $S^2 = 2$ is called a *triplet* configuration.

Referring back to p. 78 it will be seen that if

$$S^2 = \tfrac{1}{2}(3 + \sigma(1) . \sigma(2)) = 0,$$

$\sigma(1) . \sigma(2)$ must be -3. The first line of (4.19) shows that $\sigma(1) . \sigma(1) = 3$, so $\sigma(1) . \sigma(2)$ can be -3 only if $\sigma(2) = -\sigma(1)$. This is interpreted as meaning that in the singlet configuration the spins of the two electrons are oppositely directed: we then say that the spins are *antiparallel*. When $S^2 = \tfrac{1}{2}(3 + \sigma(1) . \sigma(2)) = 2$, $\sigma(1) . \sigma(2)$ must be $+1$. We interpret this as follows: If the spins have a non-zero resultant this resultant defines a direction relative to which one component of the spin of each electron may be known precisely, but the other components are then indeterminate. Thus, if the direction of the resultant is taken as one of the x-, y- or z-directions the correspondingly labelled term in the scalar product $\sigma(1) . \sigma(2) = \sigma_x(1)\sigma_x(2) + \sigma_y(1)\sigma_y(2) + \sigma_z(1)\sigma_z(2)$ will be unity, but the other two terms will be zero because our knowledge of one component of the spin of each electron precludes knowledge of the other components.

A further discussion of the representation of spin singlet and triplet configurations for a two-electron system is given in chapter 7, where we discuss the helium atom.

Combination of orbital and spin angular momenta of a single electron: L-S coupling

We shall now consider the interaction between the orbital motion and the spin of a single electron moving in a central field of force.

This interaction is the cause of the doublet structure of the lines of the principal series in the spectrum of sodium and the other alkalies.

Rather surprisingly, perhaps, it turns out that a non-relativistic calculation of the Hamiltonian for the interaction between the spin and the orbital motion of the electron gives an incorrect result, even when the speed of the electron is small compared with the speed of light. More precisely, a calculation based on non-relativistic electromagnetic theory predicts an interaction which is of the first order in its dependence on v/c (where v is the speed of the electron in a frame of reference in which the nucleus of the atom is at rest), while relativistic kinematics predicts an additional effect which is *also* of first order in v/c, and whose magnitude is half that of the other.

From non-relativistic classical electromagnetic theory it is known (see, e.g., Panofsky and Phillips, *Classical Electricity and Magnetism*, Addison-Wesley, 1962, section 18.2) that an electron moving with velocity v (which is much less than c) through a static electric field $\mathscr{E}$ experiences a magnetic field $\mathfrak{B} = -\mathbf{v} \wedge \mathscr{E}/c^2$. Due to the field $\mathfrak{B}$, in the frame of reference in which the electron is at rest a torque equal to $\boldsymbol{\mu} \wedge \mathfrak{B}/\mu_0$ acts on the magnetic moment of the electron, and the angular momentum $\mathbf{S}$ of the electron in its rest-frame therefore changes at a rate

$$\frac{\partial \mathbf{S}}{\partial t} = \boldsymbol{\mu} \wedge \mathfrak{B}/\mu_0.$$

However, relativistic kinematics shows (see S. Dancoff and D. R. Inglis, *Physical Review* (1936), **50**, p. 784) that, because the direction of $\mathbf{v}$ is changing in consequence of the electrostatic force on the electron, the rest-frame of the electron appears to an observer in the rest-frame of the nucleus to be rotating with angular velocity

$$\boldsymbol{\omega}_T = -\frac{1}{2c^2} \mathbf{v} \wedge \dot{\mathbf{v}} \quad \text{(provided } v \ll c)$$

$$= -\frac{e}{2mc^2} \mathbf{v} \wedge \mathscr{E} \quad \text{(since } \dot{\mathbf{v}} = e\mathscr{E}/m).$$

(This rotation is called the 'Thomas precession'.) The apparent rate of change of the angular momentum of the electron observed from the rest-frame of the nucleus is therefore

$$\frac{d\mathbf{S}}{dt} = \frac{\partial \mathbf{S}}{\partial t} + \boldsymbol{\omega}_T \wedge \mathbf{S}.$$

Remembering that $S = \mu m/\mu_0 e$, and using the expressions above for $\frac{\partial S}{\partial t}$ and ω_T, we can readily see that

$$\frac{dS}{dt} = -\mu \wedge (v \wedge \mathscr{E})/\mu_0 c^2 + \mu \wedge (v \wedge \mathscr{E})/2\mu_0 c^2$$
$$= -\mu \wedge (v \wedge \mathscr{E})/2\mu_0 c^2.$$

This is just the rate of change of angular momentum of a magnetic moment μ in a magnetic field $\mathfrak{B}_{eff}$, where $\mathfrak{B}_{eff} = -v \wedge \mathscr{E}/2c^2$, which is half the value of the field predicted by classical electromagnetic theory.

We conclude, therefore, that the magnetic moment of an electron moving with velocity v in an electric field $\mathscr{E}$ must contribute to the Hamiltonian an energy

$$-\mu . \mathfrak{B}_{eff}/\mu_0 = -\mu . (v \wedge \mathscr{E})/2\mu_0 c^2.$$

If the electric field is that due to a stationary nucleus, so that the electrostatic potential energy of the electron when distant r from the nucleus is $V(r)$, the electrostatic field is

$$\mathscr{E} = -\frac{\partial V(r)}{\partial r} \cdot \frac{r}{r}$$

and then

$$\mathfrak{B}_{eff} = -v \wedge \mathscr{E}/2c^2 = \frac{1}{2c^2} \cdot \frac{1}{r} \cdot \frac{\partial V}{\partial r} v \wedge r.$$

Exchanging the order of the factors of the vector product, writing $v = p/m$, and writing L for the orbital angular momentum $r \wedge p$, we get

$$\mathfrak{B}_{eff} = -\frac{1}{2mc^2} \cdot \frac{1}{r} \cdot \frac{\partial V}{\partial r} L.$$

The energy of the magnetic moment in this field, called the 'spin-orbit coupling energy', and denoted by $H_{s.o.}$, is therefore

$$H_{s.o.} = -\mu . \mathfrak{B}_{eff}/\mu_0 = -\frac{e}{m} S . \mathfrak{B}_{eff}$$

$$= \frac{e}{2m^2 c^2} \cdot \frac{1}{r} \cdot \frac{\partial V}{\partial r} L . S. \qquad (4.20a)$$

We now introduce a vector defined as $\mathbf{J} = \mathbf{L} + \mathbf{S}$, the vector sum of the orbital and spin angular momenta of the electron. $\mathbf{L}$ is as we have seen defined in terms of the position and momentum coordinate vectors $\mathbf{r}$ and $\mathbf{p}$, and commutes with the Hamiltonian H_0 for the motion in the central field for the reasons given in the first section of this chapter; $\mathbf{S}$, not being a function of these coordinates, also commutes with H. It is then easy to show that, since the components of $\mathbf{L}$ and $\mathbf{S}$ satisfy equations (4.4), so must the components of $\mathbf{J}$; and that $\mathbf{J}^2$, like $\mathbf{L}^2$ and $\mathbf{S}^2$, is a constant of the motion. Then, since $\mathbf{J}^2 = (\mathbf{L} + \mathbf{S})^2 = \mathbf{L}^2 + \mathbf{S}^2 + \mathbf{L} \cdot \mathbf{S} + \mathbf{S} \cdot \mathbf{L}$, the commutation of $\mathbf{L}$ and $\mathbf{S}$ enables us to write

$$\mathbf{J}^2 = \mathbf{L}^2 + \mathbf{S}^2 + 2\mathbf{L} \cdot \mathbf{S}$$

$$\therefore \quad \mathbf{L} \cdot \mathbf{S} = \tfrac{1}{2}(\mathbf{J}^2 - \mathbf{L}^2 - \mathbf{S}^2),$$

and $\mathbf{L} \cdot \mathbf{S}$ must be a constant of the motion; substituting in (4.20a) we get

$$H_{s.o.} = \frac{e}{4m^2c^2} \frac{1}{r} \frac{\partial V}{\partial r} (\mathbf{J}^2 - \mathbf{L}^2 - \mathbf{S}^2). \tag{4.20b}$$

Because of the spin-orbit interaction, therefore, the allowed energies for an electron for which the Hamiltonian is

$$H_0 + H_{s.o.} = \frac{p^2}{2m} + V(r) + \frac{e}{4m^2c^2} \frac{1}{r} \frac{\partial V}{\partial r} (\mathbf{J}^2 - \mathbf{L}^2 - \mathbf{S}^2)$$

differ by sharply defined amounts from the eigenvalues when the Hamiltonian is simply $H_0 = p^2/2m + V(r)$.

For instance, the outermost electron in an alkali atom moves outside a set of closed sub-shells whose resultant angular momentum and magnetic moment are zero (see *The periodic system of the elements* in chapter 7), and for that one 'optical' or 'valence' electron we can write

$$\mathbf{J}^2 = j(j+1)\hbar^2, \quad \mathbf{L}^2 = l(l+1)\hbar^2, \quad \mathbf{S}^2 = \tfrac{1}{2}(\tfrac{1}{2}+1)\hbar^2 = \tfrac{3}{4}\hbar^2,$$

so

$$\mathbf{J}^2 - \mathbf{L}^2 - \mathbf{S}^2 = \{j(j+1) - l(l+1) - \tfrac{3}{4}\}\hbar^2.$$

Now the alignment of the electron spin in the apparent magnetic field generated by the orbital motion must give $j = l \pm \tfrac{1}{2}$.
If

$$j = l + \tfrac{1}{2}, \quad \mathbf{J}^2 - \mathbf{L}^2 - \mathbf{S}^2 = l\hbar^2,$$

and if

$$j = l - \tfrac{1}{2}, \quad \mathbf{J}^2 - \mathbf{L}^2 - \mathbf{S}^2 = -(l+1)\hbar^2$$

so

$$\langle H_{s.o.} \rangle = \frac{e\hbar^2}{4m^2c^2} \left\langle \frac{1}{r}\frac{\partial V}{\partial r} \right\rangle \left\{ \begin{matrix} l \\ -(l+1) \end{matrix} \right\} \text{ according as } \left\{ \begin{matrix} j = l + \tfrac{1}{2} \\ j = l - \tfrac{1}{2} \end{matrix} \right. .$$

By inspection, we should expect that $\left\langle \dfrac{1}{r}\dfrac{\partial V}{\partial r} \right\rangle$ will usually be positive for a bound state, so the state with $j = l + \tfrac{1}{2}$ has higher energy than that with $j = l - \tfrac{1}{2}$.

In the case of the sodium atom there is no spin-orbit splitting of the ground state, for in the ground state the valence electron has $n = 3$, $l = 0$, and there is no orbital motion. In the first excited state, however, $n = 3$, $l = 1$, and $j = \tfrac{3}{2}$ or $\tfrac{1}{2}$. The state with $j = \tfrac{3}{2}$ must, because of the spin-orbit interaction, have higher energy than the state with $j = \tfrac{1}{2}$, and it is this energy difference which gives rise to the 5·9 Å separation between the two D-lines which result from the decay of these two states to the ground state.

We stated above that the orbital and spin angular momenta of a single electron must combine to give $j = l \pm \tfrac{1}{2}$. We shall now investigate this point formally, partly for the deeper insight into the effects of $L - S$ coupling which this will give us, and partly in preparation for the discussion of the anomalous Zeeman effect in chapter 6.

We know that we can diagonalize, at one and the same time, the matrices for the central field part (say H_0) of the Hamiltonian, and for the quantities $\mathbf{L}^2 = l(l+1)\hbar^2$, $\mathbf{S}^2 = \tfrac{3}{4}\hbar^2$, $L_z = m_l\hbar$, $S_z = m_s\hbar$, $J_z = (m_l + m_s)\hbar = m\hbar$ (say); and we note that

$$m_s = \pm\tfrac{1}{2}, \quad -(l+\tfrac{1}{2}) \leq m \leq (l+\tfrac{1}{2}).$$

In this representation the total Hamiltonian $H_0 + H_{s.o.}$ is not in general diagonal, because although $\mathbf{L} \cdot \mathbf{S}$ commutes with J_z, it does not commute with either L_z or S_z (see problem 10 on p. 92). Consequently, the matrix of $\mathbf{L} \cdot \mathbf{S}$ has elements which couple states of the same $J_z = m\hbar$, but different L_z and S_z. One such pair of states might be denoted by

$$\psi_{m-\frac{1}{2}, \frac{1}{2}} = f(r)\, Y_{l,\, m-\frac{1}{2}}(\theta, \phi) \times \begin{bmatrix} 1 \\ 0 \end{bmatrix} = f(r)\, Y_{l,\, m-\frac{1}{2}}\alpha$$

and

$$\psi_{m+\frac{1}{2},-\frac{1}{2}} = f(r)\, Y_{l,\, m+\frac{1}{2}}(\theta,\, \phi) \times \begin{bmatrix} 0 \\ 1 \end{bmatrix} = f(r)\, Y_{l,\, m+\frac{1}{2}}\beta.$$

In these equations $m-\frac{1}{2}$ and $m+\frac{1}{2}$ are integers specifying the z-component of the orbital angular momentum, the functions Y are eigenfunctions of the orbital angular momentum operators $\mathbf{L}^2$ and L_z, and the two-component vectors denoted by α and β are the eigenvectors of the corresponding spin operators.

We can expand $\mathbf{L} \cdot \mathbf{S}$ in terms of the four ladder operators $L_x - iL_y$, $L_x + iL_y$, $S_x - iS_y$, $S_x + iS_y$, along with L_z and S_z, thus:

$$\mathbf{L} \cdot \mathbf{S} = \tfrac{1}{2}(L_x + iL_y)(S_x - iS_y) + \tfrac{1}{2}(L_x - iL_y)(S_x + iS_y) + L_z S_z.$$

It follows from the discussion of the ladder operators N and N^* defined earlier in this chapter (see equations (4.7) and (4.8), and (4A.2) of the appendix to this chapter with m, $m+1$ replaced by $m-\frac{1}{2}$, $m+\frac{1}{2}$) that

$$(L_x + iL_y)\, Y_{l,\, m-\frac{1}{2}} = \hbar\sqrt{(l+\tfrac{1}{2})^2 - m^2}\, Y_{l,\, m+\frac{1}{2}}$$

$$(L_x + iL_y)\, Y_{l,\, m+\frac{1}{2}} = \hbar\sqrt{(l+\tfrac{1}{2})^2 - m^2}\, Y_{l,\, m-\frac{1}{2}}$$

$$(S_x + iS_y)\beta = \hbar\alpha, \quad (S_x + iS_y)\alpha = 0$$

$$(S_x - iS_y)\alpha = \hbar\beta, \quad (S_x - iS_y)\beta = 0$$

$$\therefore \ (\mathbf{L} \cdot \mathbf{S})\psi_{m-\frac{1}{2},\, \frac{1}{2}} = \{\tfrac{1}{2}(L_x + iL_y)(S_x - iS_y) + L_z S_z\}f(r)\, Y_{l,\, m-\frac{1}{2}}\alpha$$

$$= \frac{\hbar^2}{2}(m-\tfrac{1}{2})\psi_{m-\frac{1}{2},\, \frac{1}{2}} + \frac{\hbar^2}{2}\sqrt{(l+\tfrac{1}{2})^2 - m^2}\, \psi_{m+\frac{1}{2},\, -\frac{1}{2}}$$

$$(4.21a)$$

and similarly

$$(\mathbf{L} \cdot \mathbf{S})\psi_{m+\frac{1}{2},\, -\frac{1}{2}} = \{\tfrac{1}{2}(L_x - iL_y)(S_x + iS_y) + L_z S_z\}f(r)Y_{l,\, m+\frac{1}{2}}\beta$$

$$= \frac{\hbar^2}{2}\sqrt{(l+\tfrac{1}{2})^2 - m^2}\, \psi_{m-\frac{1}{2},\, \frac{1}{2}} - \frac{\hbar^2}{2}(m+\tfrac{1}{2})\psi_{m+\frac{1}{2},\, -\frac{1}{2}}.$$

$$(4.21b)$$

The coefficients on the right hand side of these equations are the elements of the matrix of $(\mathbf{L} \cdot \mathbf{S})$:

$$(\mathbf{L} \cdot \mathbf{S}) = \frac{\hbar^2}{2}\begin{bmatrix} (m-\tfrac{1}{2}) & \sqrt{(l+\tfrac{1}{2})^2 - m^2} \\ \sqrt{(l+\tfrac{1}{2})^2 - m^2} & -(m+\tfrac{1}{2}) \end{bmatrix}.$$

The eigenvalues of this matrix can easily be shown to be $\frac{1}{2}l\hbar^2$ and $-\frac{1}{2}(l+1)\hbar^2$, in agreement with our previous conclusion that $\mathbf{J}^2 - \mathbf{L}^2 - \mathbf{S}^2 = 2\mathbf{L} \cdot \mathbf{S} = l\hbar^2$ or $-(l+1)\hbar^2$. The corresponding eigenvectors can then be found, and are, in normalized form:

$$\left[\begin{matrix} \left(\dfrac{l+m+\frac{1}{2}}{2l+1}\right)^{\frac{1}{2}} \\[2mm] \left(\dfrac{l-m+\frac{1}{2}}{2l+1}\right)^{\frac{1}{2}} \end{matrix} \right] \quad \text{and} \quad \left[\begin{matrix} -\left(\dfrac{l-m+\frac{1}{2}}{2l+1}\right)^{\frac{1}{2}} \\[2mm] \left(\dfrac{l+m+\frac{1}{2}}{2l+1}\right)^{\frac{1}{2}} \end{matrix} \right].$$

When $(\mathbf{L} \cdot \mathbf{S}) = \frac{1}{2}l\hbar^2$, $\mathbf{J}^2$ can be written as

$$\mathbf{J}^2 = j_+(j_+ + 1)\hbar^2 \text{ with } j_+ = l+\tfrac{1}{2},$$

and when $\qquad\qquad (\mathbf{L} \cdot \mathbf{S}) = -\frac{1}{2}(l+1)\hbar^2$

$$\mathbf{J}^2 = j_-(j_- + 1)\hbar^2 \text{ with } j_- = l-\tfrac{1}{2}.$$

These two cases are those which, in the vector model, are pictured in terms of the *parallel* (j_+) and *antiparallel* (j_-) alignments of **L** and **S**.

The elements of the eigenvectors can be computed for specified values of m and l. Thus, for an alkali atom in its first excited state the valence electron is in a p-state ($l=1$), and the possible values of j are $\frac{3}{2}$ (in spectroscopic notation this is the state $^2P_{\frac{3}{2}}$) and $\frac{1}{2}$ (this being the state $^2P_{\frac{1}{2}}$). The eigenvector elements are then found from the table:

j	m	l	$\left(\dfrac{l+m+\frac{1}{2}}{2l+1}\right)^{\frac{1}{2}}$	$\left(\dfrac{l-m+\frac{1}{2}}{2l+1}\right)^{\frac{1}{2}}$
$\frac{3}{2}$	$\frac{3}{2}$	1	1	0
	$\frac{1}{2}$	1	$(\frac{2}{3})^{\frac{1}{2}}$	$(\frac{1}{3})^{\frac{1}{2}}$
	$-\frac{1}{2}$	1	$(\frac{1}{3})^{\frac{1}{2}}$	$(\frac{2}{3})^{\frac{1}{2}}$
	$-\frac{3}{2}$	1	0	1
$\frac{1}{2}$	$\frac{1}{2}$	1	$(\frac{2}{3})^{\frac{1}{2}}$	$(\frac{1}{3})^{\frac{1}{2}}$
	$-\frac{1}{2}$	1	$(\frac{1}{3})^{\frac{1}{2}}$	$(\frac{2}{3})^{\frac{1}{2}}$

Hence the angular momentum properties of the $^2P_{\frac{3}{2}}$ and $^2P_{\frac{1}{2}}$ configurations are represented by the following state-functions:

State	m	Angular part of state-function
$^2P_{\frac{3}{2}}$	$\frac{3}{2}$	$Y_{1,1}\alpha$
	$\frac{1}{2}$	$(\frac{2}{3})^{\frac{1}{2}}Y_{1,0}\alpha \;\; +(\frac{1}{3})^{\frac{1}{2}}Y_{1,1}\beta$
	$-\frac{1}{2}$	$(\frac{1}{3})^{\frac{1}{2}}Y_{1,-1}\alpha+(\frac{2}{3})^{\frac{1}{2}}Y_{1,0}\beta$
	$-\frac{3}{2}$	$Y_{1,0}\beta$
$^2P_{\frac{1}{2}}$	$\frac{1}{2}$	$-(\frac{1}{3})^{\frac{1}{2}}Y_{1,0}\alpha \;\; +(\frac{2}{3})^{\frac{1}{2}}Y_{1,1}\beta$
	$-\frac{1}{2}$	$-(\frac{2}{3})^{\frac{1}{2}}Y_{1,-1}\alpha+(\frac{1}{3})^{\frac{1}{2}}Y_{1,0}\beta$

Thus the eigenstates of the total Hamiltonian $H_0+H_{s.o.}$ can be represented by superpositions of the eigenstates of the central-field Hamiltonian H_0, and the tables illustrate the way in which the spin-orbit interaction mixes or couples states with different L_z and S_z to form states which are characterized by their sharp values of $\mathbf{J}^2$ and J_z. The coefficients which occur in such superposition expansions as these are called *Clebsch-Gordan coefficients*, and are tabulated in a number of monographs and treatises, e.g. in Condon and Shortley's *Theory of Atomic Spectra* (Cambridge University Press, 1957).

Angular momentum in wave-mechanics

It is now necessary to outline the wave-mechanical treatment of angular momentum in a central field of force. The Hamiltonian is

$$H = \frac{p^2}{2m}+V(r)$$

so the eigenvalue equation is

$$\left\{\frac{p^2}{2m}+V(r)\right\}\psi = E\psi.$$

When we substitute the wave-mechanical operators this becomes

$$-\frac{\hbar^2}{2m}\nabla^2\psi+V(r)\psi = E\psi \tag{4.22}$$

where m is the mass of the moving particle if the centre of force is fixed, and is the reduced mass $\dfrac{m_1 m_2}{m_1+m_2}$ if the force acts between two free particles. In spherical polar coordinates (4.22) is

$$-\frac{\hbar^2}{2m}\left\{\frac{1}{r^2}\frac{\partial}{\partial r}\ r^2\ \frac{\partial}{\partial r}+\frac{1}{r^2\sin\theta}\frac{\partial}{\partial\theta}\sin\theta\frac{\partial}{\partial\theta}+\frac{1}{r^2\sin^2\theta}\frac{\partial^2}{\partial\phi^2}\right\}\psi(r,\theta,\phi)$$

$$+V(r)\,\psi(r,\theta,\phi)=E\psi(r,\theta,\phi).$$

We attempt to solve this by the method of separation of variables. We put $\psi(r,\theta,\phi)=R(r)Y(\theta,\phi)$ and after multiplying the equation through by r^2/ψ and rearranging terms it becomes

$$\frac{\hbar^2}{R}\frac{d}{dr}\left(r^2\frac{dR}{dr}\right)+2mr^2(E-V(r))$$

$$=-\frac{\hbar^2}{Y}\left\{\frac{1}{\sin\theta}\frac{\partial}{\partial\theta}\left(\sin\theta\frac{\partial Y}{\partial\theta}\right)+\frac{1}{\sin^2\theta}\frac{\partial^2 Y}{\partial\phi^2}\right\}.$$

The left-hand side of this equation depends only on r, the right-hand side only on θ and ϕ. Each side must then be equal to the same constant, say λ.

Thus

$$\frac{\hbar^2}{2m}\frac{1}{r^2}\frac{d}{dr}\left(r^2\frac{dR}{dr}\right)+\left[E-V(r)-\frac{\lambda}{2mr^2}\right]R=0 \qquad (4.23)$$

$$-\hbar^2\left\{\frac{1}{\sin\theta}\frac{\partial}{\partial\theta}\left(\sin\theta\frac{\partial Y}{\partial\theta}\right)+\frac{1}{\sin^2\theta}\frac{\partial^2 Y}{\partial\phi^2}\right\}=\lambda Y. \qquad (4.24)$$

(4.23) depends only on r; it involves the potential $V(r)$ and the total energy E. It can be solved only for a very few specific potentials, three of which will be studied in the next chapter. For the moment we leave it, for it does not involve the angle variables, and so tells us nothing about the angular momentum.

(4.24) on the other hand does not involve the total energy and is independent of the detailed form of $V(r)$ – but remember that we arrived at (4.24) after assuming that the potential is independent of θ and ϕ. (4.24) refers therefore to the purely angular – i.e. rotational – part of the motion, and by inspection λ has the dimensions of $\hbar^2$, which are those of [angular momentum]^2. The bracketed operator of (4.24), multiplied by a factor $-\hbar^2$, is in fact the operator for the square of the total angular momentum, and λ is its eigenvalue. The moment of inertia of the system is mr^2, so the energy of the rotational motion will be $\lambda/2mr^2$, and the energy of the radial motion is represented by the quantity $E-\lambda/2mr^2$ which occurs in (4.23).

To solve (4.24) we complete the separation of the variables by setting

$$Y(\theta,\phi)=\Theta(\theta)\Phi(\phi)$$

and get, after some rearrangement,

$$\frac{\sin\theta}{\Theta}\frac{d}{d\theta}\left(\sin\theta\frac{d\Theta}{d\theta}\right)+\frac{\lambda}{\hbar^2}\sin^2\theta = -\frac{1}{\Phi}\frac{d^2\Phi}{d\phi^2} = m^2 \quad \text{(say)}$$

where m is a constant.
Thus

$$\frac{d^2\Phi}{d\phi^2}+m^2\,\Phi = 0 \tag{4.25}$$

and

$$\frac{1}{\sin\theta}\frac{d}{d\theta}\left(\sin\theta\frac{d\Theta}{d\theta}\right)+\left(\frac{\lambda}{\hbar^2}-\frac{m^2}{\sin^2\theta}\right)\Theta = 0. \tag{4.26}$$

(4.25) has solutions

$$\Phi = \frac{1}{\sqrt{2\pi}}\,\varepsilon^{\pm im\phi}$$

which is the same as (4.12), save that here we have m for $\mu/\hbar$ and have replaced the constant Φ_0 by $1/\sqrt{2\pi}$; the latter substitution ensures that Φ is normalized to unity, i.e. that

$$\oint \Phi^* \Phi \, d\phi = 1.$$

As we remarked in connection with (4.12), Φ is the eigenfunction for the z-component of angular momentum; the eigenvalue of the operator $\frac{\hbar}{i}\frac{\partial}{\partial\phi}$ is $m\hbar$, and well-behaved eigenfunctions of (4.25) exist only for integral quantum numbers, so that m must be a positive or negative integer or zero.

To solve (4.26) we put $\cos\theta = x$, $\sin\theta = \sqrt{1-x^2}$, $dx = -\sin\theta\,d\theta$, $\Theta(\theta) = P(x)$ and remember that m is integral. The equation becomes

$$\frac{d}{dx}(1-x^2)\frac{dP}{dx}+\left(\frac{\lambda}{\hbar^2}-\frac{m^2}{1-x^2}\right)P = 0.$$

This is known as Legendre's Equation. Its solutions are polynomials in x; they are found by writing $P=\sum a_n x^n$ and solving the equations that are obtained for the a_n. Solutions which are everywhere finite and well behaved exist only when

$$\frac{\lambda}{\hbar^2} = l(l+1) \quad \text{and} \quad l \geq |m|, \quad l \text{ being an integer.}$$

The eigenfunction determined by (4.26) for a given l and m is one of the Associated Legendre Polynomials of order l. It is written as $P_l^{|m|}(\cos\theta)$.† These functions are discussed in detail in e.g. Margenau and Murphy, *The Mathematics of Physics and Chemistry* (Van Nostrand, 1956), chapter 3, and a useful list of them is given in chapter 5 of Pauling and Wilson's *Introduction to Quantum Mechanics* (McGraw-Hill, 1935). For a given l equation (4.24) has $2l+1$ solutions, called spherical harmonics of the type

$$Y(\theta, \phi) = \frac{1}{\sqrt{2\pi}}\, \varepsilon^{im\phi}\, P_l^{|m|}(\cos\theta).$$

These correspond to the $2l+1$ values of m in the range from $-l$ to $+l$. In terms of the vector model they refer to the allowed orientations of the total angular momentum vector relative to the (arbitrary) z-axis. It must be remembered, however, that in order to distinguish between states with different values of m and the same value of l we should have to set up an experimental arrangement which marks out one direction in space as the z-axis – e.g. by applying an electric or magnetic field whose direction is taken as the z-direction; this destroys the spherical symmetry which characterizes the central field of force. Thus in a truly central field the $2l+1$ states for a given l are indistinguishable.

APPENDIX

The angular momentum eigenfunctions

From (4.8a) and (4.8b) we have

$$N^*N = \theta - m_3^2 - \hbar m_3$$
$$\text{and} \qquad NN^* = \theta - m_3^2 + \hbar m_3 \qquad (4\text{A}.1)$$

From these elements of the matrices for N and N^* can be found by an argument very similar to that used to find the elements of the shifting operators R and R^* of chapter 3, and it turns out that for any given l the matrices of N and N^* contain only elements of the type $N_{m+1, m}$ and $N^*_{m, m+1}$.

† An alternative derivation of these functions is given as an appendix to this chapter (pp. 89-91).

$$N^*_{m,\,m+1}\,N_{m+1,\,m} = \{l(l+1)-m(m+1)\}\hbar^2$$

$$\therefore \;|N^*_{m,\,m+1}|^2 = |N_{m+1,\,m}|^2 = \{l(l+1)-m(m+1)\}\hbar^2$$

$$= (l-m)(l+m+1)\hbar^2$$

$$\therefore \;|N^*_{m,\,m+1}| = |N_{m+1,\,m}| = \{(l-m)(l+m+1)\}^{\frac{1}{2}}\hbar. \quad (4\text{A}.2)$$

If required, the matrix elements of m_1 and m_2 can be found from this relation, cf. (4.13).

Putting $N=m_1+im_2$ in differential operator form, it becomes

$$N \to \hbar\,\varepsilon^{i\phi}\left(\frac{\partial}{\partial\theta}+i\cot\theta\,\frac{\partial}{\partial\phi}\right).$$

The solution of (4.24) for $m=l$ can be written

$$Y_{ll}(\theta,\phi) = (2\pi)^{-\frac{1}{2}}\,\varepsilon^{il\phi}\,\Theta_{ll}\,(\theta) \qquad (4\text{A}.3)$$

and since m cannot exceed l

$$NY_{ll}(\theta,\phi) = 0$$

$$\therefore\; \hbar(2\pi)^{-\frac{1}{2}}\,\varepsilon^{i\phi}\left(\frac{\partial}{\partial\theta}+i\cot\theta\,\frac{\partial}{\partial\phi}\right)\varepsilon^{il\phi}\,\Theta_{ll}\,(\theta) = 0$$

whence

$$\frac{d}{d\theta}\,\Theta_{ll}\,(\theta)-l\cot\theta\,\Theta_{ll}\,(\theta) = 0$$

so

$$\Theta_{ll}\,(\theta) = \text{const} \times \sin^l\theta$$

$$= (-)^l\sqrt{\tfrac{1}{2}(2l+1)!}\backslash\,\frac{2^{-l}}{l!}\sin^l\theta, \qquad (4\text{A}.4)$$

taking into account the normalization requirements.
Then since

$$N^*Y_{l,\,m+1} = \{(l-m)(l+m+1)\}^{\frac{1}{2}}\hbar Y_{l,\,m},$$

$$\sqrt{\frac{(l-m)!}{(l+m)!}}\backslash\,\hbar^{l-m}\,Y_{lm} = \{(2l)!\}^{-\frac{1}{2}}(m_1-im_2)^{l-m}\,Y_{ll}$$

$$= \{(2l)!\}^{\frac{1}{2}}\,\hbar^{l-m}\,\varepsilon^{im\phi}\sin^{-m}\theta\,\frac{d^{l-m}}{d(\cos\theta)^{l-m}}\left(\sin^l\theta\,\Theta_{ll}\,(\theta)\right)$$

$$\therefore\Theta_{lm}(\theta)=(-)^l\sqrt{\frac{(2l+1)(l+m)!}{2(l-m)!}}\backslash\,\frac{1}{2^l l!\sin^m\theta}\frac{d^{l-m}}{d(\cos\theta)^{l-m}}\sin^{2l}\theta. \quad (4\text{A}.5)$$

(4A.5) multiplied by $(2\pi)^{-\frac{1}{2}}\,\epsilon^{im\phi}$ is the complete angular momentum eigenfunction for any l and m.

Problems

(1) Obtain the results of pp. 59 and 61 by arguments which employ explicitly commutation relations like (2.11), instead of by the Poisson bracket algebra used in the text.

(2) Use (4A.2) and the results of the first section of this chapter to construct the matrices of m_1, m_2, m_3 and θ for $l=0$, $l=\frac{1}{2}$, $l=1$, $l=\frac{3}{2}$.

(3) If $\mathbf{L}$ is the vector whose components are the m_1, m_2 and m_3 of eqns. (4.4), show that (4.4) can be written as $\mathbf{L}\wedge\mathbf{L}=i\hbar\mathbf{L}$.

Note that in the classical limit of a macroscopic rotator, for which $|\mathbf{L}|\gg\hbar$, this is tantamount to $\mathbf{L}\wedge\mathbf{L}=0$, which is what we should expect classically for the vector product of a vector with itself.

(4) Show that if three matrices M_1, M_2 and M_3 satisfy the relations $M_1{}^2=M_2{}^2=M_3{}^2=1$, and $M_2M_3-M_3M_2=iM_1$, then M_1 'anti-commutes' with M_2 and M_3, i.e.
$$M_1M_2+M_2M_1 = 0 = M_1M_3+M_3M_1.$$
Hence show that the spin matrices σ_x, σ_y and σ_z anticommute in pairs.

(5) Verify that the matrices defined in (4.18a) satisfy the commutation relations (4.4), have eigenvalues $\pm\hbar/2$, and satisfy (4.18b).

(6) Use the two equations (4A.1) to obtain two expressions for the product N^*NN^*, and hence show that the matrices for N and N^* contain only elements of the type $N_{m+1,\,m}$ and $N^*_{m,\,m+1}$. Check this using the explicit forms of the angular momentum matrices for $l=\frac{1}{2}$ and $l=1$ which you found for problem (1).

(7) When $\theta=m_x{}^2+m_y{}^2+m_z{}^2$, and the z-direction is identified as the axis of quantization, show that
(i) $(\Delta m_x)^2 = \langle m_x{}^2\rangle$, $(\Delta m_y)^2 = \langle m_y{}^2\rangle$,
(ii) $\langle m_x{}^2\rangle = \langle m_y{}^2\rangle$ (because of symmetry),
(iii) $\therefore$ $\Delta m_x\Delta m_y = \frac{1}{2}(\langle\theta\rangle-\langle m_z{}^2\rangle)$
$$= \frac{1}{2}(l(l+1)-m^2)\hbar^2.$$
Consider the implications of (iii) for the several states with a given l and different values of m.

(8) A system is in a state ψ represented by $\psi=\sum a_m\,\varepsilon^{im\phi}$ where ϕ is a cyclic coordinate. Show that the expectation value of any

observable P will be single-valued, i.e. will be unaffected when ϕ is increased or decreased by 2π, if all the m's in the above expansion are integral, or if they are all half-integral, but will not be single-valued if both integral and half-integral m's are present.

(9) In a Stern-Gerlach apparatus certain conditions have to be satisfied in order that the two beams may be separated. These conditions relate to *inter alia* the inhomogeneity of the magnetic field and the time spent by the atoms in the field. Investigate these requirements, and verify the statement on p. 77 which concludes the section titled 'The Stern-Gerlach experiment . . .'.

(10) If $\mathbf{L}$ and $\mathbf{S}$ represent the orbital and spin angular momenta of an electron moving in a central field of force, and $\mathbf{J}=\mathbf{L}+\mathbf{S}$, show that the components of $\mathbf{J}$ satisfy (4.4) (which means that $\mathbf{J}$ represents an angular momentum), and that
$$\{\mathbf{L}.\mathbf{S}, J_x\} = \{\mathbf{L}.\mathbf{S}, J_y\} = \{\mathbf{L}.\mathbf{S}, J_z\} = 0$$
but that
$$\{\mathbf{L}.\mathbf{S}, L_z\} \neq 0, \quad \{\mathbf{L}.\mathbf{S}, S_z\} < 0.$$
Note: This means that eigenstates of the spin-orbit Hamiltonian $H_{s.o.}$ (see p. 82) are not eigenstates of the operator representing the z-component of either the spin or orbital angular momentum, and must therefore be *mixtures* of such eigenstates.

(11) Show that the angular momentum eigenfunctions (4A.5) are even or odd according as l is even or odd.

(12) Show that the matrices
$$m_x = \hbar \begin{bmatrix} 0 & 0 & 0 \\ 0 & 0 & i \\ 0 & -i & 0 \end{bmatrix}, \quad m_y = \hbar \begin{bmatrix} 0 & 0 & i \\ 0 & 0 & 0 \\ -i & 0 & 0 \end{bmatrix}, \quad m_z = \hbar \begin{bmatrix} 0 & i & 0 \\ -i & 0 & 0 \\ 0 & 0 & 0 \end{bmatrix}$$

represent the angular momentum components of a system whose (total angular momentum)^2 is $\theta = l(l+1)\hbar^2$ with $l=1$.

Find the unitary transformation which diagonalizes one of these, say m_z; apply it also to m_x and m_y, and compare the results with those you obtained for problem (1).

CHAPTER FIVE

THE RADIAL FUNCTION, AND THE TOTAL ENERGY

General remarks about the radial wave-function

The separation of the wave-equation in spherical polars yielded first two equations, (4.23) and (4.24), of which (4.24) is concerned only with the angular motion, and does not contain the total energy, while (4.23) is concerned with the radial motion, and contains the energy of this motion as $E - \lambda/2mr^2$. Since we now know that λ is to be written as $l(l+1)\hbar^2$ we can – in principle, at any rate – solve (4.23) and find the total energy E. The total energy determined in this way may be a function of l, but cannot depend on m, since (4.23) does not contain m. This accords with the remark in the last chapter, that the states with different m-values but the same l-values must be indistinguishable in a central field.

If in (4.23) we replace λ by $l(l+1)\hbar^2$ and replace $R(r)$ by $\chi(r)/r$ we get a simpler equation:

$$-\frac{\hbar^2}{2m}\frac{d^2\chi}{dr^2} + \left\{V(r) + \frac{l(l+1)\hbar^2}{2mr^2}\right\}\chi = E\chi. \qquad (5.1)$$

This is the Schrödinger equation for a one-dimensional motion under the influence of an effective potential $V(r) + l(l+1)\hbar^2/2mr^2$. The second term is called the *centrifugal potential*; it is necessarily positive, and alters the shape of the potential well in such a way as to 'drive the particle away from the origin'.

Let us consider in a qualitative way the problem of solving (5.1). Much of the discussion in the remainder of this section will be independent of the form of $V(r)$, but when we require to assume a specific form we shall use the attractive Coulomb potential $V(r) = -Ze^2/4\pi\varepsilon_0 r$. (The substitution $\varepsilon_0 = 1/4\pi$ puts the equation into the form associated with unrationalized Gaussian units.) The effective potentials for $l = 0$, 1 and 2 are sketched in Fig. 5.1 and the horizontal lines are drawn at levels on the energy scale corresponding to the four lowest eigenvalues of the energy, according to eqn. (5.11). It seems to be generally true that the potentials encountered in

93

94 QUANTUM MECHANICS

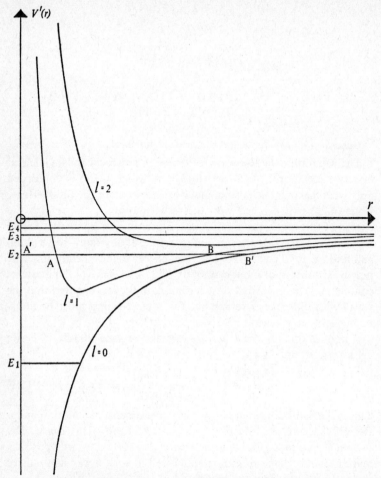

FIG. 5.1. The effective potential and the four lowest energy levels of a particle
moving in a Coulomb field.

physical problems do not decrease near the origin as rapidly as
$-1/r^2$, so that the addition of the true potential $V(r)$ and the centrifugal potential gives an effective potential, $V'(r)$ say, which rises to
infinity as r tends to zero.

Examination of (5.1) in the form

$$\frac{d^2\chi}{dr^2} = -\frac{2m}{\hbar^2}(E - V'(r))\chi$$

shows that the graph of $\chi(r)$ will be concave towards the r-axis when

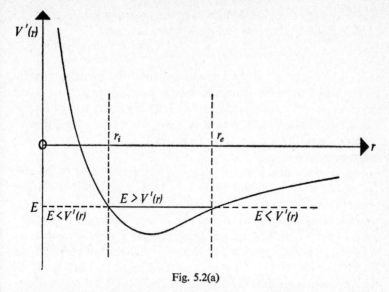

Fig. 5.2(a)

FIG. 5.2. Between the origin and r_i, and beyond r_e, $\chi(r)$ is convex towards the axis; between r_i and r_e it is concave. If $\chi(r)$ represents a bound state the graph must tend towards the axis beyond r_e, like 1 and 1′, not 2 or 2′.

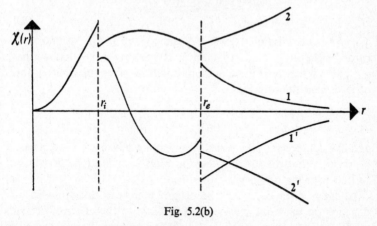

Fig. 5.2(b)

$E > V'(r)$, and convex towards the r-axis when $E < V'(r)$. Since $V'(r)$ tends to zero as r tends to infinity any negative E will give rise to a function χ which is convex towards the axis beyond a certain value of r, shown as r_e in Fig. 5.2(a). Such a function must either approach the axis asymptotically, like curves 1, 1′ of Fig. 5.2(b), or must diverge from it, like curves 2, 2′ of that figure. The latter pair cannot depict state-functions for bound states, for the probability of finding the particle distant between r and $r + \delta r$ from the origin is

$$4\pi r^2 \delta r \mid R(r) \mid^2 = 4\pi \delta r \mid \chi(r) \mid^2,$$

so if $\chi(r)$ diverges from the axis as r increases the particle is certain to be found very far from the origin and therefore beyond the influence of the attractive potential. It follows that the χ-function for a bound state must have a negative slope at r_e, and that its tendency towards the axis as r increases is controlled only by the magnitude of E.

Nearer to the origin than r_e, $\chi(r)$ will be concave towards the axis, and may oscillate. Finally there may be a region near the origin where again $E < V'(r)$, and the χ-function is again convex towards the axis. This is the region $r < r_i$ of Fig. 5.2(a). Finally as r approaches zero $\chi(r)$ must tend to zero at least as rapidly as r, for otherwise $R(r)$ would become infinite. In fact the behaviour of $\chi(r)$ near the origin depends on l. We can see this if we recall that in Fig. 5.1 all the effective potentials for $l > 0$ are dominated by the centrifugal term near the origin of r, so that for small r the equation (5.1) can be written as

$$\frac{d^2\chi}{dr^2} = \frac{l(l+1)}{r^2}\chi.$$

This has two solutions: $\chi = kr^{l+1}$ and $\chi = kr^{-l}$. The second is discarded because it tends to infinity at the origin, so that we have $\chi \propto r^{l+1}$. When $l = 0$ the Coulomb potential gives the limiting form of (5.1) near the origin as

$$\frac{d^2\chi}{dr^2} = -\frac{k}{r}\chi$$

and if χ is expressed as a series of ascending powers of r it can easily be verified that the lowest non-vanishing term must be that in $(r)^1$ so that near the origin $\chi \propto r$ when $l = 0$.

At great distances from the origin, then, the behaviour of $\chi(r)$ depends on the total energy E, while close to the origin it depends on l. Possible forms of the solution for different l are sketched in Fig. 5.3.

The 'wavelength' of the oscillations in χ (indicated in Fig. 5.3) depends on the extent to which the graph of $V'(r)$ dips below the level of E – the greater that dip the shorter the wavelength. If the level of the line $A'ABB'$ of Fig. 5.1 represents a value of E for which

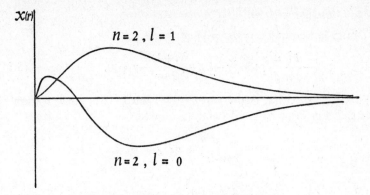

FIG. 5.3. The two functions $\chi(r)$ for $n = 2$.

stationary states exist with $l = 0$ and 1 it is easy to see that the number of oscillations in the range AB for the $\chi(r)$ corresponding to $l = 1$ must be less than the number in the range $A'B'$ for the χ-function for $l = 0$. The two possible functions will in fact be as shown in Fig. 5.3, the state-function with the highest possible l having in general no zeroes, that with the next lower l having one zero, and so on.

The three terms of the Hamiltonian operator on the left-hand side of (5.1) represent in order the kinetic energy of radial motion, the potential energy and the kinetic energy of rotation. The radial motion may be pictured as an oscillation in one of the potential wells of Fig. 5.1. For each of these wells there will be a number of energy levels whose spacing depends on the detailed shape of the well – the well is not parabolic in shape so the oscillator is not simple harmonic and the results of chapter 3 do not apply. For certain shapes of well the second lowest level in the well for $l = 2$ (say) may coincide in energy with the lowest level in the well for $l = 3$, the extra energy of radial oscillation of the one matching the extra rotational energy of the other. If this happens there is degeneracy between these levels of different l. This argument shows that such degeneracy must be a property of specific potential functions, and is not a necessary feature of the energies in the general central field problem.

The general conclusions of this qualitative discussion will be illustrated in the following sections of this chapter, where we solve (5.1) for three special potentials. First we treat the isotropic oscillator – which was discussed in a different way in chapter 3 – then the hydrogen atom, and finally the rectangular potential well.

The isotropic oscillator

In (5.1) we put $V(r) = \alpha r^2 = \frac{1}{2} m \omega^2 r^2$ and get

$$-\frac{\hbar^2}{2m} \frac{d^2 \chi}{dr^2} + \alpha r^2 \chi - E\chi + \frac{l(l+1)\hbar^2}{2mr^2} \chi = 0. \tag{5.2}$$

First we ask: what is the asymptotic form of $\chi(r)$ when r is very large? For large r (5.2) becomes

$$-\frac{\hbar^2}{2m} \frac{d^2 \chi}{dr^2} + \alpha r^2 \chi = 0$$

$$\therefore \frac{d^2 \chi}{dr^2} = \frac{m^2 \omega^2}{\hbar^2} r^2 \chi. \tag{5.3}$$

We note that this does not contain l.

Now if we try as a solution

$$\chi = \varepsilon^{\pm m\omega r^2/2\hbar} \tag{5.4}$$

we have

$$\frac{d\chi}{dr} = \pm \frac{m\omega}{\hbar} r \, \varepsilon^{\pm m\omega r^2/2\hbar}$$

and

$$\frac{d^2 \chi}{dr^2} = \pm \frac{m\omega}{\hbar} \varepsilon^{\pm m\omega r^2/2\hbar} + \frac{m^2 \omega^2}{\hbar^2} r^2 \, \varepsilon^{\pm m\omega r^2/2\hbar}.$$

For large r this agrees with (5.3), so (5.4) is a suitable asymptotic solution. We have to reject the positive exponent, as it would make χ diverge rapidly as r increases, so we take

$$\chi_{as} \propto \varepsilon^{-m\omega r^2/2\hbar}.$$

For the complete solution we shall try

$$\chi = f(r) \, \varepsilon^{-m\omega r^2/2\hbar}$$

and we must try to find a suitable polynomial form for $f(r)$. Differentiating twice we get

$$\frac{d^2 \chi}{dr^2} = \left\{ f''(r) - 2\frac{m\omega r}{\hbar} f'(r) + \left(\frac{m^2 \omega^2 r^2}{\hbar^2} - \frac{m\omega}{\hbar} \right) f(r) \right\} \varepsilon^{-m\omega r^2/2\hbar}.$$

The differential equation satisfied by $f(r)$ is therefore

$$f''(r) - \frac{2m\omega}{\hbar} r f'(r) - \left(\frac{m\omega}{\hbar} - \frac{2mE}{\hbar^2} \right) f(r) - \frac{l(l+1)}{r^2} f(r) = 0.$$

We now put $f(r) = \sum_j a_j r^j$ and equate the coefficients of each power of r to zero. For the term in r^{j-2} we have

$$a_j j(j-1) - a_{j-2}\frac{2m\omega}{\hbar}(j-2) - a_{j-2}\left(\frac{m\omega}{\hbar} - \frac{2mE}{\hbar^2}\right) - a_j l(l+1) = 0$$

or

$$a_j\{j(j-1) - l(l+1)\} = a_{j-2}\left\{\frac{m\omega}{\hbar}(2j-3) - \frac{2mE}{\hbar^2}\right\}. \qquad (5.5)$$

This recursion relation for the coefficients will generate two sets of solutions, one containing only odd powers of r, and the other containing only even powers.

Since the probability of finding the particle in a spherical shell of thickness δr is $4\pi \mid R(r) \mid^2 r^2 \delta r = 4\pi \mid \chi(r) \mid^2 \delta r$, $\chi(r)$ must not contain negative powers of r, for otherwise this probability would tend to infinity as r tends to zero. It follows that the series for $f(r)$ must terminate at the lower end, so there must be some j for which $a_j \neq 0$ but $a_{j-2} = 0$. If j' is the minimum j we have from (5.5)

$$j'(j'-1) = l(l+1) \qquad \therefore \; j' = l+1. \qquad (5.6a)$$

Thus the lowest term in the solution for a given l is r^{l+1}. If $l=0$ the lowest term in $f(r)$ is that in r, and since

$$R(r) = \frac{\chi(r)}{r} = f(r)\frac{\varepsilon^{-m\omega r^2/2\hbar}}{r}$$

the lowest term in the series for $R(r)$ is a constant.

The series for $f(r)$ must also terminate at the upper end: for the ratio of successive terms is

$$\frac{a_j r^j}{a_{j-2} r^{j-2}} = \frac{2m\omega j}{\hbar j^2} r^2 \qquad \text{for large } j$$

$$= \frac{2m\omega}{\hbar}\frac{r^2}{j}$$

which is the ratio of successive terms in the series

$$\sum_{j=0}^{\infty} \frac{1}{j!}\left(\frac{2m\omega}{\hbar} r^2\right)^j = \varepsilon^{2m\omega r^2/\hbar};$$

if this were the limiting form of $f(r)$ we should have

$$\chi(r) \to \varepsilon^{\frac{3}{2}m\omega r^2/\hbar}$$

which diverges as r tends to infinity. To prevent this the series must be terminated at the upper end, so there must be some j, say j'', for which $a_{j''-2} \neq 0$ but $a_{j''} = 0$.

From (5.5) this means that

$$\frac{m\omega}{\hbar}(2j''-3) = \frac{2mE}{\hbar^2}$$

$$\therefore E = (j'' - \tfrac{3}{2})\hbar\omega. \qquad (5.6b)$$

If we put $j''-2=n'+1$ we get E in the form

$$E = (n' + \tfrac{3}{2})\hbar\omega$$

as we had it at (3.16). In fact it is more usual to put $j''-2=n$ so that the ground-state has the quantum number 1. Then $E_n=(n+\tfrac{1}{2})\hbar\omega$ with $n\geq 1$. The highest term in $f(r)$ is then the one in r^n, and since the lowest term is the one in r^{l+1} it follows that $n>l$, and that for any possible E there is an upper limit to l. The lowest energy, occurring when $l=0$ and $n=1$, is $E_1=\tfrac{3}{2}\hbar\omega$.

We can now look into the question of the degeneracy of the eigenstate for a given E. This state is specified by the value of n and we have to decide how many l- and m-values may occur with this n. If n is odd j'' is odd, since the highest power of r in $f(r)$ is $r^n=r^{j''-2}$. It follows from (5.5) that all the j's in the various $f(r)$ for this energy are odd, and in particular that in each case the lowest value, j', is odd: hence from (5.6a) the possible l must be even. Thus if n is odd l must be even, and similarly if n is even l must be odd. To each value of l there correspond $2l+1$ values of m, and so the degree of degeneracy for the various states can be evaluated:

n	l	Degeneracy
1 (ground-state)	0	1
2	1	3
3	0, 2	$1+5 = 6$
4	1, 3	$3+7 = 10$
5	0, 2, 4	$1+5+9 = 15$
.		
n	$\ldots n-3, n-1$	$\tfrac{1}{2}n(n+1)$

This agrees with the conclusion we reached about the degeneracy in chapter 3, though there our discussion was in terms of eigen-functions in a Cartesian coordinate system. These different representations must of course be equivalent, in the sense that each must contain the same number of independent eigenfunctions, and it must be possible to express the eigenfunctions of the one coordinate system in terms of those of the other. The decision as to which coordinate system to use in any problem will depend on the nature of that problem, and the symmetries of the system with which it deals.

For our present purpose we are not much concerned to know the explicit form of the radial eigenfunctions; they can be found, apart from the normalizing factors, by determining the coefficients a_j in the recursion relation (5.5). For the states with $l = 0$ – called s-states in spectroscopy – the various $\chi(r)$ are state-functions of the one-dimensional oscillator, and may be found by the procedure indicated in connection with eqns. (3.13) and (3.14). (See also problem 3 on p. 57.) More generally the solutions of (5.1) are confluent hyper-geometric functions, and can be expressed in terms of the Associated Laguerre Polynomials; see Morse and Feshbach: *Methods of Theoretical Physics* (McGraw-Hill, 1953), chapter 6, pp. 788-9.

The hydrogen atom

The attractive potential between a nucleus of charge Ze and an electron is described by $V(r) = -Ze^2/4\pi\varepsilon_0 r$ and the motion of the system is therefore controlled by the Hamiltonian

$$H = \frac{p^2}{2m} - \frac{Ze^2}{4\pi\varepsilon_0 r}.$$

We are not interested in the motion of the centre of mass so m represents the reduced mass, i.e.

$$m = \frac{m_e M}{m_e + M} \qquad \text{(See problem 1, p. 114)}$$

For this case, then, (5.1) becomes

$$-\frac{\hbar^2}{2m}\frac{d^2\chi}{dr^2} - \left\{\frac{Ze^2}{4\pi\varepsilon_0 r} - \frac{l(l+1)\hbar^2}{2mr^2}\right\}\chi = E\chi. \qquad (5.7)$$

The asymptotic solution for large r is found by solving

$$\frac{\hbar^2}{2m}\frac{d^2\chi}{dr^2} + E\chi = 0,$$

which shows that the behaviour of $\chi(r)$ for large r is independent of l, as we should expect.

If E is positive the solution of this equation is

$$\chi(r) \propto e^{\pm i\left(\frac{2mE}{\hbar^2}\right)^{\frac{1}{2}} r}.$$

This solution does not represent a bound state, for it gives the probability of finding the electron at a distance between r and $r+\delta r$ from the centre of mass as

$$4\pi \left| \chi(r) \right|^2 \delta r = \text{constant} \times \delta r,$$

so the electron is not localized or bound. On the other hand, if E is negative, say $E = -W$, there are solutions

$$\chi(r) \propto \varepsilon^{+\left(\frac{2mW}{\hbar^2}\right)^{\frac{1}{2}} r} \quad \text{and} \quad \varepsilon^{-\left(\frac{2mW}{\hbar^2}\right)^{\frac{1}{2}} r},$$

of which the second is acceptable. We therefore conclude that E must be negative for a bound state, and that the corresponding asymptotic form for the radial function is

$$\chi_{\text{as}} \propto \varepsilon^{-\left(\frac{2mW}{\hbar^2}\right)^{\frac{1}{2}} r}.$$

We now assume that the complete form for the radial function is

$$\chi(r) = f(r) \, \varepsilon^{-\left(\frac{2mW}{\hbar^2}\right)^{\frac{1}{2}} r} \tag{5.8}$$

with

$$f(r) = \sum_j a_j \, r^j.$$

Inserting (5.8) in (5.7) we get

$$\frac{2mW}{\hbar^2} f(r) - 2\left(\frac{2mW}{\hbar^2}\right)^{\frac{1}{2}} f'(r) + f''(r) + \left(\frac{2m}{\hbar^2} \frac{Ze^2}{4\pi\varepsilon_0 r} - \frac{l(l+1)}{r^2}\right) f(r)$$

$$= \frac{2mW}{\hbar^2} f(r)$$

$$\therefore \ f''(r) - 2\left(\frac{2mW}{\hbar^2}\right)^{\frac{1}{2}} f'(r) + \left(\frac{2m}{\hbar^2} \frac{Ze^2}{4\pi\varepsilon_0 r} - \frac{l(l+1)}{r^2}\right) f(r) = 0.$$

Now we employ the series form of $f(r)$ and equate to zero the coefficients of each power of r. For the $(j-2)$th power this gives

$$a_j\{j(j-1) - l(l+1)\} = a_{j-1}\left\{2\left(\frac{2mW}{\hbar^2}\right)^{\frac{1}{2}}(j-1) - \frac{2mZe^2}{4\pi\varepsilon_0 \hbar^2}\right\}. \tag{5.9}$$

This relation will determine the coefficients in a series which contains both odd and even powers of r. The termination of the series at the lower end – to prevent the probability $4\pi \mid \chi(r) \mid^2 \delta r$ going to infinity at the origin – means that there is a minimum j, say j', such that $a_{j'} \neq 0$ but $a_{j'-1} = 0$.

From (5.9) we deduce that

$$j'(j'-1) = l(l+1)$$
$$\therefore \ j' = l+1. \tag{5.10a}$$

If the series does not terminate at the upper end, the ratio of successive terms tends, for large j, to

$$\frac{a_j r^j}{a_{j-1} r^{j-1}} = \frac{2(j-1)\left(\dfrac{2mW}{\hbar^2}\right)^{\frac{1}{2}}}{j(j-1)} r$$

$$= 2\left(\frac{2mW}{\hbar^2}\right)^{\frac{1}{2}} \frac{r}{j},$$

which is the ratio of successive terms in the series

$$\sum_{j=0}^{\infty} \frac{\left\{2\left(\dfrac{2mW}{\hbar^2}\right)^{\frac{1}{2}} r\right\}^j}{j!} = \varepsilon^{2\left(\frac{2mW}{\hbar^2}\right)^{\frac{1}{2}} r}.$$

But in that case

$$f(r) \ \varepsilon^{-\left(\frac{2mW}{\hbar^2}\right)^{\frac{1}{2}} r} = \varepsilon^{+\left(\frac{2mW}{\hbar^2}\right)^{\frac{1}{2}} r}$$

and this diverges as r tends to infinity. To prevent this the series must be terminated at its upper end, i.e. there must be some j, say j'', for which

$$a_{j''-1} \neq 0 \quad \text{but} \quad a_{j''} = 0.$$

In this case (5.9) shows that

$$2\left(\frac{2mW}{\hbar^2}\right)^{\frac{1}{2}} (j''-1) = \frac{2mZe^2}{4\pi\varepsilon_0 \hbar^2}. \tag{5.10b}$$

If we write $j''-1 = n$ we can rearrange this to read

$$W = \frac{mZ^2 e^4}{(4\pi\varepsilon_0)^2 2n^2 \hbar^2}$$

and so the total energy of the states with quantum number n is

$$E_n = -\frac{mZ^2e^4}{(4\pi\varepsilon_0)^2 2n^2\hbar^2}, \quad \text{with } n = 1, 2, 3 \ldots \quad (5.11)$$

Since the lowest term in the series $f(r)$ is that in r^{l+1} it must always be true that $n \geq l+1$ or $n > l$. For any n, both odd and even l are allowed (except of course when $n = 1$ in which case only $l = 0$ satisfies the above inequality). The energy does not depend on l, so again we have degeneracy, and the degeneracy is greater in this case than in the case of the oscillator, where the l-values were more restricted. In fact, we can list the degenerate states as we did on p. 100:

n	l	Degeneracy
1	0	1
2	0, 1	$1+3 = 4$
3	0, 1, 2	$1+3+5 = 9$
n	$0, 1, \ldots n-1$	$1+3+5+ \ldots +2n-1 = n^2$

The degree of degeneracy of the nth state is then n^2. This, the greatest possible degree of degeneracy, occurs only in a Coulomb field.

For the hydrogen atom itself Z is of course unity, but since it is often assumed that the states of individual electrons in more complex atoms may be represented approximately by hydrogen-like wave-functions – functions which are solutions of (5.7) with an appropriate value of Z – it is useful to notice how a change of Z affects the results of this discussion. First we see that the energy eigenvalues (5.11) are proportional to Z^2. Secondly, the scale of the wave-function varies inversely as Z, for if we start with $Z = 1$ in (5.7) the equation is unaltered if we subsequently replace E by Z^2E and r by r/Z. (5.7) is sometimes simplified by writing $4\pi\varepsilon_0\hbar^2/me^2$ as a_0, the Bohr unit of radius, which is numerically $0\cdot529 \times 10^{-8}$ cm. Then a_0 appears as a characteristic unit of size for the hydrogen atom, while a_0/Z plays the same role in the general case.

The energies of (5.11) are exactly those predicted by the original Bohr theory of the hydrogen atom. Using the virial theorem (problem 2 of chapter 3) we can quickly see, in further agreement with the Bohr theory, that

$$\langle \text{P.E.} \rangle = -2\,E_n, \qquad \langle \text{K.E.} \rangle = E_n.$$

These results can also be obtained if the explicit forms of the radial functions $R_{nl}(r)$ or $\chi_{nl}(r)$ are obtained. These functions are discussed in detail in, for example, Margenau and Murphy's *The Mathematics of Physics and Chemistry*, chapter 3. Chapter 5 of Pauling and Wilson's *Introduction to Quantum Mechanics* includes very useful lists of the radial functions themselves and of the expectation values of various powers of r. For instance, for a state with quantum numbers n and l the expectation value of $\dfrac{1}{r^2}$ is

$$\left\langle \frac{1}{r^2} \right\rangle_{nl} = \frac{Z^2}{a_0{}^2 n^3 (l+\frac{1}{2})}.$$

Since the rotational kinetic energy appears in the Hamiltonian as

$$\frac{l(l+1)\hbar^2}{2mr^2}$$

its expectation value must be

$$\frac{Z^2 l(l+1)\hbar^2}{2ma_0{}^2 n^3 (l+\frac{1}{2})}.$$

If this is compared with the total kinetic energy

$$-E_n = \frac{Z^2 \hbar^2}{2ma_0{}^2 n^2}$$

it will be seen that the rotational kinetic energy is always less than the total kinetic energy, the difference being the energy associated with the radial degree of freedom; this can never be zero because of the uncertainty principle.

The energies E_n increase from a minimum – for the ground-state – to zero, becoming more closely spaced as they tend to this limit. Although we ignored solutions with positive energy because they could not represent bound states, they are nevertheless physically significant; they exist for all $E>0$, and represent the states which occur when free electrons are scattered by protons, the classical analogue being the hyperbolic orbits in the Kepler problem. These states manifest themselves spectroscopically in the continuum which appears on the short wavelength side of the series limit, when free electrons are captured into bound levels.

The rectangular potential well

The solutions of the radial wave-equation for the three-dimensional rectangular potential well, for which $V = -V_0$ when $r \leqq a$ and $V=0$ when $r>a$ (Fig. 5.4a), differ in a number of important respects from those of the two previous cases. The most obvious difference is that, because of the discontinuity of the potential where $r>a$, the solution has to be constructed by fitting together the solutions of two distinct wave-equations, one for the 'interior' region and the other for the 'exterior' region; the eigenvalues are fixed by the requirements of continuity at the boundary between those regions. The second important difference between this and the previous cases is that the energies of the bound states in the rectangular well show no degeneracy between states with different values of l. A third difference is that, for a well of finite width and depth, the number of bound states is finite; the quantity $V_0 a^2$ which controls the number of bound states is called the *strength of the well*.

The solutions with zero orbital momentum are found most readily. When $l=0$ the interior and exterior forms of the wave-equation for $\chi(r)$ are, from (5.1),

Interior: $\qquad -\dfrac{\hbar^2}{2m}\dfrac{d^2\chi}{dr^2} - V_0\chi = E\chi \qquad$ when $r \leqq a$;

Exterior: $\qquad -\dfrac{\hbar^2}{2m}\dfrac{d^2\chi}{dr^2} = E\chi \qquad$ when $r > a$.

In both cases we want to find solutions representing bound states, for which $E<0$; if we put $E=-W$, where the *binding energy* W is positive, the above equations become

Interior: $\qquad \dfrac{d^2\chi}{dr^2} + \dfrac{2m}{\hbar^2}(V_0 - W)\chi = 0;$ $\qquad$ (5.12a)

Exterior: $\qquad \dfrac{d^2\chi}{dr^2} - \dfrac{2m}{\hbar^2}W\chi = 0.$ $\qquad$ (5.12b)

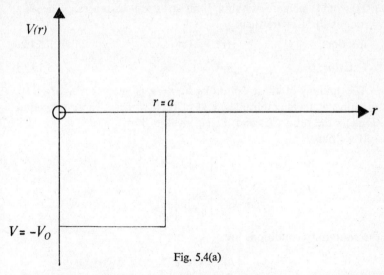

Fig. 5.4(a)

FIG. 5.4. The continuity of $\chi(r)$ and its first derivative at $r=a$ is achieved by the suitable choice of the binding energy W and the ratio $C=A$.

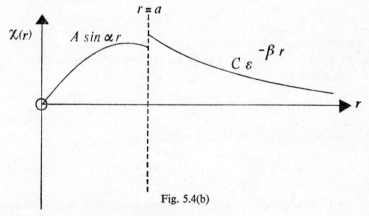

Fig. 5.4(b)

The solutions of these equations are

Interior: $\chi(r) = A \sin \alpha r + B \cos \alpha r$, where $\alpha^2 = \dfrac{2m}{\hbar^2}(V_0 - W)$;

Exterior: $\chi(r) = C \varepsilon^{-\beta r} + D \varepsilon^{\beta r}$, where $\beta^2 = \dfrac{2m}{\hbar^2}W$.

B must be zero, for otherwise the radial wave-function $R(r) = \chi(r)/r$ would be infinite at the origin, and D must be zero for otherwise

$R(r)$ would increase without limit at great distances. The final solutions for $\chi(r)$ are then

Interior: $\qquad\qquad\qquad \chi(r) = A \sin \alpha r;$ $\qquad\qquad$ (5.13a)

Exterior: $\qquad\qquad\qquad \chi(r) = C \, \varepsilon^{-\beta r}.$ $\qquad\qquad$ (5.13b)

The joining of these solutions at $r=a$ (Fig. 5.4b) involves the equating of their amplitudes, and of their slopes. These two equations fix the ratio C/A and the eigenvalue W.

If we put

$$\xi = \alpha a = +\left\{\frac{2m}{\hbar^2}(V_0 - W)\right\}^{\frac{1}{2}} a$$

$$\eta = \beta a = +\left\{\frac{2m}{\hbar^2}W\right\}^{\frac{1}{2}} a$$

the continuity conditions are

$$A \sin \xi = C \, \varepsilon^{-\eta}$$

$$A\xi \cos \xi = -C\eta \, \varepsilon^{-\eta}$$

whence

$$\xi \cot \xi = -\eta.$$

A solution which is only just bound exists whenever $\eta = 0$; then apart from $\xi = 0$, which is physically inadmissible, the solutions of this equation are

$$\xi = (2n-1)\frac{\pi}{2}, \qquad \text{where } n = 1, 2, 3 \ldots$$

In view of the definition of ξ, this means that

$$\frac{2m}{\hbar^2}V_0 a^2 = \left\{(2n-1)\frac{\pi}{2}\right\}^2. \qquad\qquad (5.14)$$

As the strength of the well is increased from zero the first bound state appears when $\dfrac{2m}{\hbar^2} V_0 a^2 = \dfrac{\pi^2}{4}$. Its state-function has exactly a quarter of a wavelength inside the well. As the well-strength increases further this state becomes more tightly bound, and a new weakly bound state with three quarters of a wavelength within the well appears when $\dfrac{2m}{\hbar^2} V_0 a^2 = \dfrac{9\pi^2}{4}$.

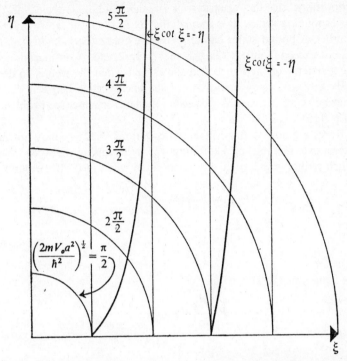

FIG. 5.5. Graphical solution for the binding energies of states with zero orbital momentum in the three-dimensional rectangular potential well.

The binding energies are found by solving for η the equations

$$\xi \cot \xi = -\eta$$

and

$$\xi^2 + \eta^2 = \frac{2m}{\hbar^2} V_0 a^2.$$

Fig. 5.5 illustrates a graphical solution of these equations, and helps us to visualize the way in which the number of solutions and their binding energies depend on the well-strength $V_0 a^2$. We draw in the first quadrant – since ξ and η are by definition positive quantities – the loci of $\xi \cot \xi = -\eta$ and $\xi^2 + \eta^2 = 2mV_0 a^2/\hbar^2$. The latter are circles whose radii are proportional to the square root of the well-strength. The intersections of the two sets of loci correspond to solutions of the equations, the ordinates η of the intersections being proportional to the square root of the binding energies of the corresponding states. It is immediately clear from the figure that the number of bound states cannot exceed 1 unless $(2mV_0a^2/\hbar^2)^{\frac{1}{2}} > \pi/2$, cannot exceed 2 unless $(2mV_0a^2/\hbar^2)^{\frac{1}{2}} > 3\pi/2$, etc. Consideration of the geometry of the figure also shows that when the well is so deep that there are many bound states the energy gaps between neighbouring states increase as we ascend the level scheme (see problem 4 on p. 115).

Reverting now to the differential equations (5.12) we may note an alternative method of exhibiting the relationship between them which reduces the labour of solving them when $l \neq 0$. If we put

$$\rho = \left\{\frac{2m}{\hbar^2}(V_0 - W)\right\}^{\frac{1}{2}} r$$

and

$$\rho' = \left\{\frac{2m}{\hbar^2} W\right\}^{\frac{1}{2}} r$$

the equations (5.12) become

$$\frac{d^2\chi}{d\rho^2} + \chi = 0 \qquad (5.15a)$$

and

$$\frac{d^2\chi}{d\rho'^2} - \chi = 0. \qquad (5.15b)$$

Now replacing ρ by $i\sigma$ in (5.15a) gives

$$\frac{d^2\chi}{d\sigma^2} - \chi = 0$$

which is the same as (5.15b).

The solution (5.13a) which we found to satisfy the boundary condition at the origin can now be written

$$\chi(\rho) = \frac{A}{2i}(\varepsilon^{i\rho} + \varepsilon^{-i\rho})$$

and replacing ρ by $i\sigma$ gives

$$\chi(\sigma) \propto (\varepsilon^{-\sigma} + \varepsilon^{+\sigma})$$

from which we get (5.13b) by neglecting the second diverging term – which we must do because the boundary conditions to be satisfied by the exterior solution differ from those for the interior solution.

Now, when $l > 0$ (5.1) can be put in the forms

Interior:
$$\frac{d^2\chi}{d\rho^2} + \chi - \frac{l(l+1)}{\rho^2}\chi = 0; \tag{5.16a}$$

Exterior:
$$\frac{d^2\chi}{d\rho'^2} - \chi - \frac{l(l+1)}{\rho'^2}\chi = 0. \tag{5.16b}$$

If in (5.16a) we put $\chi = \sum_j = a_j\rho^j$ and equate the coefficient of ρ^{j-2} to zero, we get

$$a_j\{j(j-1) - l(l+1)\} = a_{j-2}. \tag{5.17}$$

If $R(r)$ is not to become infinite at the origin the series must terminate at the lower end, so as in the other cases considered in the earlier sections of this chapter there is a minimum j, say j', given by

$$j' = l+1. \tag{5.18}$$

For small ρ, then, $\chi(\rho)$ must behave like ρ^{l+1}; further, (5.17) shows that the solutions will be even or odd, involving only alternate powers of ρ. Our solution (5.13a) for $l = 0$ satisfies these requirements.

The solution for $l = 1$ will therefore be even, and will behave near the origin like ρ^2. The function

$$\frac{1}{\rho}(\sin\rho - \rho\cos\rho)$$

has these properties, and it is easy to verify by direct substitution that it satisfies (5.16a). Writing this function in terms of complex exponentials,

$$\frac{1}{\rho}\left\{\frac{1}{2i}(\varepsilon^{i\rho} - \varepsilon^{-i\rho}) - \frac{\rho}{2}(\varepsilon^{i\rho} + \varepsilon^{-i\rho})\right\}$$

and putting $\rho = i\sigma$ we get

$$-\tfrac{1}{2}\left(\frac{1}{\sigma}+1\right)\varepsilon^{-\sigma} + \tfrac{1}{2}\left(\frac{1}{\sigma}-1\right)\varepsilon^{\sigma}.$$

Excluding the terms in ε^{σ} we obtain the solution of (5.16b). The complete solution when $l = 1$ is then

Interior:
$$\chi(\rho) = \frac{1}{\rho}(\sin\rho - \rho\cos\rho); \tag{5.19a}$$

Exterior:
$$\chi(\rho') = \frac{1}{\rho'}(1+\rho')\varepsilon^{-\rho'}. \tag{5.19b}$$

The continuity requirements at $r=a$, expressed as before in terms of ξ and η, become

$$\frac{\cot \xi}{\xi} - \frac{1}{\xi^2} = \frac{1}{\eta} + \frac{1}{\eta^2}$$

with again

$$\xi^2 + \eta^2 = \frac{2m}{\hbar^2} V_0 a^2.$$

If the well-strength is increased from zero, bound states appear whenever η is zero, i.e. whenever $\cot \xi$ is infinite, or

$$\xi = \pi, 2\pi, 3\pi \ldots$$

$$\therefore \frac{2m}{\hbar^2} V_0 a^2 = \left(2n\frac{\pi}{2}\right)^2 \quad \text{with } n = 1, 2, 3 \ldots \text{(cf. 5.14).} \quad (5.20)$$

For $l=2$ the solution of (5.16a) must be odd and must behave near the origin like ρ^3. A function satisfying these requirements may be constructed in the form

$$\frac{1}{\rho^2}\{(1 + a\rho^2)\sin \rho + b\rho \cos \rho\}.$$

Expanding the circular functions in powers of ρ, we ensure the correct dependence on ρ near the origin by choosing a and b to make the terms in ρ^{-1} and ρ^{+1} vanish. We find that the interior function must be

Interior: $\quad \chi(\rho) = \dfrac{1}{\rho^2}\{(3-\rho^2)\sin \rho - 3\rho \cos \rho\}$ $\quad\quad$ (5.21a)

and direct substitution in (5.16a) will show that this is a solution for $l=2$. More generally the interior solution for any l is of the form

$$\chi_l(\rho) = \frac{1}{\rho^l}\{F(\rho)\sin \rho + G(\rho)\cos \rho\}, \quad\quad (5.22)$$

where $F(\rho)$ is a polynomial in even powers of ρ and $G(\rho)$ is a polynomial in odd powers of ρ; one terminates at ρ^l and the other at ρ^{l-1}. The exterior solution is then derived from this by the method illustrated above. When $l=2$, for example, the exterior solution derived from (5.21a) is

Exterior: $\quad \chi(\rho') = \dfrac{1}{\rho'^2}\{3 + 3\rho' + \rho'^2\} \, \varepsilon^{-\rho'}.$ $\quad\quad$ (5.21b)

The continuity requirements at $r=a$ relate the binding energy to the well-strength through the equations

$$\frac{3}{\xi^2} + \frac{1}{\xi \cot \xi - 1} = -\frac{3}{\eta^2} - \frac{1}{1+\eta}$$

and

$$\xi^2 + \eta^2 = \frac{2m}{\hbar^2} V_0 a^2.$$

Bound solutions just appear whenever $\eta = 0$, so that

$$\xi \cot \xi = 1$$
$$\therefore \quad \tan \xi = \xi$$
$$\therefore \qquad \xi = 0, 4\cdot49, 7\cdot72, 10\cdot9, 14\cdot1 \ldots$$

a sequence of values which tend towards but are always slightly below the terms of the sequence $(2n+1)\pi/2$ with $n = 1, 2, 3 \ldots$

Thus for comparison with (5.14) and (5.20) we may write

$$\frac{2m}{\hbar^2} V_0 a^2 \lesssim \left\{(2n+1)\frac{\pi}{2}\right\}^2 \quad \text{with } n = 1, 2, 3 \ldots \qquad (5.23)$$

It is now clear that in this potential well there is no degeneracy between the eigenvalues for different values of l. Because of the discontinuity in the potential at $r=a$ the eigenvalues are determined by the behaviour of the eigenfunctions at $r=a$ – rather than as $r \to \infty$, as was the case for the isotropic oscillator or in the Coulomb field – and this depends on the detailed form of the eigenfunctions. The degeneracy in the case of the isotropic oscillator and the Coulomb potential appears to result from the determination of the eigenvalues through the asymptotic behaviour of the wave-functions, which as we saw in the first section of this chapter does not discriminate between the functions for different values of l.

The problem of the energy levels in the rectangular potential well is of interest in nuclear physics, as it represents a first approximation to the short-range neutron-proton force. If the binding between the neutron and proton in the deuteron is due to such a potential the strength of the well may be inferred from the fact that the deuteron has just one bound state, whose binding energy is $2\cdot225$ MeV. If this is assumed negligible compared with the well-depth, $V_0 a^2$ has the value $1\cdot02 \times 10^{-24}$ MeV cm.^{2}; putting $a = 2.10^{-13}$ cm., which is approximately the range of the nuclear forces, we find that V_0 is about 25 MeV, so the binding energy of the deuteron is indeed much less than the well-depth. The exterior solution of the wave-equation is $\varepsilon^{-\beta r}$ with $1/\beta = 4\cdot3 \times 10^{-13}$ cm. It follows that the amplitude of the wave-function falls off rather slowly in the exterior region, and that the expectation value of the radius is considerably greater than the range of the neutron-proton force.

Problems

(1) The Hamiltonian for two particles of masses m_1 and m_2 at the points whose coordinate vectors are $\mathbf{r}_1$ and $\mathbf{r}_2$, and whose mutual interaction is described by the potential $V(\mathbf{r}_1 - \mathbf{r}_2)$, is

$$H = -\frac{\hbar^2}{2m_1}\nabla_1{}^2 - \frac{\hbar^2}{2m_2}\nabla_2{}^2 + V(\mathbf{r}_1 - \mathbf{r}_2).$$

Show that if $\boldsymbol{\xi} = \mathbf{r}_1 - \mathbf{r}_2 =$ separation between the particles

and $\quad \boldsymbol{\eta} = \dfrac{m_1\mathbf{r}_1 + m_2\mathbf{r}_2}{m_1 + m_2} =$ coordinate of centre of mass

$$H = -\frac{\hbar^2}{2(m_1 + m_2)}\nabla_\eta{}^2 - \frac{\hbar^2(m_1 + m_2)}{2m_1 m_2}\nabla_\xi{}^2 + V(\xi)$$

and that the motion can therefore be separated into
  (i) the motion of the mass-centre of the system
  (ii) the motion relative to the mass-centre of a particle with the *reduced mass*

$$m = \frac{m_1 m_2}{m_1 + m_2}.$$

(2) Solve the wave-equation for the two-dimensional isotropic oscillator in the forms:

(i) $\quad -\dfrac{\hbar^2}{2m}\left(\dfrac{\partial^2}{\partial x^2} + \dfrac{\partial^2}{\partial y^2}\right)\psi + \alpha(x^2 + y^2)\psi = E\psi$

(ii) $\quad -\dfrac{\hbar^2}{2m}\left(\dfrac{\partial^2}{\partial r^2} + \dfrac{1}{r}\dfrac{\partial}{\partial r} + \dfrac{1}{r^2}\dfrac{\partial^2}{\partial \theta^2}\right)\psi + \alpha r^2\psi = E\psi$

and investigate the degeneracy of the solutions.

(3) Find the explicit forms, including normalization factors, of the radial eigenfunctions for the states of the hydrogen atom with $n=1, 2$ and 3. Calculate the mean radii of these states and compare them with the radii of the circular orbits in the Bohr theory, and with the positions of the minimum of the effective potential

$$-\frac{e^2}{4\pi\varepsilon_0 r}+\frac{l(l+1)\hbar^2}{2mr^2}.$$

(4) Show, from a consideration of the geometry of Fig. 5.5 or otherwise, that when the spherical potential well is deep enough to contain a large number of levels with $l=0$ the separations of neighbouring low-lying levels increase in the ratio $3:5:7:9:\ldots$ etc. as we ascend the level scheme. Compare this with the results of problem 6 of chapter 2, p. 40.

(5) Verify that the functions $F(\rho)$ and $G(\rho)$ in equation (5.22) contain just sufficient disposable constants for them to satisfy and be completely defined (apart from a normalizing factor) by the requirement that, for small ρ, $\chi_l(\rho)$ must behave like ρ^{l+1}; and show that a $\chi_l(\rho)$ constructed in this way satisfies (5.16a).

(6) Take the binding energy of the deuteron as $2\cdot23$ MeV and the range of the nuclear forces as $2\cdot00\times10^{-13}$ cm., and compute V_0 to three significant figures. Fit the interior and exterior solutions of the wave-function together in accordance with the continuity conditions at the edge of the well, and calculate the mean radius of the deuteron.

(7) Express the radial momentum operator p_r of chapter 2, problem (7), in differential operator form, and hence construct equation (4.23) for the radial eigenfunction as a symbolic representation of the statement:

Total energy = radial kinetic energy + rotational kinetic energy + potential energy.

(8) Show that $\psi(r, \theta, \phi)=Ar\,\varepsilon^{-r^2}\sin\theta\,\varepsilon^{i\phi}$ is a state function belonging to the first excited state of the three-dimensional isotropic oscillator, and express it as a combination of wave-functions in the Cartesian representation.

CHAPTER SIX

THE PERTURBATION METHOD AND THE VARIATION METHOD IN QUANTUM STATICS

Methods for approximate solution of the eigenvalue equation

While there are a number of cases in which the Schrödinger equation – or the equivalent matrix mechanical eigenvalue problem – can be solved exactly, it more often happens that exact solution is not possible or not practicable. This may happen either because of the complexity of the system itself, or because of the complex nature of the interactions between some of its members. The energy levels and eigenfunctions for the helium atom, for instance, cannot be found exactly; in quantum mechanics – as in classical mechanics – exact solution of the three-body problem is in principle impossible and the solution has to be approached by methods of approximation.

A number of techniques of approximation have been developed, and two will be discussed in this chapter. The first of these, called the *perturbation method*, is the quantum-mechanical analogue of a technique used extensively in celestial mechanics. It is mainly useful in those cases in which, although the actual wave-equation cannot be solved, solutions can be obtained of a wave-equation which differs from the actual one only in the omission of terms whose effect is small. The simpler equation is solved, and the effect of the omitted terms is then introduced as a correction or as a series of corrections. The terms which are neglected in the first instance are called perturbations, and it is necessary to assume that the perturbations are small, so that although they change the energies of the stationary states by small amounts they do not alter drastically the general arrangement of the levels.

The other approximation method which will be introduced in this chapter, called the *variation method*, is often useful when the perturbation method cannot be made to give a good approximation without an excessive amount of work. The variation method is most useful for approximating to the state-function and energy of the ground-state of a system, although it can be used more generally.

The perturbation method

There are two branches of perturbation theory, of which one belongs to quantum statics – the study of the properties of stationary states – and the other to quantum dynamics, which deals with the changes that a system undergoes in time. It is the first of these that concerns us now; the second is treated in chapter 10. In any problem in stationary perturbation theory we are in a sense comparing the properties of two systems. The state-functions and eigenvalues for one of these systems can be found exactly, and from these solutions we infer approximate solutions for the other. As long as the perturbation is small one stationary state of the perturbed system corresponds to each stationary state of the unperturbed system, but with a slightly modified state-function, and a slightly different energy. Very often the most important practical effect of a perturbation is the removal of a degeneracy. To start with, though, we shall assume that the unperturbed system is non-degenerate, and as we proceed we shall see how to do away with the need for this assumption.

In the absence of degeneracy the stationary states of an unperturbed system are found by determining canonical matrices P_0 and Q_0 which make the Hamiltonian matrix diagonal:

$$H_0 = H(P_0, Q_0) = \begin{vmatrix} E_1 & \cdot & \cdot & \cdot & \cdot & \cdot \\ \cdot & E_2 & \cdot & \cdot & \cdot & \cdot \\ \cdot & \cdot & E_3 & \cdot & \cdot & \cdot \\ \cdot & \cdot & \cdot & E_4 & \cdot & \cdot \\ \cdot & \cdot & \cdot & \cdot & E_5 & \cdot \\ \cdot & \cdot & \cdot & \cdot & \cdot & E_6 \end{vmatrix}$$

The coordinate system (in function space) associated with these matrices will be designated K_0; the coordinate axes coincide in direction with the eigenvectors of H_0, and are mutually orthogonal as long as H_0 is non-degenerate (see chapter 1). We shall continue to use this coordinate system for the description of the perturbed states, so each perturbed state will be represented by a superposition of unperturbed states.

To illustrate this by a three-dimensional example, if the unperturbed state u_2 is represented by a vector along the y-axis (Fig. 6.1) a perturbation will modify the state to $(\psi)_2$ whose representative vector makes a small angle with u_2. $(\psi)_2$ has components in the directions of all three axes, and must be written

$$(\psi)_2 = a_2 u_2 + a_1 u_1 + a_3 u_3$$

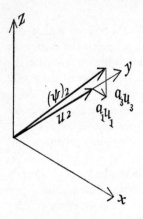

FIG. 6.1. The effect of applying a perturbation to a system in the state u_2. a_1u_1 and a_3u_3 represent the modification produced by the perturbation.

where u_1 and u_3 are unit vectors along the x- and z-axes; if the perturbation is small a_2 will be nearly equal to 1 and a_1 and a_3 will be much less than 1.

The perturbed state vectors will be mutually orthogonal as were the unperturbed state vectors, and the perturbed state vectors will be eigenvectors of the total Hamiltonian (including the perturbation); since the perturbed state vectors define a coordinate system K' which is rotated slightly relative to K_0, the total Hamiltonian will not be diagonal in the K_0 system, and we can write it as

$$H = H_0 + H' \qquad (6.1)$$

where H_0 is diagonal, and H' is the non-diagonal perturbation matrix.

State-functions and energies of the perturbed system

Let us now assume that a physical system is known, in the absence of any perturbation, to be in an eigenstate u_k of H_0 for which

$$H_0u_k = E_ku_k. \qquad (6.2)$$

When the perturbation is applied the state of the system becomes ψ, say, and the energy W; knowing the form of H_0 and H' (in (6.1)) we want to find the corrections

$$\psi - u_k \quad \text{and} \quad W - E_k.$$

We expand the perturbed eigenfunction and eigenvalue as power series in a parameter λ which expresses the magnitude of the perturbation, and serves to label the terms according to their relative importance.

$$\psi = \psi_0 + \lambda\psi_1 + \lambda^2\psi_2 + \ldots$$
$$W = W_0 + \lambda W_1 + \lambda^2 W_2 + \ldots$$
$$H\psi = W\psi$$

and

$$H = H_0 + \lambda H'.$$

Here each ψ_i will be a superposition of eigenfunctions of H_0. Combining these equations we get

$$(H_0 + \lambda H')(\psi_0 + \lambda\psi_1 + \lambda^2\psi_2 + \ldots) = (W_0 + \lambda W_1 + \lambda^2 W_2 + \ldots)(\psi_0 + \lambda\psi_1 + \lambda^2\psi_2 + \ldots$$

and if we collect and equate terms in equal powers of λ we get

$$H_0\psi_0 = W_0\psi_0 \qquad \text{(unperturbed)}$$
$$H_0\psi_1 + H'\psi_0 = W_0\psi_1 + W_1\psi_0 \qquad \text{(1st order)}$$
$$H_0\psi_2 + H'\psi_1 = W_0\psi_2 + W_1\psi_1 + W_2\psi_0 \qquad \text{(2nd order)}$$

$$\vdots$$

$$(6.3)$$

etc.

The first of these equations is that for the unperturbed system; we therefore write $\psi_0 = u_k$, $W_0 = E_k$ and substitute these in the second, to find

$$H_0\psi_1 + H'u_k = E_k\psi_1 + W_1 u_k. \qquad (6.4)$$

We now expand ψ_1 in terms of the unperturbed eigenvectors, writing

$$\psi_1 = \sum_n a_n^{(1)} u_n.$$

The superscript $^{(1)}$ indicates that the coefficients $a_n^{(1)}$ are those appropriate to the first-order approximation. Making this substitution for ψ_1 in (6.4) we find

$$\sum_n a_n^{(1)} E_n u_n + H'u_k = E_k \sum_n a_n^{(1)} u_n + W_1 u_k.$$

If we multiply through from the left by $u_m{}^*$ it follows from the orthonormality of the eigenvectors that

QM I

$$a_m^{(1)} E_m + u_m^* H' u_k = a_m^{(1)} E_k + W_1 \delta_{mk}. \tag{6.5}$$

δ_{mk} is the Krönecker symbol, which $=1$ if $m=k$ and $=0$ if $m \neq k$.

(6.5) assumes different forms, according as m is or is not equal to k. If $m=k$ it becomes

$$W_1 = u_k^* H' u_k = \langle H' \rangle_k = H'_{kk}. \tag{6.6a}$$

If $m \neq k$
$$a_m^{(1)} = \frac{H'_{mk}}{E_k - E_m}. \tag{6.6b}$$

Thus
$$(\psi)_k = u_k(1 + a_k^{(1)}) + \sum_{m \neq k} \frac{H'_{mk}}{E_k - E_m} u_m.$$

The requirement that $(\psi)_k$ be normalized leads to

$$1 = \int (\psi)_k^* (\psi)_k d\tau = 1 + a_k^{(1)*} + a_k^{(1)} + \text{terms in } | a_m^{(1)} |^2, \text{ etc.}$$

To the degree of approximation in which terms in the second and higher powers of the coefficients $a_m^{(1)}$ are neglected this means that

$$a_k^{(1)} + a_k^{(1)*} = 0$$

whence
$$a_k^{(1)} = \text{imaginary} = i\gamma_k, \text{ say.}$$

Then, still to the same degree of approximation,

$$1 + a_k^{(1)} = 1 + i\gamma_k = \varepsilon^{i\gamma_k}$$

so
$$\psi_k = u_k \varepsilon^{i\gamma_k} + \sum_{m \neq k} \frac{H'_{mk}}{E_k - E_m} u_m.$$

If, next, we were to consider the effect of the perturbation on the system, supposing it to have been initially in some other state, u_l or u_n, rather than u_m, we should be led by the same argument to introduce phase-angles γ_l or γ_n respectively into the expressions for the corresponding perturbed states $(\psi)_l$ or $(\psi)_n$. Then the condition that $(\psi)_k$, $(\psi)_l$ and $(\psi)_n$ must be mutually orthogonal leads to $\gamma_k = -\gamma_l$, $\gamma_l = -\gamma_n$, $\gamma_n = -\gamma_k$, and similarly for the phases associated with all pairs of perturbed states. These relations can be satisfied only by setting all these phase angles equal to zero. Thus, finally,

$$(\psi)_k = u_k + \sum_{m \neq k} \frac{H'_{mk}}{E_k - E_m} u_m. \tag{6.7a}$$

The energy of this state is, from (6.6a),

$$(W)_k = E_k + H'_{kk}. \tag{6.7b}$$

In the wave-mechanical representation, of course,

$$H'_{kk} = \int u_k{}^* H' u_k \, d\tau$$

$$H'_{mk} = \int u_m{}^* H' u_k \, d\tau$$

(where the integration is over all the space coordinates). If the first-order approximation is not good enough we substitute the results of the first-order theory into the third of eqns. (6.3) and proceed exactly as before. If $m=k$ we get

$$W_2 = \sum_{n \neq k} \frac{H'_{nk} H'_{kn}}{E_k - E_n} = \sum_{n \neq k} \frac{|H'_{kn}|^2}{E_k - E_n} \tag{6.8a}$$

and if $m \neq k$ we get an equation which determines the $a_m{}^{(2)}$:

$$a_m{}^{(2)} = \sum_{\substack{n \neq k \\ m \neq k}} \frac{H'_{mn} H'_{nk}}{(E_k - E_m)(E_k - E_n)} - \frac{H'_{mk} H'_{kk}}{(E_k - E_m)^2}. \tag{6.8b}$$

To the first approximation, then, the perturbation changes the energies of the stationary states by the magnitudes of the diagonal elements of the perturbation matrix, while in the second approximation the energy changes involve the energy differences between the initial state and all other states which are 'coupled' to it by non-vanishing elements of H'. In chapter 10 we shall see that these are the states to which the perturbation is likely to cause transitions.

If the initial state of the system is degenerate the argument given above is inapplicable. This is because it starts by assuming that for small perturbations each state $(\psi)_k$ of the perturbed system is closely related to, and indeed closely resembles, a state u_k of the unperturbed system. But when the unperturbed system is degenerate, the eigenfunctions representing the degenerate states are not uniquely determined – a point to which reference was made in chapter 1. In fact, if the degeneracy is n-fold, then if a suitable set of n orthogonal eigenfunctions is known, any number of other sets of n orthogonal linear combinations of these eigenfunctions can be constructed, but the only set which will be a suitable set of zero-order functions for a perturbation calculation will comprise those to which the perturbed functions approach as the perturbation is reduced to zero. It is therefore necessary to approach the eigenvalue problem for those groups of states which are degenerate, by first constructing the submatrix of the perturbation matrix H' *for each such degenerate group* using any convenient set of linearly independent state-functions, and diagonalizing these various sub-matrices. This diagonalization selects those linear combinations of the initially-chosen state-functions which are eigenfunctions of H', and determines the corresponding perturbation energies. The eigenfunctions determined in this way are, of course, orthogonal, and will remain so even if the magnitude of the perturbation is reduced to zero.

We shall now apply the perturbation method to the Zeeman and Stark effects in the hydrogen atom, dealing with problems of degeneracy as they arise.

The first-order normal Zeeman effect

Neglecting electron spin the Hamiltonian for an electron moving in a central field of force on which is superposed a uniform magnetic field of intensity $\mathscr{H}$ parallel to the z-axis is†

$$H = -\frac{\hbar^2}{2m_e}\left(\frac{\partial^2}{\partial r^2}+\frac{2}{r}\frac{\partial}{\partial r}+\frac{l(l+1)}{r^2}\right) - \frac{\mu_0 e\mathscr{H}}{2m_e}\frac{\hbar}{i}\frac{\partial}{\partial\phi} + \frac{\mu_0^2 e^2\mathscr{H}^2}{8m_e}\rho^2 + e.V(r)$$

$$(6.9)$$

where $x^2+y^2=\rho^2$.

This follows if we write $H = \dfrac{p'^2}{2m_e}+e.V(r)$ and put $\mathbf{p}'=\mathbf{p}-e\mathbf{A}$, since

for the uniform field the components of $\mathbf{A}$ can be chosen as

$$A_x = -\tfrac{1}{2}\mu_0\mathscr{H}y$$
$$A_y = \tfrac{1}{2}\mu_0\mathscr{H}x$$
$$A_z = 0.$$

For small field strengths the term in $\mathscr{H}^2$ may be neglected compared with that in $\mathscr{H}$, which contributes the *first-order Zeeman effect*. Now if we omit the terms in $\mathscr{H}$, we are left with the unperturbed Hamiltonian, whose eigenfunctions we know are of the form

$$R_{nl}(r)\, P_l^{|m|}(\cos\theta)\, \varepsilon^{im\phi}.$$

These are already eigenfunctions of the first-order perturbing term $\dfrac{\mu_0 e\mathscr{H}}{2m_e}\dfrac{\hbar}{i}\dfrac{\partial}{\partial\phi}$, so the matrix of this perturbation is diagonal; its eigenvalues are

$$\frac{\mu_0 e\mathscr{H}}{2m_e}\, m\hbar$$

† Where there is risk of confusion between the symbol for electron mass and the angular momentum quantum number m, the electron mass will be written as m_e.

so the total energy must be $E_0 - \dfrac{\mu_0 e \mathscr{H}}{2m_e} \, m\hbar$.

This perturbation reduces the degeneracy, states of different m having energies differing in units of $\dfrac{\mu_0 e \mathscr{H}}{2m_e}$. The quantity $\dfrac{\mu_0 e \hbar}{2m_e}$, which has the dimensions of a magnetic moment, is called the *Bohr magneton*, and agrees with the magnetic moment calculated from Bohr's theory for the ground-state orbit of the hydrogen atom.[†]

The quantity $\dfrac{\mu_0 e \mathscr{H}}{4\pi m_e}$, which has the dimensions of a frequency, is called the *Larmor frequency*; it is the precessional frequency calculated from classical physics for a circulating electron.

It will be shown in chapter 11 that the only transitions which are likely to occur are those in which m changes by 0 or ± 1. This, coupled with the above expressions, suffices to explain the spectrum of the normal Zeeman effect.

The first-order anomalous Zeeman effect

When the atom in a magnetic field has both orbital and spin angular momentum the Hamiltonian contains terms representing the interaction of both the orbital and the spin magnetic moments with the field, and generally gives rise to a more complicated splitting of energy levels and spectral lines. In spectroscopy this more complicated splitting of spectral lines was called the 'anomalous Zeeman effect', not because it was less common than the 'normal Zeeman effect' discussed above (in fact, the opposite is the case), but because the one seemed 'normal' in that it could be accounted for by the classical electron theory, whereas the other was inexplicable in such terms.

In a magnetic field the energy of the magnetic moments associated with the orbital and spin angular momenta is $H_{mag} = -\dfrac{\mu_0 e \mathscr{H}}{2m_e}(L_z + 2S_z)$.

If we take the unperturbed Hamiltonian as $H_0 = \dfrac{p^2}{2m_e} + e.V(r)$, the perturbation H' must include both the magnetic interaction H_{mag} and the spin-orbit interaction $H_{s.o.}$ discussed in chapter 4, i.e.,

$$H' = H_{s.o.} + H_{mag} = \frac{e^2}{2m_e{}^2 c^2} \cdot \frac{V'(r)}{r} (\mathbf{L} . \mathbf{S}) - \frac{\mu_0 e \mathscr{H}}{2m_e}(L_z + 2S_z).$$

[†] See also chapter 9, pp. 192–4.

As in our previous discussion of spin-orbit coupling, we shall assume that we are dealing with an alkali atom for which $S^2 = \frac{3}{4}\hbar^2$, and $S_z = \pm\frac{\hbar}{2}$. Then the quantities $\mathbf{L}^2$, $\mathbf{S}^2$, and $m\hbar = L_z + S_z$ all commute with H', but H' does not commute with L_z or S_z (see p. 83). The perturbation therefore removes the two-fold degeneracy which arises from the identity of the energies of those unperturbed states which have the same J_z, but different L_z and S_z; and the perturbation matrix couples, by its non-zero off-diagonal elements, pairs of eigenfunctions of the unperturbed system having the same $\mathbf{L}^2 = l(l+1)\hbar^2$ and $J_z = m\hbar$, but different values of L_z and S_z, specifically $m_l = m + \frac{1}{2}$, $m_s = -\frac{1}{2}$, and $m_l = m - \frac{1}{2}$, $m_s = \frac{1}{2}$. If we define

$$k\hbar = \frac{e^2\hbar^2}{2m_e^2 c^2}\int V'(r)R_{nl}^2(r) \cdot r dr,$$

the spin-orbit coupling contribution to the matrix of H' which couples such a pair of states is (see p. 84)

$$H_{s.o.} = \frac{k\hbar}{2}\begin{bmatrix} (m-\frac{1}{2}) & \sqrt{(l+\frac{1}{2})^2 - m^2} \\ \sqrt{(l+\frac{1}{2})^2 - m^2} & -(m+\frac{1}{2}) \end{bmatrix}$$

and the magnetic field interaction contributes

$$H_{mag} = -\frac{\mu_0 e \mathcal{H}\hbar}{2m_e}\begin{bmatrix} m+\frac{1}{2} & 0 \\ 0 & m-\frac{1}{2} \end{bmatrix}$$

since both m_l and m_s are diagonal in this representation. Thus the perturbation matrix coupling these states is

$$H' = \begin{bmatrix} \frac{k\hbar}{2}(m-\frac{1}{2}) - \frac{\mu_0 e \mathcal{H}\hbar}{2m_e}(m+\frac{1}{2}) & \frac{k\hbar}{2}\sqrt{(l+\frac{1}{2})^2 - m^2} \\ \frac{k\hbar}{2}\sqrt{(l+\frac{1}{2})^2 - m^2} & -\frac{k\hbar}{2}(m+\frac{1}{2}) - \frac{\mu_0 e \mathcal{H}\hbar}{2m_e}(m-\frac{1}{2}) \end{bmatrix}.$$

Inspecting this matrix we note that if $|m| = (l+\frac{1}{2})$ the off-diagonal elements vanish, and the matrix is diagonal; thus there is no mixing of unperturbed states in the cases when m has the extreme values $\pm(l+\frac{1}{2})$. The eigenvalues are then

$$\lambda_1 = \frac{k\hbar}{2}(m-\frac{1}{2}) - \frac{\mu_0 e \mathcal{H}\hbar}{2m_e}(m+\frac{1}{2})$$

and

$$\lambda_2 = -\frac{k\hbar}{2}(m+\frac{1}{2}) - \frac{\mu_0 e \mathcal{H}\hbar}{2m_e}(m-\frac{1}{2})$$

The significance of these two values becomes clearer if we refer back to equations (4.21a) and (4.21b), which we repeat here for convenience:

$$(\mathbf{L} \cdot \mathbf{S})\psi_{m-\frac{1}{2}, \frac{1}{2}} = \frac{\hbar^2}{2}(m-\tfrac{1}{2})\psi_{m-\frac{1}{2},\frac{1}{2}} + \frac{\hbar^2}{2}\sqrt{(l+\tfrac{1}{2})^2 - m^2}\,\psi_{m+\frac{1}{2},-\frac{1}{2}}$$
$$(4.21a)$$

$$(\mathbf{L} \cdot \mathbf{S})\psi_{m+\frac{1}{2}, -\frac{1}{2}} = \frac{\hbar^2}{2}\sqrt{(l+\tfrac{1}{2})^2 - m^2}\,\psi_{m-\frac{1}{2}, \frac{1}{2}} - \frac{\hbar^2}{2}(m+\tfrac{1}{2})\psi_{m+\frac{1}{2}, \frac{1}{2}}.$$
$$(4.21b)$$

When $m^2 = (l+\tfrac{1}{2})^2$, (4.21a) becomes

$$(\mathbf{L} \cdot \mathbf{S})\psi_{m-\frac{1}{2}, \frac{1}{2}} = \frac{\hbar^2}{2}(m-\tfrac{1}{2})\psi_{m-\frac{1}{2}, \frac{1}{2}}$$

in which case $l = m-\tfrac{1}{2}$, or $m = l+\tfrac{1}{2}$. Then

$$(L_z + 2S_z)\psi_{m-\frac{1}{2}, \frac{1}{2}} = \{(m-\tfrac{1}{2}) + 2 \cdot \tfrac{1}{2}\}\hbar\psi_{m-\frac{1}{2}, \frac{1}{2}} = (l+1)\hbar\psi_{m-\frac{1}{2}, -\frac{1}{2}}$$

so

$$H'_{m=l+\frac{1}{2}} = H_{s.o.} + H_{mag} = \frac{k\hbar}{2}l - \frac{\mu_0 e \mathscr{H}\hbar}{2m_e}(l+1),$$

which is the eigenvalue denoted above by λ_1. On the other hand, when $m^2 = (l+\tfrac{1}{2})^2$, (4.21b) becomes

$$(\mathbf{L} \cdot \mathbf{S})\psi_{m+\frac{1}{2}, -\frac{1}{2}} = -\frac{\hbar^2}{2}(m+\tfrac{1}{2})\psi_{m+\frac{1}{2}, -\frac{1}{2}}.$$

In this case we cannot have $m = l+\tfrac{1}{2}$, for then the subscript $m+\tfrac{1}{2}$ which specifies the z-component of the orbital moment would be $l+1$, i.e. greater than l. This then must be the case $-m = l+\tfrac{1}{2}$, with $m+\tfrac{1}{2} = -l$, which is allowed. Now, therefore

$$(L_z + 2S_z)\psi_{m+\frac{1}{2}, -\frac{1}{2}} = \{(m+\tfrac{1}{2}) - 2 \cdot \tfrac{1}{2}\}\hbar\psi_{m+\frac{1}{2}, -\frac{1}{2}} = -(l+1)\hbar\psi_{m+\frac{1}{2}, -}$$

$$\therefore \quad H'_{m=-(l+\frac{1}{2})} = H_{s.o.} + H_{mag} = \frac{k\hbar l}{2} + \frac{\mu_0 e \mathscr{H}\hbar}{2m_e}(l+1).$$

This is the eigenvalue denoted earlier by λ_2. The absence of mixing when $|m| = l+\tfrac{1}{2}$ has already been indicated in the table (p. 86) of the eigenstates of the Hamiltonian of the spin-orbit interaction. Since the H_{mag} matrix is diagonal it cannot contribute any further mixing.

When $|m| < l+\tfrac{1}{2}$ the matrix of H' is non-diagonal, and mixing of states will in general occur. When the magnetic field is zero the matrix of H' becomes that for $H_{s.o.}$, and the effect of applying a *weak* magnetic field is simply to separate, in energy, eigenstates of the spin-orbit coupling Hamiltonian which are otherwise degenerate. Solution of the secular equation for the eigenvalues of H' gives, after some work,

$$H' = -\frac{\mu_0 e \mathcal{H} \hbar}{2m_e} \cdot m - \frac{k\hbar}{4} \pm \frac{1}{2} \sqrt{k^2 \hbar^2 (l+\tfrac{1}{2})^2 - \frac{2\mu_0 e \mathcal{H} \hbar}{2m_e} k\hbar m + \left(\frac{\mu_0 e \mathcal{H} \hbar}{2m_e}\right)^2}.$$

In the limit of weak magnetic fields, such that

$$\frac{\mu_0 e \mathcal{H}}{2m_e} \ll k, \text{ this reduces to}$$

$$H'_{\text{weak field}} = \tfrac{1}{2} k\hbar l - \frac{\mu_0 e \mathcal{H} \hbar}{2m_e} \cdot m \cdot \frac{2l+2}{2l+1} \text{ for } j_+ = l+\tfrac{1}{2}$$

(which agrees with our previous results, for the special cases $m = \pm(l+\tfrac{1}{2})$), and

$$H'_{\text{weak field}} = -\tfrac{1}{2} k\hbar(l+1) - \frac{\mu_0 e \mathcal{H} \hbar}{2m_e} \cdot m \cdot \frac{2l}{2l+1} \text{ for } j_- = l-\tfrac{1}{2}.$$

When $\mathcal{H}$ vanishes these expressions reduce to those found in chapter 4 for the spin-orbit coupling energies for the 'parallel' (j_+) and 'antiparallel' (j_-) configurations. The magnetic interaction contributes an additional energy proportional to the magnetic field strength and to the magnetic quantum number m, and the spacing of the magnetic sub-levels depends on the additional factor, $\frac{2l+2}{2l+1}$ or $\frac{2l}{2l+1}$ for the single electron case considered here, according as the spin and orbital moments are parallel or antiparallel. Such a factor is known as the *g-factor* or *gyromagnetic ratio*[†] of the state; it is the ratio of the resultant magnetic moment in Bohr magnetons to the resultant angular momentum in units of $\hbar$. For a state with zero l and non-zero s the gyromagnetic ratio is 2; if l is non-zero and s is zero the gyromagnetic ratio is 1. For the first excited state of an alkali atom, with $l=1$ and $s=\tfrac{1}{2}$, the gyromagnetic ratio is $\tfrac{4}{3}$ for the quadruplet configuration and $\tfrac{2}{3}$ for the doublet configuration.

In the limit of very strong magnetic fields, such that $\frac{\mu_0 e \mathcal{H}}{2m_e} \gg k$,

[†] A more suitable name, which is occasionally used, is 'magneto-mechanical ratio'.

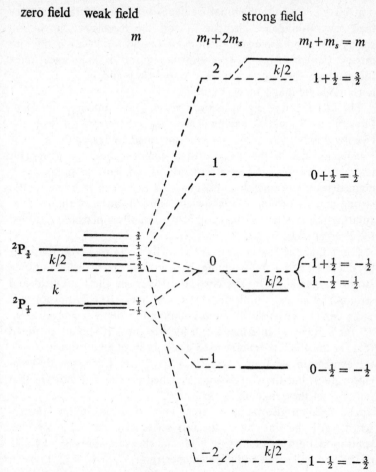

FIG. 6.2. Spin-orbit coupling effect, Zeeman splitting, and Paschen-Back effect, for an alkali atom state with $l = 1$, $s = \frac{1}{2}$.

the eigenvalues of H′ become

$$H'_{\text{strong field}} = -\frac{\mu_0 e \mathcal{H} \hbar}{2m_e}(m \pm \tfrac{1}{2}) - \frac{k\hbar}{2}(\tfrac{1}{2} \mp m).$$

In the strong-field limit the splitting pattern is simpler than in the weak-field case, and the separation of the sub-levels is, apart from the relatively small spin-orbit contributions, the same as that found in the normal Zeeman effect. Referring back to the matrix for H' we see that in the strong-field limit the matrix is effectively diagonal

128   QUANTUM MECHANICS

– at least one of the diagonal elements being considerably greater than the off-diagonal elements – and the eigenfunctions in the strong-field limit are eigenfunctions of L_z and S_z. There is then no mixing, though there is not a complete removal of degeneracy, since for example the states with $m_l=1$, $m_s=-\tfrac{1}{2}$ and $m_l=-1$, $m_s=\tfrac{1}{2}$ have the same magnetic energy.

The fact that the eigenfunctions of $H_{s.o.}$ are mixtures of eigenfunctions of L_z and S_z having sharp values of $\mathbf{J}^2$ and J_z, while the eigenfunctions of H_{mag} are *not* such mixtures, underlies the familiar statements that in the absence of a magnetic field the spin-orbit interaction couples the spin and orbital moments to give a well-defined resultant, and that this coupling is broken in a sufficiently strong magnetic field. The associated simplification of the Zeeman splitting pattern as the magnetic field strength is increased is called *the Paschen-Back effect*.

Fig. 6.2 shows, for a state specified by $l=1$, $s=\tfrac{1}{2}$, the splittings produced by spin-orbit coupling, by a weak magnetic field, and by a strong magnetic field. The correlation between the weak-field and strong-field states is indicated by dotted lines. The justification of these correlations follows from computation of the eigenvalues of H' for a series of intermediate field-strengths. It should be noted that for the alkali atom case used as the basis of all our illustrations, the expression we found for H' strong field predicts seven different eigenvalues, but the correlations sketched on Fig. 6.2 indicate that only five of these actually occur.

The Zeeman effect was of great importance in atomic spectroscopy. All the lines of a spectral series give the same Zeeman splitting pattern in a magnetic field, and this eases the disentangling of the line series in a complicated spectrum.

The second-order Zeeman effect

If the perturbation is large the $\mathscr{H}^2$ term may become important, particularly if $x^2+y^2=\rho^2$ is large, i.e. for highly excited states. The effect of this term on the energy of the state u_n will be

$$\left\langle \frac{\mu_0^2 e^2 \mathscr{H}^2}{8m}\rho^2 \right\rangle_n = \frac{\mu_0^2 e^2 \mathscr{H}^2}{8m}\langle x^2+y^2\rangle_n$$

which is
$$= \frac{\mu_0^2 e^2 \mathscr{H}^2}{8m}\frac{2}{3}\langle r^2\rangle_n$$

if the state is spherically symmetrical.

For the ground-state of the hydrogen atom, for instance,

$$u_n = \frac{1}{(\pi a_0{}^3)^{\frac{1}{2}}} \varepsilon^{-r/a_0}$$

where
$$a_0 = \frac{4\pi\varepsilon_0\hbar^2}{me^2} = 0.529 \text{ Å}.$$

and
$$\langle r^2\rangle_{gd.\,state} = \frac{4}{a_0{}^3} \int_0^\infty r^4\, \varepsilon^{-2r/a_0}\, dr.$$

Successive integrations by parts give

$$\langle r^2\rangle = 3a_0{}^2$$

$$\therefore \quad \langle H'\rangle = \frac{\mu_0{}^2 e^2 \mathscr{H}^2}{4m}\, a_0{}^2. \tag{6.10}$$

More generally, it has been shown (see Pauling and Wilson, chapter 5, pp. 144-5) that, for a state with quantum numbers nlm in a hydrogen-like atom with nuclear charge Z,

$$\langle r^2\rangle_{nlm} = \frac{a_0{}^2 n^4}{Z^2}\left\{1 + \frac{3}{2}\left(1 - \frac{l(l+1)-\frac{1}{3}}{n^2}\right)\right\}.$$

For large n, i.e. for highly excited states, this is proportional to n^4.

We can easily see the link between this effect and diamagnetism. If an atom is polarized by a magnetic field, so that it acquires a magnetic moment $\alpha\mathscr{H}$, the associated energy is $-\frac{1}{2}\alpha\mathscr{H}^2$. Comparing with (6.10) we have

$$\alpha = -\frac{\mu_0 e^2}{2m}\, a_0{}^2$$

or more generally

$$\alpha = -\frac{\mu_0 e^2}{4mZ^2}\, \langle\rho^2\rangle.$$

Summing this over all the electrons in a gram molecule gives the molar diamagnetic susceptibility. Values of atomic radii deduced in this way from measurements of diamagnetism agree with those found from X-ray scattering cross-sections.

The second-order Zeeman effect may also be detected spectroscopically. In a transition from a highly excited state to the ground-state the energy shift of the ground-state will be negligible compared with that of the excited state. Further, states which can decay straight to the ground-state will have small values of l (because of the selection rule $\Delta l = \pm 1$; see chapter 11), so the energy change will be approximately

$$\frac{\mu_0^2 e^2 \mathcal{H}^2}{m} \frac{5a_0^2}{2} n^4 \frac{2}{3} \frac{1}{Z^2}$$

which is

$$\frac{n^4 \mu_0^2 \mathcal{H}^2}{Z^2} \times 10^{-11} \text{ eV.}$$

If $Z = 1$, $n = 30$, $\mu_0 \mathcal{H} = 3$ weber/sq. metre, the energy change is $7 \cdot 3 \times 10^{-4}$ eV and in the middle of the visible spectrum where $\hbar \omega \approx 2$ eV the wavelength change is

$$\Delta \lambda \approx 2 \text{ Å.}$$

This effect has been demonstrated in the laboratory by Jenkins and Segré (1939).

The first-order Stark effect in the hydrogen atom

The unperturbed Hamiltonian

$$-\frac{\hbar^2}{2m}\nabla^2 - \frac{e^2}{4\pi\varepsilon_0 r}$$

has eigenfunctions of the type

$$R_{nl}(r)\, P_l^{|m|}(\cos\theta)\, \varepsilon^{im\phi}$$

and the perturbation is

$$H' = -e\mathcal{E}z = -e\mathcal{E}r\cos\theta.$$

The energy change in the ground state is zero because the perturbation is an odd function of the coordinates; explicitly, the expression for $\langle H' \rangle$ is the product of three integrals, with respect to r, θ and ϕ respectively, of which one is

$$\int_0^\pi \cos\theta \sin\theta \, d\theta = \int_{-1}^{+1} \cos\theta \, d(\cos\theta) = 0$$

and so $\langle H' \rangle$ vanishes.

The first excited state is four-fold degenerate (see p. 104) and at first sight it appears that the discussion of p. 121 requires us to diagonalize a 4×4 matrix. In fact the problem is simpler than this. We are representing the perturbed states as superpositions of eigenstates of the unperturbed Hamiltonian, and these are eigenstates of the operator m_z, so the matrix of m_z is diagonal. Now the perturbation is proportional to z, which commutes with m_z, so that

$$H'm_z - m_z H' = 0.$$

Putting this in terms of a typical element of the commutator matrix

$$(H'm_z - m_z H')_{rs} = 0$$
$$\therefore \quad H'_{rs}(m_z)_s - (m_z)_r H'_{rs} = 0$$
$$\therefore \quad H'_{rs} = 0 \quad \text{unless} \quad (m_z)_r = (m_z)_s.$$

This means that the non-vanishing elements of H' must all refer to pairs of states which have the same m-values. Of the four degenerate components of the first excited state, labelled $(2, 0, 0)$ $(2, 1, 1)$ $(2, 1, 0)$ $(2, 1, -1)$, only the first and third have the same m-value, so the matrix to be diagonalized is a 2×2 matrix referring to these states only. The diagonal elements of this matrix vanish, for the reasons given above in connection with the ground-state, and the off-diagonal elements are found from the state-functions (for which see Pauling and Wilson, chapter 5):

$$\psi_{210} = \frac{1}{4(2\pi a_0{}^3)^{\frac{1}{2}}} \frac{r}{a_0} \varepsilon^{-r/2a_0} \cos\theta$$

$$\psi_{200} = \frac{1}{4(2\pi a_0{}^3)^{\frac{1}{2}}} \left(2 - \frac{r}{a_0}\right) \varepsilon^{-r/2a_0}.$$

The off-diagonal elements are easily shown to be both equal to $3e\mathscr{E}a_0$. The relevant part of the H' matrix is therefore

$$\begin{bmatrix} 0 & 3e\mathscr{E}a_0 \\ 3e\mathscr{E}a_0 & 0 \end{bmatrix}.$$

The secular equation which determines its eigenvalues is

$$\lambda^2 - (3e\mathscr{E}a_0)^2 = 0$$

giving $\lambda = \pm 3e\mathscr{E}a_0$ as the energy changes due to the perturbation. The corresponding eigenvectors are

$$\frac{1}{\sqrt{2}} \begin{bmatrix} 1 \\ 1 \end{bmatrix} \quad \text{and} \quad \frac{1}{\sqrt{2}} \begin{bmatrix} 1 \\ -1 \end{bmatrix}$$

for which the appropriate linear combinations of eigenstates are

$$\Psi_+ = \frac{1}{\sqrt{2}}\{\psi_{210}+\psi_{200}\} \quad \text{and} \quad \Psi_- = \frac{1}{\sqrt{2}}\{\psi_{210}-\psi_{200}\}.$$

The energy levels after perturbation are therefore

$$\Psi_+ \quad\text{———}\quad l = 1, 0; \; m = 0$$
$$\psi_{211} \text{ and } \psi_{21-1} \quad\text{———}\quad l = 1; \; m = \pm 1$$
$$\Psi_- \quad\text{———}\quad l = 1, 0; \; m = 0.$$

It will be noted that the states Ψ_+ and Ψ_- do not have sharp values of l; it is only in a central field that eigenstates of the energy operator are bound to be eigenstates of the total angular momentum.

The perturbation of the second excited state, which is ninefold degenerate, is again less complex than might appear at first sight. Grouping the nine sets of quantum numbers according to their m-values we have

$$
\begin{array}{llllll}
m = & 0 & : & (3\ 2\ 0) & (3\ 1\ 0) & (3\ 0\ 0) \\
m = & 1 & : & (3\ 2\ 1) & (3\ 1\ 1) & \\
m = & -1 & : & (3\ 2\ -1) & (3\ 1\ -1) & \\
m = & 2 & : & (3\ 2\ 2) & & \\
m = & -2 & : & (3\ 2\ -2). & & \\
\end{array}
$$

The states with $m=2$ and $m=-2$ will not be affected by the perturbation, and the perturbation of the others is found by diagonalizing the appropriate 2×2 and 3×3 matrices. The two 2×2 matrices are identical apart from the signs of the complex exponents in the off-diagonal elements, so they both determine the same pair of energy shifts. The diagonal elements of the perturbation matrices all vanish, for the reasons discussed before, and for the same reason the corner elements of the 3×3 matrix vanish. The form of the matrices is therefore

$$
\begin{bmatrix} 0 & H'_{12} \\ \\ H'_{12} & 0 \end{bmatrix}
\quad \text{and} \quad
\begin{bmatrix} 0 & H''_{01} & 0 \\ H''_{01} & 0 & H''_{12} \\ 0 & H''_{12} & 0 \end{bmatrix}
$$

where the elements are labelled by the l-values of the states to which they refer. Calculation gives the values of these elements as

$$H'_{12} = \tfrac{3}{2}3e\mathscr{E}a_0; \qquad\qquad H''_{01} = \sqrt{6}\ 3e\mathscr{E}a_0$$
$$H''_{12} = \sqrt{3}\ 3e\mathscr{E}a_0$$

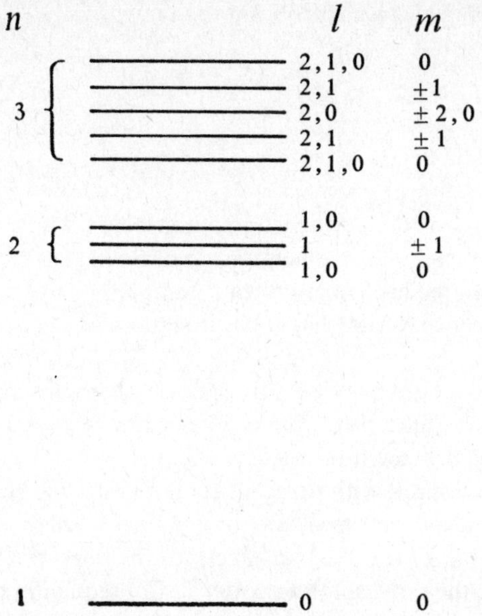

FIG. 6.3. Stark splitting of the three lowest states of the hydrogen atom.

and the eigenvalues of the perturbation obtained by diagonalizing the matrices are

$$\lambda_{m=1} = \pm\tfrac{3}{2}3e\mathscr{E}a_0; \qquad \lambda_{m=0} = 0, \pm 3.3e\mathscr{E}a_0.$$

For the case $m = \pm 1$ the eigenvectors are

$$\frac{1}{\sqrt{2}}\begin{bmatrix} 1 \\ \pm 1 \end{bmatrix}$$

so that the wave-mechanical state-functions are

$$\Psi_+ = \frac{1}{\sqrt{2}}\{\psi_{32\pm1} + \psi_{31\pm1}\}$$

and

$$\Psi_- = \frac{1}{\sqrt{2}}\{\psi_{32\pm1} - \psi_{31\pm1}\}.$$

For the case $m = 0$ the eigenvectors corresponding to the eigenvalues $0, \pm 3.3e\mathscr{E}a_0$, are respectively

$$\frac{1}{\sqrt{3}}\begin{bmatrix} 1 \\ 0 \\ -\sqrt{2} \end{bmatrix} \quad \text{and} \quad \frac{1}{\sqrt{6}}\begin{bmatrix} \sqrt{2} \\ \pm\sqrt{3} \\ 1 \end{bmatrix};$$

the corresponding eigenfunctions are therefore

$$\Psi_0 = \frac{1}{\sqrt{3}}\{\psi_{300} - \sqrt{2}\,\psi_{320}\}$$

and

$$\Psi_\pm = \frac{1}{\sqrt{6}}\{\sqrt{2}\,\psi_{300} \pm \sqrt{3}\,\psi_{310} + \psi_{320}\}.$$

These eigenstates of the perturbation are states in which the energy, z-component of angular momentum, and z-component of electric dipole moment are sharp; they form a complete specification of the states. It is easy to verify that these functions are mutually orthogonal.

The ninefold degeneracy of this state is therefore reduced, the level becoming a quintuplet. The results of this section are summarized in the level scheme illustrated in Fig. 6.3.

The mixing of states with different total angular momenta by this perturbation makes the spectrum of the Stark effect much more complex than that of the Zeeman effect, for the lines of a given series do not all have the same splitting pattern. Consequently the Zeeman effect was the more important historically for its help in elucidating atomic level schemes.

The second-order Stark effect

Although there is no first-order Stark effect on the ground-state of the hydrogen atom, there is a second-order effect. Since $H' = -e\mathscr{E}z$ (6.8a) can be written

$$W_2 = e^2\mathscr{E}^2 \sum_{n \neq k} \frac{|z_{kn}|^2}{E_k - E_n}.$$

This energy change can be used to define an atomic polarizability α by writing it as

$$W_2 = -\tfrac{1}{2}\alpha\mathscr{E}^2$$

whence if we put $k = 1$ for the ground-state

$$\alpha = 2e^2 \sum_{n > 1} \frac{|z_{1n}|^2}{E_n - E_1}. \tag{6.11}$$

The polarizability is important in the theories of the dielectric constant, and of optical dispersion.

If we define a dimensionless quantity f_n, called the *oscillator strength* for the transition $1 \to n$, by the equation

$$f_n = \frac{2m}{\hbar^2}(E_n - E_1)|z_{1n}|^2 \tag{6.12}$$

the expression for α becomes

$$\alpha = \frac{e^2\hbar^2}{m} \sum_{n>1} \frac{f_n}{(E_n-E_1)^2} = \frac{e^2}{m} \sum_{n>1} \frac{f_n}{\omega_{n1}^2}.$$

This expression for the polarizability is familiar in classical physics. (See also chapter 11, equations (11.17) and (11.19).)

It can be shown fairly readily that the sum of the oscillator strengths f_n is unity; this result is known as the *f-sum-rule*. We know from (3.1) that

$$\{H, z\} = \dot{z} = p_z/m$$
$$\therefore \quad i(Hz - zH) = \hbar p_z/m$$

and so

$$i(H_n - H_1)z_{n1} = \hbar(p_z)_{n1}/m$$

and

$$i(H_1 - H_n)z_{1n} = \hbar(p_z)_{1n}/m.$$

From the first of these

$$i(H_n - H_1)|z_{n1}|^2 = \frac{\hbar}{m} z_{1n}(p_z)_{n1}$$

and from the second

$$i(H_n - H_1)|z_{n1}|^2 = -\frac{\hbar}{m}(p_z)_{1n}z_{n1}$$

$$\therefore \quad i(H_n - H_1)|z_{n1}|^2 = \frac{\hbar}{2m}\left(z_{1n}(p_z)_{n1} - (p_z)_{1n}z_{n1}\right)$$

$$\therefore \quad i\sum_n (H_n - H_1)|z_{n1}|^2 = \frac{\hbar}{2m} \sum_n \left(z_{1n}(p_z)_{n1} - (p_z)_{1n}z_{n1}\right)$$

$$= \frac{\hbar}{2m}(z\,p_z - p_z z)_{11}$$

$$\therefore \quad \sum_n (H_n - H_1)|z_{n1}|^2 = \frac{\hbar^2}{2m}$$

(from the commutation relation for z and p_z)

$$\therefore \quad \sum_n f_n = 1.$$

We can get a rough estimate of the polarizability α if we assume that the oscillator strength for the transition $1 \rightarrow 2$ is very much stronger than the others. Then (6.11) and (6.12) give

$$\alpha \approx \frac{e^2\hbar^2}{m} \frac{1}{(E_2-E_1)^2}$$

Since

$$E_2-E_1 = -\frac{1}{4\pi\varepsilon_0}\frac{e^2}{2a_0}\left(\frac{1}{2^2}-\frac{1}{1^2}\right) = \frac{1}{4\pi\varepsilon_0}\frac{3e^2}{8a_0}$$

we see that

$$\frac{\alpha}{4\pi\varepsilon_0} \approx \frac{64}{9}a_0^3 \approx 7\cdot1\,a_0^3. \tag{6.13}$$

This will be an over-estimate of α, because the energy differences in the denominator are greater in the terms referring to higher excited states, when they occur; hence by putting $f_2=1$ we have over-weighted the term with the smallest denominator. Another estimate of the polarizability is obtained below, using the variation method (and see also chapter 11, problem 5).

The variation method

The variation method used in quantum mechanics evolved from a technique developed by Ritz to determine the solutions of partial differential equations. In quantum mechanics it is most often used to obtain approximations to the ground-state state-function and energy, but the method can be extended to investigate higher states. The variation method is important partly because it is applicable when the assumptions which underlie perturbation theory – that there is a closely related problem capable of exact solution, and that the effect of the perturbation is small – are not valid.

Suppose that an arbitrary normalized function ϕ is expanded in energy eigenfunctions ψ_i, for which the corresponding eigenvalues are E_i. Then

$$\phi = \sum_i a_i \psi_i$$

and the expectation value of the energy for the state represented by ϕ is

$$\langle H \rangle_\phi = \int \phi^* H\phi d\tau = \sum_i |a_i|^2 E_i. \tag{6.14}$$

Now if E_1 is the energy of the ground state ψ_1,

$$\langle H \rangle_\phi = \sum_i |a_i|^2 E_i \geq \sum_i |a_i|^2 E_1 \geq E_1 \tag{6.15}$$

where the last step depends on the fact that for a normalized function $\sum |a_i|^2 = 1$. The equality applies if ϕ is identical with ψ_1, the true ground-state wave-function. Otherwise $\langle H \rangle_\phi > E_1$.

We therefore choose a *trial eigenfunction* $\phi(\lambda_1, \lambda_2 \ldots)$ which is normalized to unity and depends on a number of parameters $\lambda_1, \lambda_2 \ldots$ We evaluate the integral $\int \phi^* H \phi d\tau$, the result being of course a function of the λ's. The integral is then minimized with respect to the parameters. (6.15) shows that the result cannot be less than E_1, and so is an upper limit to the ground-state energy. This upper limit will be close to the true energy if the trial function closely resembles the true eigenfunction. Thus approximations to both the ground-state eigenfunctions and energy are found.

The criterion used in the variation method to select the 'best' from the family of functions generated by the variation of the trial parameters can be written

$$\delta \sum_i |a_i|^2 (E_i - E_1) = 0.$$

It may sometimes be important to remember that this, though obviously a relevant criterion when an estimate of the energy is wanted, may not select the function that gives the closest approximation to the value of some other observable.

If the approximate ground-state eigenfunction found in this way is ϕ_1, any function of the type $\phi_2 = \phi - \phi_1 \int \phi_1^* \phi d\tau$ is orthogonal to ϕ_1. As long as ϕ_1 is a good approximation to the true ground-state eigenfunction ψ_1 there will be no term in ψ_1 in the eigenfunction expansion of ϕ_2, which is therefore of the form

$$\phi_2 = \sum_{i>1} a_i \psi_i.$$

Then

$$\langle H \rangle_{\phi_2} = \int \phi_2^* H \phi_2 d\tau = \sum_{i>1} |a_i|^2 E_i > E_2,$$

so by varying the parameters on which ϕ_2 depends an upper limit can be found for E_2, and an approximation is obtained to the state-function of the first excited state. The process may be extended to find approximations to the higher states, but the errors in the process are cumulative. An extension of the variation method enables the fixing of a *lower* limit to the energy, but the integrals to be evaluated for this purpose are usually a good deal more difficult than those which fix the upper limit.

We shall now illustrate the method by a simple example. The Hamiltonian for the simple harmonic oscillator is

$$-\frac{\hbar^2}{2m}\frac{d^2}{dx^2}+\tfrac{1}{2}m\omega^2x^2.$$

If we take as a trial solution $\phi=C\varepsilon^{-\lambda x^2}$, with $C=\sqrt[4]{2\lambda/\pi}$ in order that the trial function shall be correctly normalized – and note that the normalization of the trial function usually, as here, introduces a factor which is a function of the variation parameter – we then have

$$H\phi = -\frac{C\hbar^2}{2m}(4\lambda^2x^2-2\lambda)\,\varepsilon^{-\lambda x^2}+\tfrac{1}{2}Cm\omega^2x^2\,\varepsilon^{-\lambda x^2}$$

and

$$\langle H\rangle = C^2\int_{-\infty}^{+\infty}\left\{-\frac{\hbar^2}{2m}(4\lambda^2x^2-2\lambda)+\tfrac{1}{2}m\omega^2x^2\right\}\varepsilon^{-2\lambda x^2}dx$$

which gives

$$\langle H\rangle = \frac{\hbar^2\lambda}{2m}+\frac{m\omega^2}{8\lambda}.$$

Minimizing $\langle H\rangle$ with respect to λ we get

$$\frac{d\langle H\rangle}{d\lambda} = \frac{\hbar^2}{2m}-\frac{m\omega^2}{8\lambda^2} = 0 \quad\text{when}\quad \lambda = \frac{m\omega}{2\hbar}$$

whence

$$\langle H\rangle = \tfrac{1}{2}\hbar\omega = E_1 \qquad \text{(cf. (3.9a))}$$

and the corresponding eigenfunction is

$$\sqrt[4]{\frac{m\omega}{\pi\hbar}}\;\varepsilon^{-m\omega x^2/2\hbar} \qquad \text{(cf. (3.13)).}$$

In this case we obtained the correct result by a particularly suitable choice of trial function!

Atomic polarizability by the variation method

When an electric field is applied to an atom the polarization of the atom can be visualized as the result of a separation of the nucleus and the centroid of the electronic wave-function. The electronic wave-function will be distorted and will lose its spherical symmetry, while retaining axial symmetry about a line through the nucleus and the centroid of the negative charge-distribution; this line will be parallel to the electric field vector. It is therefore reasonable to attempt to estimate the polarizability of the hydrogen atom from the trial function

$$\phi = (\pi a_0{}^3)^{-\frac{1}{2}}\, \varepsilon^{-r/a_0}\, (1+\lambda z).$$

The factors $(\pi a_0{}^3)^{-\frac{1}{2}}\varepsilon^{-r/a_0}=\psi_1$ form the ground-state wave-function for the unperturbed hydrogen atom, which is shown as a continuous curve in Fig. 6.4, while the factor $(1+\lambda z)$ distorts the wave-function into the form indicated by the dotted line. The function ϕ is not normalized. In fact

$$\int \phi^*\, \phi d\tau = \langle(1+\lambda z)^2\rangle_{\psi_1}$$
$$= \langle 1+\lambda^2 z^2\rangle_{\psi_1}$$

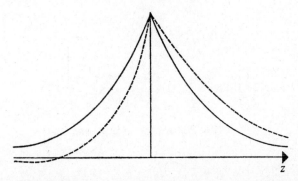

FIG. 6.4.   Solid curve: the unperturbed ground-state wave-function for the hydrogen atom, $\psi(r)$. Dotted curve: the trial function $(1 + \lambda z)\psi(r)$ for the variation calculation of the polarizability.

(since $\langle z\rangle_{\psi_1}=0$, being the mean value of an odd function)

$$= 1+\frac{\lambda^2}{3}\langle r^2\rangle_{\psi_1} \quad \text{(cf. p. 129)}$$

$$= 1+\lambda^2 a_0{}^2.$$

When an electric field is applied to the atom, the Hamiltonian can be written as $H=H_0-e\mathscr{E}z=H_0+H'$ so

$$(1+\lambda^2 a_0{}^2)\langle H\rangle_\phi = \langle(1+\lambda z)(H_0+H')(1+\lambda z)\rangle_{\psi_1}$$
$$= \langle H_0\rangle_{\psi_1}-2\lambda e\mathscr{E}\langle z^2\rangle_{\psi_1}+\lambda^2\langle zH_0z\rangle_{\psi_1}-e\mathscr{E}\langle z\rangle_{\psi_1}$$
$$+\lambda\langle zH_0\rangle_{\psi_1}+\lambda\langle H_0z\rangle_{\psi_1}-\lambda^2 e\mathscr{E}\langle z^3\rangle_{\psi_1}.$$

The first two terms here do not vanish, while the rest do. Dealing first with the terms which vanish, we see by inspection that $\langle z\rangle_{\psi_1}$

and $\langle z^3 \rangle_{\psi_1}$ must average to zero, since they are the means of odd functions; in the same way

$$\langle z H_0 \rangle_{\psi_1} = \langle z E_1 \rangle_{\psi_1} = 0$$

for E_1 is a constant; and using (3.1) we have

$$\langle H_0 z \rangle_{\psi_1} = \langle z H_0 \rangle_{\psi_1} + \frac{\hbar}{im} \langle p_z \rangle_{\psi_1}$$

which is the sum of the means of odd functions, and is therefore zero. Finally, using (3.1) and (2.11) we see that $\langle z H_0 z \rangle_{\psi_1}$ vanishes, because

$$z H_0 z = z \left(z H_0 + \frac{\hbar}{i} \dot{z} \right)$$

and

$$z H_0 z = \left(H_0 z - \frac{\hbar}{i} \dot{z} \right) z$$

$$\therefore 2 z H_0 z = z^2 H_0 + H_0 z^2 + \frac{\hbar}{i} (z\dot{z} - \dot{z}z)$$

$$= 2 z^2 H_0 + \frac{\hbar}{i} \frac{d}{dt} z^2 + \frac{\hbar}{i} (z\dot{z} - \dot{z}z)$$

$$\therefore 2 \langle z H_0 z \rangle_{\psi_1} = 2 \langle z^2 H_0 \rangle_{\psi_1} + \frac{\hbar}{i} \frac{d}{dt} \langle z^2 \rangle_{\psi_1} + \frac{\hbar^2}{m}$$

$$= 2 \langle z^2 \rangle_{\psi_1} E_1 + \frac{\hbar^2}{m}$$

$$= -2 a_0^2 \frac{\hbar^2}{2m a_0^2} + \frac{\hbar^2}{m}$$

$$\therefore \langle z H_0 z \rangle_{\psi_1} = 0.$$

The non-vanishing terms are

$$\langle H_0 \rangle_{\psi_1} = E_1 = -\frac{\hbar^2}{2m a_0^2}$$

and

$$2\lambda e\mathscr{E} \langle z^2 \rangle_{\psi_1} = 2\lambda e\mathscr{E} a_0^2,$$

so that finally

$$(1 + \lambda^2 a_0^2) \langle H \rangle_\phi = -\frac{\hbar^2}{2m a_0^2} - 2\lambda e\mathscr{E} a_0^2$$

$$\therefore \langle H \rangle_\phi = -\frac{(\hbar^2 / 2m a_0^2) + 2\lambda e\mathscr{E} a_0^2}{1 + \lambda^2 a_0^2}. \tag{6.16}$$

This is a minimum when

$$2\lambda^2 e\mathscr{E}a_0{}^4 + \frac{\lambda\hbar^2}{m} - 2e\mathscr{E}a_0{}^2 = 0$$

whence

$$\lambda = \frac{2e\mathscr{E}a_0{}^2 m}{\hbar^2}.$$

(The other root of the quadratic is negative and gives a higher value of $\langle H \rangle$. Since we want to find an upper limit for $\langle H \rangle$, we choose the positive root.)

Substituting this in (6.16) and expanding as far as terms in $\mathscr{E}^2$, we find

$$\langle H \rangle_\phi = -\frac{\hbar^2}{2ma_0{}^2} - 4\pi\varepsilon_0 \cdot 2\mathscr{E}^2 a_0{}^3.$$

The first term here is the energy in the absence of the electric field, while the second term is the energy of electric polarization. The polarizability is defined by setting this equal to $-\tfrac{1}{2}\alpha\mathscr{E}^2$ whence

$$\frac{\alpha}{4\pi\varepsilon_0} = 4a_0{}^3 \qquad \text{(cf. (6.13)).}$$

Since the polarization energy is negative, and since the variation method gives an upper limit to the energy, it must give a lower limit here for the value of α. This result and that in eqn. (6.13) lie therefore on either side of the true value. In fact it can be shown that the correct value for $\alpha/4\pi\varepsilon_0$ is $4\cdot5a_0{}^3$. This follows from a detailed solution of the wave-equation (see e.g. Mott and Sneddon, *Wave Mechanics and its Applications*, O.U.P., 1948, pp. 166-8), and the same result can be obtained by the variation method using the trial function $\varepsilon^{-r/a_0}(1 + \lambda z + \mu zr)$.

Problems

(1) Show that the spacing of the energy levels of a one-dimensional simple harmonic oscillator is not changed by a perturbation $H' = \beta x$.

(2) A perturbation βx^2 is applied to a one-dimensional simple harmonic oscillator. Find its effect on the energy levels using the perturbation method and compare this with the result of an exact solution.

(3) A rigid body with moment of inertia I and electric dipole moment μ rotates in a plane, the axis passing through the centre of mass. An electric field $\mathscr{E}$ is applied, in the plane. Using the wave-equation

$$\frac{\hbar^2}{2I}\frac{d^2\psi}{d\phi^2}+(W+\mu\mathscr{E}\cos\phi)\psi = 0$$

find the perturbation energy as far as second order, and thus show that the polarizability α is proportional to $I/(4m^2-1)$, m being the rotational quantum number. What is the physical significance of the difference in the sign of α according as $m=0$ or $m>0$?

(4) Calculate the magnitude of the splittings of the atomic hydrogen states with $n=2$ and $n=3$ in a field of 10^7 volts/metre. (This is an obtainable field strength.) Using the selection rules $\Delta l=\pm1$, $\Delta m=0, \pm1$, find the number of components, and their separations in Ångström units, of the spectral line arising from the transition between these states.

(5) Using the trial function $\left(\dfrac{\lambda^3}{\pi}\right)^{\frac{1}{2}}\varepsilon^{-\lambda r}$ find an upper limit to the energy of the ground-state of the isotropic three-dimensional oscillator.

(For this hydrogen-like trial function $\left\langle\dfrac{1}{r}\right\rangle = \lambda$ and $\langle r^2\rangle = \dfrac{3}{\lambda^2}$.)

The result is $\langle H\rangle = \sqrt{3}\,\hbar\omega$.

(6) In the case of the sodium D doublet, which shows a spin-orbit splitting of about 6 Å, the production of the Paschen-Back effect would require a magnetic field of about 400,000 G or 40 weber/sq. metre. Justify this statement.

The corresponding transition in the lithium spectrum has a spin-orbit splitting of 0·15 Å. Show that in this case the Paschen-Back effect should be demonstrable with a field of 6,000 G or 0·6 weber/sq. metre.

CHAPTER SEVEN

MANY-ELECTRON ATOMS, AND THE HYDROGEN MOLECULE

So far we have been applying quantum theory to the description of extremely simple systems – a single oscillator, rotator, or an atom containing only one electron. Now we want to see how to describe the system which is formed when two or more such systems are brought together, so that they interact. We shall consider first the case of the helium atom, in which either electron can – in first approximation at any rate – be thought of as moving in the central field of the nucleus, but with its motion perturbed by the repulsion of the other electron. We shall then go on to consider more complex cases.

The helium atom

We suppose that the helium atom has an infinitely massive nucleus, round which move two electrons, labelled 1 and 2. We take the nucleus as the origin of coordinates; r_1 and r_2 are the distances of the two electrons from the nucleus, and r_{12} is the separation of the two electrons. The Hamiltonian is

$$H = \frac{p_1{}^2}{2m} + \frac{p_2{}^2}{2m} - \frac{2e^2}{4\pi\varepsilon_0 r_1} - \frac{2e^2}{4\pi\varepsilon_0 r_2} + \frac{e^2}{4\pi\varepsilon_0 r_{12}} \qquad (7.1)$$

$$= H_1 + H_2 + H'$$

where

$$H_1 = \frac{p_1{}^2}{2m} - \frac{2e^2}{4\pi\varepsilon_0 r_1}, \qquad H_2 = \frac{p_2{}^2}{2m} - \frac{2e^2}{4\pi\varepsilon_0 r_2},$$

$$H' = \frac{e^2}{4\pi\varepsilon_0 r_{12}}.$$

If we delete the perturbing term H' the remainder of the Hamiltonian leads to an eigenvalue equation which is separable into equations each representing the behaviour of a single electron in a Coulomb field. For the eigenvalue equation is $H\chi = E\chi$

$$\therefore \quad (H_1 + H_2)\chi = E\chi$$

and if we put

$$\chi = \psi(r_1)\phi(r_2)$$

this becomes

$$\phi(r_2)H_1\psi(r_1)+\psi(r_1)H_2\phi(r_2) = E\psi(r_1)\phi(r_2).$$

Now divide through by χ and we get

$$\frac{1}{\psi(r_1)} H_1 \psi(r_1)+\frac{1}{\phi(r_2)} H_2 \phi(r_2) = E$$

which gives

$$\begin{array}{c} H_1 \psi(r_1) = E_1 \psi(r_1) \\ H_2 \phi(r_2) = E_2 \phi(r_2) \end{array} \text{ with } E_1+E_2 = E.$$

The functions $\psi(r_1)$ and $\phi(r_2)$ are eigenfunctions of a Hamiltonian of exactly the same type as that for the hydrogen atom. We shall call these functions 'single-particle wave-functions'.

In zero-th order, then, it appears that the state-functions for the helium atom are the products of two single-particle wave-functions, and the energies are the sums of the corresponding single-particle energies. This seems reasonable enough if we recall that each single-particle function defines a probability distribution, and in the absence of interaction these are independent probabilities.

But there is another solution with the same energy, viz. $\psi(r_2)\phi(r_1)$, so the level with energy E is twofold degenerate. We shall write these two solutions as

$$\psi(r_1)\phi(r_2) = \chi_1(r_1, r_2), \qquad \psi(r_2)\phi(r_1) = \chi_2(r_1, r_2).$$

To determine the effect of the perturbation H' we must diagonalize the matrix of the perturbation for this pair of states. The diagonal matrix elements of H' with respect to χ_1 and χ_2 are

$$H'_{11} = \int \psi^*(r_1) \phi^*(r_2) \frac{e^2}{4\pi\varepsilon_0 r_{12}} \psi(r_1) \phi(r_2) \, d\tau_1 \, d\tau_2$$

$$= \int |\psi(r_1)|^2 |\phi(r_2)|^2 \frac{e^2}{4\pi\varepsilon_0 r_{12}} \, d\tau_1 \, d\tau_2 \qquad (7.2a)$$

and

$$H'_{22} = \int \phi^*(r_1) \psi^*(r_2) \frac{e^2}{4\pi\varepsilon_0 r_{12}} \phi(r_1) \psi(r_2) \, d\tau_1 \, d\tau_2$$

$$= \int |\phi(r_1)|^2 |\psi(r_2)|^2 \frac{e^2}{4\pi\varepsilon_0 r_{12}} \, d\tau_1 \, d\tau_2.$$

Clearly

$$H'_{11} = H'_{22} = L, \text{ say.}$$

L is called the 'direct integral'. If we write

$$\left. \begin{array}{l} e\,|\,\psi(r_1)\,|^2 = \rho_1 \\ e\,|\,\phi(r_2)\,|^2 = \rho_2 \end{array} \right\} \text{ where } \rho_1 \text{ and } \rho_2 \text{ are charge densities,}$$

L is of the form

$$\int \frac{\rho_1 d\tau_1 \rho_2 d\tau_2}{4\pi\varepsilon_0 r_{12}}$$

and represents the energy of electrostatic repulsion between two classical charge-distributions. The non-diagonal matrix elements are

$$H'_{12} = \int \psi^*(r_1)\,\phi^*(r_2)\frac{e^2}{4\pi\varepsilon_0 r_{12}}\,\psi(r_2)\,\phi(r_1)\,d\tau_1\,d\tau_2 = K$$

and

$$H'_{21} = \int \phi^*(r_1)\,\psi^*(r_2)\frac{e^2}{4\pi\varepsilon_0 r_{12}}\,\phi(r_2)\,\psi(r_1)\,d\tau_1\,d\tau_2 = K.$$

(7.2b)

K is called the 'exchange integral' and has no classical analogue; it is small unless the state-functions ϕ and ψ overlap appreciably.

Then the matrix of H' with respect to the degenerate unperturbed states χ_1 and χ_2 is

$$H' = \begin{bmatrix} L & K \\ K & L \end{bmatrix}$$

and the secular equation for its eigenvalues is

$$\begin{vmatrix} L-\lambda & K \\ K & L-\lambda \end{vmatrix} = 0$$

$$\therefore \quad (L-\lambda)^2 = K^2$$

$$\therefore \quad \lambda = L \pm K = \text{perturbation energies.}$$

The corresponding eigenfunctions are

$$\chi_s = \frac{1}{\sqrt{2}}\left\{\chi_1 + \chi_2\right\} \qquad \text{for} \quad E' = L+K$$

and

$$\chi_a = \frac{1}{\sqrt{2}}\left\{\chi_1 - \chi_2\right\} \qquad \text{for} \quad E' = L-K.$$

In full, these are

$$\chi_s = \frac{1}{\sqrt{2}} \left\{ \psi(r_1)\,\phi(r_2) + \phi(r_1)\,\psi(r_2) \right\}$$

$$\chi_a = \frac{1}{\sqrt{2}} \left\{ \psi(r_1)\,\phi(r_2) - \phi(r_1)\,\psi(r_2) \right\}. \tag{7.3}$$

These functions χ_s and χ_a are eigenfunctions of H_1, H_2 and H'; they are therefore eigenfunctions of $H = H_1 + H_2 + H'$, and the eigenvalues of H are $E_1 + E_2 + L \pm K$. Since the perturbing potential represents a force of repulsion, the effect of the perturbation must be to raise the energy levels. This means that $L \pm K$ cannot be negative, so $L \geq K$. Further χ_s has higher energy than χ_a, so that for a configuration defined by the single-particle wave-functions ψ and ϕ, where $\psi \neq \phi$, the anti-symmetric state χ_a will be the more stable. The ground-state, however, should be a state with $\psi \equiv \phi$, and the anti-symmetric combination vanishes identically in this case; the ground-state must therefore be of the non-degenerate type

$$(\chi)_{\text{ground state}} = \psi(r_1)\,\psi(r_2). \tag{7.4}$$

The symmetric and anti-symmetric state-functions represent space-distributions which differ in a way we can easily visualize. The anti-symmetric function in (7.3) vanishes when the coordinates of the two particles are the same, so when the system is in a state represented by an anti-symmetric state-function the probability of finding the two electrons at the same place is zero. In fact the motions of the two electrons are correlated so that they tend to be on opposite sides of the nucleus. If, on the other hand, the state is one whose state-function is symmetric the probability of finding the two electrons together is rather high. Their electrostatic repulsion then makes the energy of such a symmetric state higher than the energy of the corresponding anti-symmetric state.

We shall now estimate the ionization potential of the helium atom from the foregoing analysis, to see whether it agrees with the value obtained experimentally.

The ground-state energy for the hydrogen atom is

$$-\frac{e^2}{4\pi\varepsilon_0} \cdot \frac{1}{2a_0} = -13\cdot6 \text{ eV}.$$

For the single-particle states of the helium atom, with nuclear charge 2, the corresponding energy is four times as great, i.e. $-54\cdot4$ eV.

For the ground-state configuration of the helium atom, because

$$\psi = \phi = \left(\frac{Z^3}{\pi a_0^3}\right)^{\frac{1}{2}} \varepsilon^{-Zr/a_0},$$

there is only one product of single-particle state-functions, as noted at (7.4); it is

$$(\chi)_{\text{ ground state }} = \left(\frac{Z^3}{\pi a_0^3}\right)\varepsilon^{-Z(r_1 + r_2)/a_0}.$$

The perturbation energy for the ground state is therefore given by the integral

$$H' = \frac{e^2}{4\pi\varepsilon_0} \frac{Z^6}{\pi^2 a_0^6} \iint \frac{\varepsilon^{-2Z(r_1 + r_2)/a_0}}{r_{12}} \, d\tau_1 \, d\tau_2 \qquad (7.5)$$

which can be simplified if we replace the variables r_1, r_2 and r_{12} by ρ_1, ρ_2 and ρ_{12}, which are defined by $\rho_1 = 2Zr_1/a_0$, $\rho_2 = 2Zr_2/a_0$, and $\rho_{12} = 2Zr_{12}/a_0$. Then, remembering that the volume elements $d\tau_1$ and $d\tau_2$ contain factors $r_1^2 dr_1$ and $r_2^2 dr_2$, we see that

$$H' = \frac{e^2}{4\pi\varepsilon_0} \frac{Z}{32\pi^2 a_0} \iint \frac{\varepsilon^{-\rho_1} \varepsilon^{-\rho_2}}{\rho_{12}} \, dv_1 \, dv_2.$$

Apart from the factor $Ze^2/32\pi^2 a_0$ this is the electrostatic potential energy of the spherically symmetric charge distributions whose density functions are $\varepsilon^{-\rho_1}$ and $\varepsilon^{-\rho_2}$. We can evaluate it by calculating the potential due to the first of these by integrating over dv_1, and then finding the energy of the second charge-distribution in that potential field.

The potential at a point r due to a spherical shell of radius ρ_1, and total charge $4\pi\rho_1^2\varepsilon^{-\rho_1}d\rho_1$, falls off with distance outside the shell as though the charge were concentrated at the centre, so that for $r > \rho_1$ it is $4\pi\rho_1^2\varepsilon^{-\rho_1}d\rho_1/4\pi\varepsilon_0 r$. Within the shell the potential is constant at the value it has at the shell's surface, which is $4\pi\rho_1^2\varepsilon^{-\rho_1}d\rho_1/4\pi\varepsilon_0\rho_1$.

The potential $\Phi(r)$ of the whole distribution is therefore given by

$$4\pi\varepsilon_0\Phi(r) = \frac{4\pi}{r} \int_0^r \varepsilon^{-\rho_1}\rho_1^2 d\rho_1 + 4\pi \int_r^\infty \varepsilon^{-\rho_1}\rho_1 d\rho_1$$

$$= \frac{4\pi}{r}\left\{2 - \varepsilon^{-r}(r+2)\right\}.$$

The energy of the second charge-distribution in this potential is then

$$\int \Phi(\rho_2)\, \varepsilon^{-\rho_2} dv_2 \;=\; \frac{1}{4\pi\varepsilon_0}\, 16\pi^2 \int_0^\infty \{2-\varepsilon^{-\rho_2}(\rho_2+2)\}\varepsilon^{-\rho_2}\rho_2\, d\rho_2$$

$$=\; \frac{1}{4\pi\varepsilon_0}\, 20\pi^2$$

and so

$$H' = \frac{1}{4\pi\varepsilon_0}\, \frac{Ze^2}{2a_0}\, \frac{5}{4} = 2\times\frac{5}{4}\times 13\!\cdot\!6\,\text{eV}$$

$$=\; 34\ \text{eV}.$$

Hence the energy in the ground-state, represented by H_1+H_2+H', is $(-2\times 54\!\cdot\!4+34)\,\text{eV} = -74\!\cdot\!8\ \text{eV}$.

If one of the electrons is removed to infinity the energy of the remaining ion is $-54\!\cdot\!4\,\text{eV}$. The ionization potential should therefore be $(74\!\cdot\!8-54\!\cdot\!4)\,\text{V} = 20\!\cdot\!4\,\text{V}$. Experimentally it is found to be $24\!\cdot\!8\,\text{V}$, which means that the value of H' must be $29\!\cdot\!6\,\text{eV}$, rather than $34\!\cdot\!0\,\text{eV}$. This is an appreciable discrepancy, but this should not surprise us – the perturbation method assumes that the perturbation is small, but we have been applying it to a case in which the perturbation energy is about 30% of the unperturbed energy.

We can improve the approximation very strikingly by means of the variation method. The ground-state function (7.4) represents the simultaneous presence of two electrons, each moving in the field of a nucleus of charge 2; the interaction between the electrons is treated as a perturbation. Alternatively we might suppose that each electron 'screens' the nucleus to some extent, so that when electron 2 is distant r_2 from the nucleus the effective charge in whose field it moves is that of the nucleus, less the fraction of the charge of the other electron represented by the part of its wave-function for which $r_1 < r_2$. The simplest way of representing this is to suppose that the single-electron wave-functions are of the form

$$\phi(Z') = \left(\frac{Z'^3}{\pi a_0^3}\right)^{\frac{1}{2}} \varepsilon^{-Z'r/a_0} \tag{7.6}$$

where Z' is between 1 and 2 and is treated as a variation parameter.

The Hamiltonian (7.1) contains five terms, of which two represent kinetic energies, two represent the potential energies of the electrons in the field of the nucleus of charge 2, and the other is the potential energy of mutual repulsion of the electrons. With the trial function

(7.6) the expectation values of the kinetic energies are each $\dfrac{Z'^2 e^2}{8\pi\varepsilon_0 a_0}$

and those of the potential energies are each $-\dfrac{2Z'e^2}{4\pi\varepsilon_0 a_0}$. (Note that if $Z'=2$ we get the ratio $\langle\text{K.E.}\rangle : \langle\text{P.E.}\rangle = -\frac{1}{2}$, as we should expect for a single electron moving in a bound orbit in a Coulomb field.) The expectation value of the electron interaction energy is

$$\left(\frac{Z'^3}{\pi a_0^3}\right)^2 \frac{e^2}{4\pi\varepsilon_0} \iint \frac{\varepsilon^{-2Z'(r_1+r_2)/a_0}}{r_{12}} \, d\tau_1 \, d\tau_2.$$

This integral is, apart from the replacement of Z by Z', the same as (7.5) so its value is

$$\frac{5}{8} Z' \frac{e^2}{4\pi\varepsilon_0 a_0}.$$

The expectation value for the Hamiltonian with the trial function constructed from two single-particle functions like (7.6) is therefore

$$\langle H \rangle_{Z'} = \frac{e^2}{4\pi\varepsilon_0 a_0} \left(Z'^2 - 4Z' + \frac{5}{8}Z' \right)$$

$$= \frac{e^2}{4\pi\varepsilon_0 a_0} Z' \left(Z' - \frac{27}{8} \right).$$

By differentiating with respect to Z', we find that $\langle H \rangle_{Z'}$ is a minimum when $Z' = \dfrac{27}{16} = 1\cdot69$; hence the upper limit for the ground-state energy is

$$-\frac{e^2}{4\pi\varepsilon_0 a_0} \left(\frac{27}{16}\right)^2 = -77\cdot5 \text{ eV}.$$

This gives for the ionization potential $(77\cdot5 - 54\cdot4)$ V $= 23\cdot1$ V. Comparing with the result from the perturbation calculation, $20\cdot4$ V, and the experimental value of $24\cdot8$ V, we see that the variation method using this very simple trial function gives a much better estimate of the ground-state energy than the perturbation calculation. Notice that, although both calculations as given here involve the evaluation of the same integral, they start from rather different physical pictures of the effect of the electronic interactions. The effect of correlations between the motion of the electrons can be introduced into the variation calculation by choosing a trial function which contains explicitly the distance r_{12} between the electrons, say

$$\phi \propto \varepsilon^{-Z'(r_1+r_2)/a_0}(1+cr_{12})$$

with parameters Z' and c. It was shown by Hylleraas (1930) that the ionization potential deduced from this function differs by less than 0·5 V from the true value. With more complicated trial functions even better results are obtained.

Symmetry and anti-symmetry of state-functions; the exclusion principle

The fictitious forces to whose operation we might attribute the energies represented by the exchange integrals are called 'exchange forces'.† The effects associated with them – such as the splitting of the energy levels of helium, or the binding of two identical hydrogen atoms into a stable molecule – cannot be explained in classical terms. These exchange effects result from the fact that in a configuration compounded of two single-particle states ψ and ϕ we have no means of deciding which electron is in which state; what we observe is a state of the compound system in which either electron is equally likely to be in either state, and we have to represent this by a linear combination of the products $\psi(r_1)\,\phi(r_2)$ and $\psi(r_2)\,\phi(r_1)$, in which each term has equal probability amplitude. The space probability densities associated with the two products are

$$|\psi(r_1)|^2\,|\phi(r_2)|^2 \text{ and } |\psi(r_2)|^2\,|\phi(r_1)|^2$$

which are both equal to ρ, say. The space probability densities associated with the symmetric and anti-symmetric combinations

$$\frac{1}{\sqrt{2}}\left\{\psi(r_1)\,\phi(r_2) \pm \psi(r_2)\,\phi(r_1)\right\}$$

are

$$\tfrac{1}{2}\{\,|\psi(r_1)|^2\,|\phi(r_2)|^2+|\psi(r_2)|^2\,|\phi(r_1)|^2 \pm 2R[\psi(r_1)\psi(r_2)\phi(r_1)\phi(r_2)]\}$$
$$= \rho \pm R[\psi(r_1)\psi(r_2)\phi(r_1)\phi(r_2)].$$

The last term represents an 'interference of the probability waves', and is sometimes called an *overlap density*. It is zero only if the two single-particle systems do not overlap, which is effectively the case if they are each tightly bound systems, widely separated; the inter-

---

† The forces whose operation gives rise to the interaction energy in the helium atom are of course electrostatic forces, and both the direct and the exchange integrals evaluate effects which arise from electrostatics.

action between them is then negligible. If the systems are close enough to interact the probability distribution will differ from classical expectation because of interference effects, and the interaction energy will be correspondingly modified.

The property of the symmetry or anti-symmetry of a state-function is an important – indeed a fundamental – one. It is a property which is conserved through all the changes which an isolated system undergoes. We can show this in the following way:

The Hamiltonian for a system of many identical particles – particles having the same intrinsic properties, such as mass, charge, spin, magnetic moment etc. – must be symmetrical in the coordinates of these particles, for the interchange of any two such particles cannot change any observable property of the system; in particular it cannot change the energy. (This may also be deduced from Newton's Third Law.) We recall the equation of motion (2.16) of a system whose state-function changes with time:

$$H\psi = i\hbar \, \frac{\partial \psi}{\partial t}.$$

If the state-function is ψ_0 when $t=0$, after a lapse δt it will be

$$\psi_{\delta t} = \psi_0 + \frac{\partial \psi}{\partial t} \, \delta t$$

$$= \psi_0 - \frac{i}{\hbar} H\psi_0 \delta t.$$

Because H is symmetric the increment $i/\hbar \, H\psi_0 \, \delta t$ is symmetric or anti-symmetric according as ψ_0 is symmetric or anti-symmetric; hence the symmetric or anti-symmetric character of ψ is conserved.

It is found empirically that the state-functions of systems of many identical fundamental particles – neutrons, protons or electrons – are always anti-symmetric combinations of the single-particle wave-functions when these are expressed as functions of all the space and spin coordinates of the several particles. For a many-particle system let $\psi_\mu(r_m)$ represent the state of the mth particle and let the energy of this state be E_μ. Neglecting interactions, the Hamiltonian is $\sum_m H_m$ and the total energy is $\sum_\mu E_\mu$. If there are n particles, there are in all $n!$ different products of single-particle wave-functions, of the type

$$\psi_\alpha(r_1) \, \psi_\beta(r_2) \ldots \psi_\nu(r_n);$$

however there is only one anti-symmetric linear combination of these $n!$ products, and it can be written formally as a determinant:

$$\Psi = C \begin{vmatrix} \psi_\alpha(r_1) & \psi_\alpha(r_2) & \psi_\alpha(r_3) & \cdots & \psi_\alpha(r_n) \\ \psi_\beta(r_1) & \psi_\beta(r_2) & \psi_\beta(r_3) & \cdots & \psi_\beta(r_n) \\ \cdot & \cdot & \cdot & & \cdot \\ \cdot & \cdot & \cdot & & \\ \cdot & \cdot & \cdot & & \cdot \\ \psi_\nu(r_1) & \psi_\nu(r_2) & \psi_\nu(r_3) & \cdots & \psi_\nu(r_n) \end{vmatrix}$$

It is easy to see that this function is anti-symmetric, for an interchange of two particles, say the second and third, is effected symbolically by interchanging the corresponding columns of the determinant, which reverses its sign.

We can now obtain a very remarkable result if we suppose two of the single-particle state-functions to be identical. This makes two rows of the determinant identical, and the determinant then vanishes. In this case the total state-function is zero. We are led to the conclusion that *in a system of many particles two identical particles cannot be in the same state.* This is *Pauli's Exclusion Principle.*

In practice the state-function Ψ of a many-particle system may have to be written, not as a single determinant, but as a linear combination of determinants. The determinant written above takes care of the $n!$ distributions of the n particles over the n functions ψ_μ, but there is another type of degeneracy which arises from the possibility that several spin-orbit functions may correspond to the same unperturbed energy. In particular, there may be several sets of functions $\psi_\mu, \psi_\mu', \psi_\mu'' \ldots$ etc. with different values of the quantum numbers m_z and s_z, and these would have the same energies because the unperturbed energy is independent of the z-component of angular momentum. The construction of such a set of determinants was first discussed by Slater (1929) and the example of the three-electron atom lithium is treated in detail in Pauling and Wilson's *Introduction to Quantum Mechanics,* chapter 9; for the ground-state configuration of lithium there are six third-order determinants, representing six possible anti-symmetric state-functions of the unperturbed system.

Space-and-spin functions for the helium atom

We shall now examine in more detail the possible configurations of the helium atom, taking into account the exclusion principle. To do this we shall have to include a representation of the spin states. Suppose s_3 denotes the spin operator, whose eigenvalues are $\pm\hbar/2$; as in chapter 4 we shall write the spin eigenfunctions as α and β, α being the eigenfunction for an electron with spin $\frac{1}{2}$, and β being the eigenfunction for an electron with spin $-\frac{1}{2}$. The single-particle wave-functions are now products of space-and-spin functions, the possible products being

for particle 1: $\psi(1)\,\alpha(1)$, $\psi(1)\,\beta(1)$, $\phi(1)\,\alpha(1)$, $\phi(1)\,\beta(1)$;
for particle 2: $\psi(2)\,\alpha(2)$, $\psi(2)\,\beta(2)$, $\phi(2)\,\alpha(2)$, $\phi(2)\,\beta(2)$.

These may be formed into eight products representing $\psi\phi$ configurations; the resultant spin s_3 is shown for each product:

$$\psi(1)\,\alpha(1)\,\phi(2)\,\alpha(2) \quad [s_3 = 1]; \quad \psi(1)\,\alpha(1)\,\phi(2)\,\beta(2) \quad [s_3 = 0];$$
$$\psi(1)\,\beta(1)\,\phi(2)\,\alpha(2) \quad [s_3 = 0]; \quad \psi(1)\,\beta(1)\,\phi(2)\,\beta(2) \quad [s_3 = -1];$$
$$\phi(1)\,\alpha(1)\,\psi(2)\,\alpha(2) \quad [s_3 = 1]; \quad \phi(1)\,\alpha(1)\,\psi(2)\,\beta(2) \quad [s_3 = 0];$$
$$\phi(1)\,\beta(1)\,\psi(2)\,\alpha(2) \quad [s_3 = 0]; \quad \phi(1)\,\beta(1)\,\psi(2)\,\beta(2) \quad [s_3 = -1].$$

From these we can form four symmetric combinations and four anti-symmetric combinations. Only the anti-symmetric combinations are consistent with the exclusion principle. They are, neglecting normalizing factors,

$$\{\psi(1)\,\phi(2)+\psi(2)\,\phi(1)\}\{\alpha(1)\,\beta(2)-\alpha(2)\,\beta(1)\} \quad [s_3 = 0]$$
$$\{\psi(1)\,\phi(2)-\psi(2)\,\phi(1)\}\{\alpha(1)\,\alpha(2)\} \quad [s_3 = 1]$$
$$\{\psi(1)\,\phi(2)-\psi(2)\,\phi(1)\}\{\alpha(1)\,\beta(2)+\alpha(2)\,\beta(1)\} \quad [s_3 = 0]$$
$$\{\psi(1)\,\phi(2)-\psi(2)\,\phi(1)\}\{\beta(1)\,\beta(2)\} \quad [s_3 = -1].$$

Notice that the space-factor in the first is symmetric, while the space-factor in the others is anti-symmetric. Since this property remains unaltered when a system changes with time, we should expect transitions from one energy level to another to take place only between pairs of states whose space-functions are both symmetric, or both anti-symmetric. Now the energy level scheme for helium, deduced from its spectrum, shows that there are two sets of levels – a singlet set and a triplet set. (The names *parhelium* and *orthohelium* are used to refer to helium in the singlet and triplet states respectively.) Transitions occur between pairs of triplet levels, and between pairs of singlet levels, but only very rarely between singlet and triplet levels. (See White, *Introduction to Atomic Spectra*, McGraw-Hill, 1934, p. 209.) We are thus led to associate the single state-function whose space-factor is symmetric with the singlet levels, and the three whose space-factor is anti-symmetric with the triplet levels. We could verify that this association is correct by operating on the anti-symmetric and symmetric combinations of spin-functions with the operators $S^2 = \frac{1}{2}(3 + \boldsymbol{\sigma}(1) \cdot \boldsymbol{\sigma}(2))$ and $S_z = \frac{1}{2}(\sigma_z(1) + \sigma_z(2))$, which were shown in chapter 4 to be the operators for the square of the total spin angular momentum and the z-component of spin for a system of two electrons. It is easily shown (problem 1, p. 164) that the anti-symmetric spin-function has zero total angular momentum, while the symmetric functions have total angular momentum $\{\frac{1}{2}(\frac{1}{2}+1)\}^{\frac{1}{2}}\hbar$ and z-components $\hbar/2$, 0 and $-\hbar/2$. They therefore represent singlet and triplet states respectively.

Referring back to the first section of this chapter, it will be recalled that the space-symmetric (i.e. singlet) states have higher energy than the corresponding anti-symmetric (triplet) states, but that the ground-state configuration occurs only in the symmetric or singlet form. Suppose that a helium atom is singly ionized, and is neutralized by picking up an electron so as to form a triplet state. Radiative decay through the triplet state will ultimately lead to the lowest such state, which is about 20 eV above the singlet ground-state. Radiative decay to the ground-state is not normally possible, and de-excitation usually takes place by collision. (This is possible because in the collision process it is the symmetry of the combined state-function describing both the colliding atoms that is conserved, and not the symmetry of the state-function for each atom separately. If the collision reverses the symmetry for both atoms, the symmetry of the combined system is conserved.) The absence of the space-anti-symmetric ground-state in helium was one of the key facts which led Pauli to the discovery of the exclusion principle. This property is shared by all the rare-gas atoms, and is important in the technology of metal-vapour lamps and certain gas laser systems, such as the He − Ne laser.

Energy levels of an electron in a many-electron atom

In attempting to calculate energy levels and charge-probability densities for many-electron atoms it is always assumed that each electron moves in a central field due to the nucleus and all the other electrons. In our variation calculation for the helium atom we assumed that the effect of the 'other' electron was to screen the nucleus, and so reduce the effective nuclear charge, but we assumed that the resultant potential was of the Coulomb type. It would be more realistic to treat the effective nuclear charge seen by an electron as a function of the distance of the electron from the nucleus. Let us consider qualitatively the problem of predicting the energy levels of the outermost electron in the alkali metals – Li, Na, K, Rb, Cs – in which the inner closed electron shells act as a core, around and through which moves a single valence electron.

If the valence electron is remote from the nucleus it 'sees' a system whose net charge is unity; as the electron penetrates the core the screening of the nucleus by the core is progressively reduced and the electron moves in the electrostatic field of a system whose charge appears to increase towards the nuclear charge Ze. The potential then varies more rapidly than the Coulomb one, and may be written

$$V(r) = -\frac{e^2}{4\pi\varepsilon_0 r} - \delta V(r)$$

where $\delta V(r)$ is a perturbation, and the negative sign preceding it takes care of the fact that it is attractive (Fig. 7.1).

If ψ_{nlm} is a state-function for an electron moving in the Coulomb field of a nucleus with charge e, the change in the energy of this state due to the perturbation $-\delta V(r)$ is

$$\langle -\delta V \rangle_{nlm} = -\int \psi_{nlm}{}^* \, \delta V \, \psi_{nlm} \, d\tau.$$

If δV is due to closed shells,† and so represents a central perturbation, the only factor in ψ_{nlm} which needs to be taken into account is the radial factor $R_{nl}(r)$, which is the eigenfunction of the operator

$$\frac{p_r{}^2}{2m} + \frac{l(l+1)\hbar^2}{2mr^2} - \frac{e^2}{4\pi\varepsilon_0 r}.$$

As we remarked at the beginning of chapter 5 the effect of the centrifugal potential is to reduce the likelihood that an electron in a state of high angular momentum will be found near the nucleus. The expression for $\langle \delta V \rangle_{nlm}$ will be large if the probability density

† The $2n^2$ electrons which have a given value of n are said to form a *closed shell*; the $2(2l+1)$ electrons with a given n and l form a *sub-shell*. The charge density due to all the electrons in a closed shell is spherically symmetric.

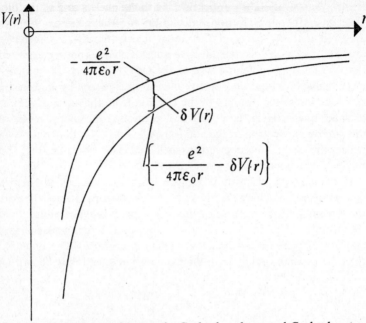

FIG. 7.1. The difference between the Coulomb and screened Coulomb potentials can be treated as a perturbation $-\delta V(r)$ operating on the known
eigenfunctions of the Coulomb field.

$|R_{nl}|^2$ is large where $\delta V(r)$ is large, that is, near the nucleus. Hence
the integral is larger for states with small l than for states of the
same unperturbed energy with large l.

The nature of the resultant splitting of the levels which are
degenerate in the Coulomb field will therefore be as indicated in
Fig. 7.2. The s-states are depressed more than the others, and as the
initial separations of the levels with neighbouring n-values decreases
with increase of n the depression of the 4s level is such that it practically coincides with the 3d level. This happens in the periodic table
in the first transition group of elements, and it shows both in the
well-known complexity of the iron-arc spectrum, and in the occurrence of ferromagnetism in iron, cobalt and nickel.

The periodic system of the elements

The exclusion principle, and what was said in the last section about
the order of the energy levels in the screened Coulomb field, enable
us to understand in a general way the classification of the elements

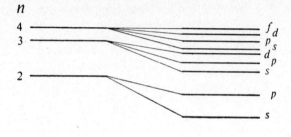

n

4 ────────

3 ────────

2 ────────

f d
p s
d
p
s

p

s

1 ────────

s

FIG. 7.2. Energy levels in the potentials of Fig. 7.1. In the Coulomb field the
energy depends only on n; in the screened Coulomb field there is also a
dependence on l.

in the periodic system. From the exclusion principle we know that
any level specified by the quantum numbers n, l, m can be occupied
by at most two electrons, with oppositely aligned spins. In the
ground-state the levels will be filled by the available electrons in
order of increasing energy; generally the levels with lowest n fill up
first and for a given n those with lowest l fill first. For any l there are
of course $2(2l+1)$ levels. The order of filling and the number of
electrons in each *shell* – a group of electrons with the same values of
n and l – could therefore be predicted unhesitatingly were it not for
the fact, noted above, that in the non-Coulomb field the ordering
of the shells is disturbed, so that, for instance, the $4s$ levels ($n=4$,
$l=0$) may be lower than the $3d$ levels. In the same way the $5s$ levels
lie lower than the $4d$, while the $6s$ levels lie lower than the $5d$ and
$4f$ levels. The order of filling of the shells, along with the atomic
number and chemical symbol for the elements which are formed by
the closure of the several shells, are shown below:

Shell	n	l	No. of electrons	Z	Element
1s	1	0	2	2	He
2s	2	0	2	4	Be
2p	2	1	6	10	Ne
3s	3	0	2	12	Mg
3p	3	1	6	18	A
{ 4s	4	0	2	20	Ca
{ 3d	3	2	10	30	Zn
4p	3	1	6	36	Kr
{ 5s	5	0	2	38	Sr
{ 4d	4	2	10	48	Cd
5p	5	1	6	54	Xe
{ 6s	6	0	2	56	Ba
{ 4f	4	3	14		
{ 5d	5	2	10	80	Hg
6p	6	1	6	86	Rn
{ 7s	7	0	2	88	Ra
{ 5f	5	3	14		
{ 6d	6	2	10	112	

The bracketed shells have energies so close that they are not filled in sequence; in such groups the two s-levels fill first, but the subsequent filling of the other shells in these groups is accomplished with the help of 'temporary loans' of one or both electrons from the s-shell; the elements which immediately precede Zn, Cd and Hg, for instance, are the 'noble' metals Cu, Ag, Au, each of which has a vacancy in the s-shell.

The chemical properties of the elements are determined by the number of electrons and vacancies in the outermost shell, and the gap between this and the next higher (empty) shell. It is the recurrence of similar configurations in the highest shell that produces the *periodic system* of the elements. Thus, for instance, the rather large energy gap between the filled p-shells and the next higher shell produces a series of inert gases, He, Ne, A, Kr, Xe, Rn. The addition of one electron in the next higher s-shell produces the alkali metals, the removal of one electron from the rare-gas structure produces the halogens; the lowering of total energy that results from the transfer of an electron from an alkali metal to a halogen, with the formation of two closed p-shell structures, accounts for the polar bonding of compounds like NaCl and KBr.

State-functions for complex atoms: Hartree's self-consistent field

Calculations of the state-functions and energies of complex atoms go beyond the scope of perturbation theory, and of the variation method, though the variation method has been applied successfully to a number of the lighter atoms and ions. For the heavier atoms, calculations start from the assumption that each electron moves in a spherically symmetric field due to the nucleus and the other electrons. Two methods have been used for the calculation of the appropriate potential for the central field. One of these, due to Thomas and Fermi, will be discussed in the next chapter as an application of quantum statistics; the other, due to Hartree, will be outlined here.

In the Hartree method it is assumed that the potential for each electron can be obtained by summing the potentials due to the nucleus and the charge probability-distributions $e \mid \psi \mid^2$ of all the other electrons. This potential is estimated from trial wave-functions ϕ_i; usually it is assumed that all the electrons in any one shell have the same wave-function. The wave-equation for, say, the kth state-function, containing the potential derived from the trial wave-functions for all the other electrons, is solved to give a solution ψ_k; this is done for each electron in turn. The solutions ψ_k will not in general agree with the trial functions ϕ_i. New trial functions are therefore estimated on the basis of these findings and the process is repeated until trial functions are found which give solutions consistent with themselves. The state-function for the whole atom is then taken to be the product of the self-consistent single-electron trial functions.

There is a close connection between Hartree's method and the variation method. Let us attempt to apply the variation method to a trial function of the type $\phi = \psi_1 \psi_2 \psi_3 \ldots \psi_n$ where the suffixes refer to the several electrons and all the ψ_i are normalized. The best such function is that which makes $\int \phi^* H \phi d\tau$ a minimum.

The Hamiltonian for the n-electron system is

$$H = \sum_{i=1}^{n} \left\{ -\frac{\hbar^2}{2m} \nabla_i{}^2 - \frac{Ze^2}{4\pi\varepsilon_0 r_i} \right\} + \sum_{i>j} \sum_{j=1}^{n} \frac{e^2}{4\pi\varepsilon_0 r_{ij}}$$

$$= \sum_{i=1}^{n} H_i + \sum_{i>j} \sum_{j=1}^{n} \frac{e^2}{4\pi\varepsilon_0 r_{ij}}.$$

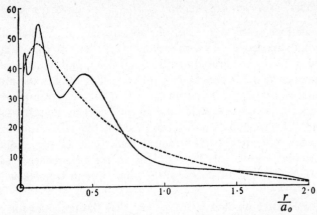

FIG. 7.3.   The radial charge distribution for the Rb⁺ ion. There are 36 electrons, forming closed $1s$, $2s$, $2p$, $3s$, $3p$, $3d$, $4s$ and $4p$ sub-shells. The continuous curve, calculated by Hartree, shows pronounced peaks due to the shells with $n=1$, 2 and 3, and a plateau ending just beyond $r=1·5a_0$ due to the two sub-shells with $n=4$. The dotted curve was calculated by Thomas (see chapter 8 for 'The Thomas–Fermi model of the atom') and was used by Hartree as the first trial function.

Both curves are normalized so that the area under them represents the total charge on the electrons.

Then

$$\int \phi^* H \phi \, d\tau$$

$$= \sum_i \int \psi_i^* H_i \psi_i \, d\tau_i + \sum_{i>j} \sum_{j=1}^n \iint \psi_i^* \psi_j^* \frac{e^2}{4\pi\varepsilon_0 r_{ij}} \psi_i \psi_j \, d\tau_i \, d\tau_j.$$

The best ϕ is found by varying each of the ψ_j in turn to minimize this quantity. Picking out the terms in a particular ψ_j we find them to be

$$\int \psi_j^* H_j \psi_j \, d\tau_j + \sum_{i \neq j} \iint \psi_i^* \psi_j^* \frac{e^2}{4\pi\varepsilon_0 r_{ij}} \psi_i \psi_j \, d\tau_i \, d\tau_j$$

and this can be written as $\int \psi_j^* H_j \psi_j \, d\tau_j$ if

$$H_j = -\frac{\hbar^2}{2m}\nabla_j^2 - \frac{Ze^2}{4\pi\varepsilon_0 r_j} + \sum_{i \neq j} \int \frac{|\psi_i|^2 e^2}{4\pi\varepsilon_0 r_{ij}} \, d\tau_i.$$

Now this is just the Hamiltonian for the jth electron moving in the combined field due to the nucleus and the charge distributions representing the other electrons. The integral $\int \psi_j^* H_j \psi_j \, d\tau_j$ is a minimum when ψ_j is a solution of the eigenvalue equation $H_j \psi_j = E \psi_j$, so the single-electron wave-functions which satisfy the variation criterion are the solutions of the wave-equations used in the Hartree method.

The trial function ϕ constructed from these single-electron wave-functions is not symmetrized in the way required by the Pauli principle. If ϕ is written as a determinant to satisfy the requirement of anti-symmetry, effects due to electron exchange are included; this refinement of the Hartree method is due to Slater, and Fock.

The total charge-distributions calculated by the Hartree method show maxima at certain distances from the nucleus corresponding to the various electron shells, as shown in Fig. 7.3. The calculated binding energies tend to be slightly but systematically high.

The hydrogen molecule

The case of the hydrogen molecule is similar to, but more complicated than, that of the helium atom; historically the wave-mechanical treatment by Heitler and London (1927) was of tremendous importance, for the formation of the homopolar bond between two identical atoms could not be understood in classical terms.

There are in this case two nuclei, which we label a and b, and two electrons, labelled 1 and 2. If we neglect the motion of the nuclei, the Hamiltonian can be written

$$H = \frac{p_1^2}{2m} + \frac{p_2^2}{2m} + \frac{1}{4\pi\varepsilon_0} \left(-\frac{e^2}{r_{a1}} - \frac{e^2}{r_{b1}} - \frac{e^2}{r_{a2}} - \frac{e^2}{r_{b2}} + \frac{e^2}{r_{12}} + \frac{e^2}{R_{ab}} \right). \qquad (7.7)$$

This can be read in two ways, depending on whether we assume that electron 1 'belongs to' nucleus a and electron 2 to nucleus b, or that electron 1 'belongs to' nucleus b and electron 2 to nucleus a. The unperturbed eigenfunctions for the two cases would be

$$\psi (r_{a1}) \, \phi (r_{b2}) \quad \text{and} \quad \psi (r_{a2}) \, \phi (r_{b1})$$

respectively, and the corresponding perturbing terms would be

$$H' = \frac{1}{4\pi\varepsilon_0} \left(-\frac{e^2}{r_{b1}} - \frac{e^2}{r_{a2}} + \frac{e^2}{r_{12}} + \frac{e^2}{R_{ab}} \right)$$

and

$$H' = \frac{1}{4\pi\varepsilon_0} \left(-\frac{e^2}{r_{a1}} - \frac{e^2}{r_{b2}} + \frac{e^2}{r_{12}} + \frac{e^2}{R_{ab}} \right).$$

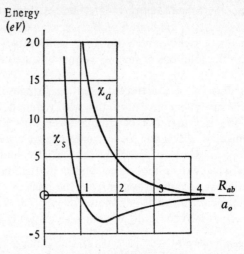

Fig. 7.4. The energy of the space-symmetric and anti-symmetric states of the hydrogen molecule as a function of the separation of the protons (calculated by Sugiura using the Heitler-London theory).

The alternative products of single-particle eigenfunctions are degenerate, and again we have to diagonalize a 2×2 perturbation matrix of the form

$$\begin{bmatrix} L & K \\ K & L \end{bmatrix}$$

whose eigenvalues $L+K$ and $L-K$ belong to symmetric and antisymmetric eigenfunctions. In this case we cannot say by inspection that the perturbation energy must be positive, as we could in the case of the helium atom, for now the Hamiltonian includes both positive and negative perturbing terms, and the relative importance of their contributions depends on the distance between the two nuclei. If the values of the direct and exchange integrals are computed for various values of the nuclear separation, it turns out that for the symmetric state the perturbing energy $L+K$ is negative provided the nuclei are not too close together, and has a minimum, whereas the perturbing energy for the anti-symmetric state is always positive. This shows that a stable molecule can be formed, and will be represented by a symmetric state-function, whereas if two hydrogen atoms in a state represented by an anti-symmetric function approach one another the force between them will always be a repulsion. Fig. 7.4 shows plots of the perturbation energy as a function of the inter-nuclear distance R_{ab} for the two types of state-function.

The value of R_{ab} for which the energy has its minimum defines the separation of the protons in a hydrogen molecule; the calculated value is $1\cdot5a_0 = 0\cdot8$ Å; the experimental value is $0\cdot74$ Å. The depth of the minimum gives the energy required to dissociate the molecule as $3\cdot14$ eV, while the experimental value is $4\cdot48$ eV. Variational calculations using more complex trial functions give improved results. For instance, a trial function of the type

$$\phi = k\{\psi_a(r_1)\psi_a(r_2) + \psi_b(r_1)\psi_b(r_2)\} + \{\psi_a(r_1)\psi_b(r_2) + \psi_b(r_1)\psi_a(r_2)\}$$

has been used, containing two parameters, of which one is the coefficient k and the other is the effective charge number Z' in the single-particle functions which are of the type $\varepsilon^{-Z'r/a_0}$. This function gives $R_{ab} = 0\cdot77$ Å, and $4\cdot00$ eV for the dissociation energy, which is a considerable improvement. The first two terms in this trial function (in which it is found that the variation criterion requires $k = 0\cdot256$, $Z' = 1\cdot193$) represent the possibility that both electrons are attached to the same nucleus. In this case the molecule can be pictured as consisting partly of a negative and a positive ion, whose electrostatic attraction contributes to the binding of the molecule. These terms are therefore called *ionic terms*. Further improvement can be effected by combining single-particle functions which are not spherically symmetric. The labour of computation is of course increased by each of these refinements.

Since the graph of $\langle H \rangle$ for the symmetric state has a minimum there will be oscillations of the nuclei along their line of centres, with a frequency determined by the curvature of the graph in the neighbourhood of the minimum. The wavelength of the resulting radiation is found by observation of infra-red band spectra to be $2\cdot27\ \mu$; the Heitler-London theory predicts a wavelength of $2\cdot08\ \mu$, and the variation method assuming an admixture of homopolar and ionic terms gives $2\cdot11\ \mu$.

The Heitler-London method has been used also to calculate the interactions between pairs of atoms with closed electron shells, such as helium or neon. In these cases it is found that the interaction energy is positive at all distances, a result which is consistent with the fact that the rare-gas molecules are monatomic.

Problems

(1) Using the operators $S_z = \frac{1}{2}\{\sigma_z(1) + \sigma_z(2)\}$ and $S^2 = \frac{1}{2}\{3 + \sigma(1).\sigma(2)\}$ introduced in chapter 4 for the spin of a two-electron system, along with eqns. (4.14), show that the symmetric and anti-symmetric spin-functions of the helium atom represent triplet and singlet states respectively.

(2) Use the Hamiltonian (7.7) for the hydrogen molecule and the trial function

$$A\phi_1 + B\phi_2 = A\,\psi_a(1)\,\psi_b(2) + B\,\psi_a(2)\,\psi_b(1)$$

where A and B are parameters to be determined.

With the abbreviations

$$H_{11} = \int\phi_1 H\phi_1 d\tau_1 = \int\phi_2 H\phi_2 d\tau_2 = H_{22}$$
$$H_{12} = \int\phi_1 H\phi_2 d\tau_1 d\tau_2 = \int\phi_2 H\phi_1 d\tau_1 d\tau_2 = H_{21}$$
$$S^2 = \int\phi_1\phi_2 d\tau_1 d\tau_2$$

show that the minimizing of $\langle H \rangle$ with respect to both A and B leads to a secular equation for $\langle H \rangle$ whose roots are

$$\langle H \rangle = \frac{H_{11} + H_{12}}{1 + S^2} \quad \text{and} \quad \frac{H_{11} - H_{12}}{1 - S^2}$$

and interpret this.

(3) The function

$$U(R) = U_0\{\varepsilon^{-2(R - R_0)/a} - 2\varepsilon^{-(R - R_0)/a}\},$$

called the *Morse potential*, is often used to represent analytically the lower curve of Fig. 7.4. Show that the value of U/U_0 has a minimum value of -1 when $R = R_0$. With $a = R_0/2$, expand $U(R)$ about its minimum and hence show that near the minimum it resembles a parabolic (harmonic oscillator) potential well. Show that this is also the case for the effective potential obtained by combining $U(R)$ with a centrifugal potential $K(K+1)\hbar^2/2MR^2$, and find the characteristic oscillator frequency in either case.

(4) The ion H^- would consist of a nucleus of charge $+1$ and two electrons. The calculations of pp. 148-149 are relevant in principle but the numerical results have to be modified by the introduction of scale-factors. Show that the perturbation calculation, suitably modified, predicts for the H^- ion a ground-

state energy of $(-2 \times 13\cdot6 + 17)$ eV $= -10\cdot2$ eV, and that the corresponding variation calculation gives

$$-\frac{e^2}{4\pi\varepsilon_0 a_0} \times \left(\frac{11}{16}\right)^2 = -12\cdot9 \text{ eV}.$$

Note that this means that the H^- ion is less stable than, and will therefore tend to decay into, a hydrogen atom and a free electron.

CHAPTER EIGHT

QUANTUM STATISTICS

General remarks about indistinguishability

The discussion in chapter 7 of the state-function of a many-particle system shows that the counting of the possible states of such systems will give different answers in quantum mechanics from those we should expect on the basis of classical ideas. If n identical particles are to be distributed over n different states, we can form $n!$ different products of single-particle state-functions, and according to the ideas of classical physics these would represent different degenerate states of the compound system. But we saw that these $n!$ products had to be formed into an anti-symmetric linear combination, and that there was one such combination, representing one quantum-mechanical state. In quantum mechanics then we do not distinguish between states which can be transformed into one another by the interchange of two or more identical particles.

In fact we adopt the view that identical particles are indistinguishable not only because they are identical but also because of the overlapping of their state-functions. In the state-function of the complex system this indistinguishability is represented by the linear superposition with equal amplitudes of all possible products of the single-particle state-functions; the states represented by the various products are themselves indistinguishable, and are therefore regarded as all representing the same state.

Sometimes it is convenient to regard a system as composed of units, each containing several fundamental particles. For example, when trying to calculate the equation of state of a gas it is convenient to think of the gas as consisting, not of protons, neutrons and electrons, but of molecules; each molecule of course contains several elementary particles. If the interactions between different molecules are very small compared with the interactions between the elementary particles within any one molecule, the representation of the system by means of the state-functions of the elementary particles would be unnecessarily complicated and general. If the molecule contains an

166

even number p of elementary particles, the bodily interchange of two molecules interchanges an even number of elementary particles. If the state-function of the whole system is expressed in terms of the elementary-particle state-functions, it must be an anti-symmetric combination of them; the interchange of any pair of them multiplies it by -1, the interchange of p pairs multiplies it by $(-1)^p$ and if p is even there is no resultant change of sign. From this it follows that the total state-function is a *symmetric* linear combination of those groupings of state-functions which represent complete molecules.†

Units whose representative functions combine symmetrically, like atoms or molecules containing even numbers of elementary particles, do not obey the Pauli principle, for as we saw on p. 146 the symmetric combination does not vanish when two of its component state-functions are identical. In this case, then, there is no limitation on the number of particles in a given state, but we still have to regard as one state those configurations which differ only through the inter-change of indistinguishable units.

Since in quantum mechanics the enumeration of the states of a many-particle system gives different results from those obtained in classical mechanics, quantum mechanics leads to different results in statistical calculations; in fact there are two branches of quantum statistics, one applying to systems with symmetrical state-functions, the other to systems with anti-symmetrical state-functions. The feature common to both branches of quantum statistics is a method of enumeration which does not distinguish between the various con-figurations which are formed by permuting the units of the system over different single-unit states; the feature which differentiates them is the possibility of multiple occupancy of states in the statistics of 'symmetric systems', and its exclusion in the statistics of 'anti-symmetric systems'.

We can quickly see that the classical and the two quantum systems of counting states give different results, from a simple example. Suppose we want to distribute two particles over three cells; we label the cells a, b and c; in the classical case we label the particles x and y, while in the quantum cases we label them – indistinguishably – as x and x. Then the possible states are

† A full and rigorous discussion of this point is given by Ehrenfest and Oppen-heimer in *Phys. Rev.*, 1931, 37, pp. 333-8.

	Classical			Quantum 'symmetric'			Quantum 'anti-symmetric'	
a	b	c	a	b	c	a	b	c
x	y	0	x	x	0	x	x	0
y	x	0						
0	x	y	0	x	x	0	x	x
0	y	x						
y	0	x	x	0	x	x	0	x
x	0	y						
x, y	0	0	x, x	0	0			
0	x, y	0	0	x, x	0			
0	0	x, y	0	0	x, x			
Total number	9			6			3	

We shall now calculate for the general case the number of ways of distributing a specified number of particles over configurations of different energies, using each of the three forms of statistics, in order to find the most probable distributions.

We shall assume that N particles are distributed over a number of states which are specified by their energies. Suppose there are g_1 single-particle states or 'cells' with energy ϵ_1, g_2 cells with energy $\epsilon_2, \ldots g_s$ cells with energy $\epsilon_s, \ldots$ etc.; and suppose also that the number of particles is less than the number of cells. We want to predict the most probable number of particles in each cell.

(i) Classical case – the Boltzmann statistics

The number of ways in which N particles can be divided up into groups with n_1 in the first group, n_2 in the second, $\ldots n_s$ in the sth group, $\ldots$ etc., is

$$\frac{N!}{\prod_s n_s!}. \tag{8.1}$$

If the particles in each group are entered in the cells of that group, any number in each, there are $g_s^{n_s}$ ways of distributing n_s particles over g_s cells. Hence the total number of recognizably different distributions is

$$W_B = N! \prod_s \frac{g_s^{n_s}}{n_s!}. \tag{8.2}$$

A more useful expression for our purpose is that for $\log W_B$, which is of course closely related to the entropy of the distribution. If the numbers we are dealing with are large enough we may use Stirling's Theorem for the logarithm of the factorial of a large number; it is often written as

$$\log n! \to n \log n - n = n(\log n - 1) \approx n \log n.$$

Using this, we find from (8.2) that

$$\log \frac{W_B}{N!} = \sum_s n_s(\log g_s - \log n_s). \tag{8.3}$$

The total energy of the distribution is

$$E = \sum_s n_s \epsilon_s \tag{8.4}$$

and the total number of particles in it is

$$N = \sum_s n_s. \tag{8.5}$$

Suppose that the numbers n_s are chosen to give the equilibrium, or most probable, distribution. Then $\log W_B$ is unaltered by any small variations in the n_s which do not alter E and N. Hence the n_s must satisfy the three conditions:

$$\delta \log \frac{W_B}{N!} = \sum_s (\log g_s - \log n_s - 1)\delta n_s = 0 \tag{8.6a}$$

$$\delta E = \sum_s \epsilon_s \delta n_s = 0 \tag{8.6b}$$

$$\delta N = \sum_s \delta n_s = 0. \tag{8.6c}$$

Let us multiply (8.6b) by a constant $-\mu$ having the dimensions of [energy]$^{-1}$, and multiply (8.6c) by a dimensionless constant $-\lambda$, and add, to obtain

$$\sum_s (\log g_s - \log n_s - 1 - \mu\epsilon_s - \lambda)\delta n_s = 0.$$

μ and λ may be chosen so as to make any two of the brackets in this summation vanish, say the first and second. Then, if we vary n_1, n_2 and n_r only, so as to keep $\log W$ constant, it follows that

$$-\log \frac{n_r}{g_r} = 1 + \mu\epsilon_r + \lambda \qquad \text{for any } r$$

$$\therefore \quad \frac{n_r}{g_r} = K \varepsilon^{-\mu\epsilon_r}.$$

It is shown in text-books on heat that if log W is to be proportional to the entropy, $\mu = 1/kT$ (see e.g. Planck, *Theory of Heat*, Macmillan, 1932, pp. 242 et seq.) so we can write for the probability that a cell with energy ϵ will be occupied at temperature T

$$\frac{n}{g} = K\varepsilon^{-\epsilon/kT} \tag{8.7}$$

which is a well-known result of classical statistics.

We shall now develop the analogous arguments for the two types of quantum statistics.

(ii) 'Symmetric' case – Bose-Einstein statistics

Since the particles are indistinguishable the various arrangements which led to expression (8.1) for the classical case must be counted simply as one. But we still have to calculate the number of ways of distributing n_s particles among the g_s states with energy ϵ_s, taking account of the *number* of particles in each cell, but disregarding their order.

In fact it simplifies the calculation if we do take account of the ordering to start with, and we can argue as follows: Of the n_s particles to be placed in the g_s cells, the first may be placed in any one of g_s positions; the second in any one of $g_s + 1$ positions, i.e. in any one of the $g_s - 1$ unoccupied cells or in the occupied cell either to right or left of the particle already there, the third in any one of $g_s + 2$ positions, i.e. $(g_s - 2) + 4$ if the first two were in separate cells, $g_s - 1 + 3$ if they were in the same cell; and so on, the last being placed in any one of $g_s + n_s - 1$ positions. The number of arrangements is then

$$g_s(g_s+1)(g_s+2)\ldots(g_s+n_s-1) = \frac{(g_s+n_s-1)!}{(g_s-1)!}.$$

But of these the $n_s!$ permutations of the particles are indistinguishable, and by taking the order into account we over-estimated by this factor. The number of recognizably different arrangements of n_s particles distributed over g_s cells is therefore

$$\frac{(g_s+n_s-1)!}{n_s!\,(g_s-1)!}.$$

Then the *total* number of recognizably different distributions is found, by multiplying together all the expressions like the above for the groups containing $n_1, n_2, \ldots, n_s, \ldots$ particles respectively, to be

$$W_{BE} = \prod_s \frac{(g_s + n_s - 1)!}{n_s! \, (g_s - 1)!}. \tag{8.8}$$

We shall now calculate the equilibrium distribution derived from (8.8) in two distinct cases.

Black-body radiation. This was the first application (1924) of the Bose-Einstein statistics. We consider the radiation enclosed in a cavity of volume V. The energy of a quantum of frequency v_s is hv_s, which we write as ϵ_s. The total energy of the radiation can then be written as

$$E = \sum_s n_s hv_s = \sum_s n_s \epsilon_s. \tag{8.9}$$

Equations (8.8) and (8.9) are analogous to (8.2) and (8.4) of the discussion of the classical case; we have in the present case no analogue of (8.5), for radiation quanta may be annihilated and created – absorbed and emitted – and the total number is therefore uncertain. If the distribution specified by the n_s is the equilibrium one, then small variations in the n_s which do not alter E do not alter $\log W$, and so

$$\delta \log W_{BE} = \sum_s \log \frac{n_s + g_s}{n_s} \delta n_s = 0 \tag{8.10a}$$

(after using Stirling's Theorem) and

$$\delta E = \sum_s \epsilon_s \delta n_s = 0. \tag{8.10b}$$

If μ is a constant with dimensions [energy]$^{-1}$, (8.10a) and (8.10b) combine into

$$\sum_s \left(\log \frac{n_s + g_s}{n_s} - \mu \epsilon_s \right) \delta n_s = 0. \tag{8.11}$$

Choosing μ to make, say, the first term in this summation vanish, we can then vary n_1 and n_r only, so as to keep $\log W_{BE}$ constant. It follows that

$$\log \frac{n_r + g_r}{n_r} = \mu \epsilon_r \qquad \text{for } any \text{ } r$$

and therefore that

$$\frac{n + g}{n} = \varepsilon^{\mu \epsilon}$$

and

$$\frac{n}{g} = \frac{1}{\varepsilon^{\mu\epsilon}-1}. \tag{8.12}$$

We now require an expression for g, the number of cells with energy in the neighbourhood of ϵ.

Suppose a wave-system is set up in a rectangular box three of whose sides, of length a_1, a_2 and a_3, lie along the x-, y- and z-axes respectively. The possible standing-wave patterns are represented by functions like

$$\sin k_1 x \ . \ \sin k_2 y \ . \ \sin k_3 z$$

where k_1, k_2 and k_3 are the components of the wave-vector $\mathbf{k}$. For a standing-wave system

$$k_1 = \frac{\pi n_1}{a_1}, \qquad k_2 = \frac{\pi n_2}{a_2}, \qquad k_3 = \frac{\pi n_3}{a_3},$$

n_1, n_2 and n_3 being positive integers. Since

$$k_1{}^2 + k_2{}^2 + k_3{}^2 = k^2 = \left(\frac{2\pi}{\lambda}\right)^2$$

we have

$$\frac{n_1{}^2}{a_1{}^2} + \frac{n_2{}^2}{a_2{}^2} + \frac{n_3{}^2}{a_3{}^2} = \frac{4}{\lambda^2} \ .$$

The points whose coordinates are the positive integers n_1, n_2, n_3 form a regular lattice in one octant of a three-dimensional space, and represent in that n-space the normal modes of vibration of the standing-wave system. The number of normal modes with wavelength greater than λ_m is the number of lattice points within one octant of the ellipsoid

$$\frac{n_1{}^2}{\left(\dfrac{2a_1}{\lambda_m}\right)^2} + \frac{n_2{}^2}{\left(\dfrac{2a_2}{\lambda_m}\right)^2} + \frac{n_3{}^2}{\left(\dfrac{2a_3}{\lambda_m}\right)^2} = 1.$$

If the ellipsoid is large enough this is simply the volume of one of its octants, i.e.

$$\frac{1}{8} \frac{4\pi}{3} \frac{8a_1 a_2 a_3}{\lambda^3} = \frac{4\pi}{3} \frac{V}{\lambda^3}$$

where $V = a_1 \, a_2 \, a_3$ is the volume of the box.

This may also be interpreted as the number of normal modes with frequency less than ν if we put $\nu = c/\lambda$, so that it becomes

$$\frac{4\pi V}{3c^3} v^3.$$

In the case of light waves the number of modes is twice as great, since two independent states of polarization are allowed. Taking this into account, we find by differentiation that the number of states with frequencies between v and $v + \delta v$ is

$$g(v)\delta v = \frac{8\pi V}{c^3} v^2 \delta v.$$

Putting this for g,† and remembering that $\epsilon = hv$, we get

$$n = \frac{8\pi V}{c^3} \frac{v^2 \delta v}{\epsilon^{\mu h v} - 1}.$$

As before, we must put $\mu = 1/kT$; the energy density in the spectrum, u_v, is then given by

$$u_v \delta v = \frac{nhv}{V} = \frac{8\pi h}{c^3} \frac{v^3 \delta v}{\epsilon^{hv/kT} - 1}. \tag{8.13}$$

This is Planck's Radiation Law.

Bose-Einstein gas in equilibrium. The molecules of most gases contain an even number of elementary particles, so at normal temperatures and pressures they will obey Bose-Einstein rather than classical statistics. Since classical statistical mechanics has proved successful in its application to the description of the gaseous state it seems that the Bose-Einstein distribution for a normal gas should reduce to the Boltzmann distribution. We shall investigate this point. The equilibrium state is now specified by three conditions, analogous to (8.6a), (8.6b) and (8.6c); two of these are (8.10a) and (8.10b), and the third expresses the constancy of the number of gas molecules,

$$\delta N = \sum_s \delta n_s = 0. \tag{8.10c}$$

† The correctness of the assumption that all the states represented by lattice points in an ellipsoidal shell in n-space are degenerate, and differ in energy from those in the adjacent shells, is not at once obvious, and the uncertainty principle has to be invoked to justify it. The states represented by the lattice points are not infinitely sharp, because the lifetime of a photon in one of these states is finite; hence the lattice point has to be imagined as 'smeared out', and if this smear extends over a region occupied by several lattice points the corresponding levels are degenerate. Light waves, for instance, normally are not coherent over distances greater than about $10^7\lambda$, so the energy of the corresponding state is unsharp, the uncertainty being about 1 part in 10^7, or (say) 10^{-19} erg. In a cubical box of side 1 cm. the number of normal modes for visible radiation in this energy range is about 10^7; the modes within this energy range can be regarded as degenerate. Similar arguments can be adduced in the case of, for instance, the energy-states of the conduction electrons in a metal.

Using undetermined multipliers μ and λ we combine these into

$$\sum_s \left(\log \frac{n_s + g_s}{n_s} - \mu\epsilon_s - \lambda \right) \delta n_s = 0.$$

Arguing as before, we find from this that

$$\frac{n_r + g_r}{n_r} = \varepsilon^{\mu\epsilon_r + \lambda} \qquad \text{for any } r,$$

and so, putting $\mu = 1/kT$, we get

$$n = \frac{g}{\varepsilon^{\lambda + \epsilon/kT} - 1}. \tag{8.14}$$

The energy of the molecules is $p^2/2m$ (p being the momentum), so

$$\epsilon = \frac{p^2}{2m}, \qquad \delta\epsilon = \frac{1}{m} p\delta p.$$

For a standing-wave system in an enclosure of volume V, the number of wave-modes with wavelength greater than λ is, as we have seen,

$$f_\lambda = \frac{4\pi}{3} \frac{V}{\lambda^3}.$$

Using de Broglie's relation $p = h/\lambda$ this gives

$$f_p = \frac{4\pi V}{3h^3} p^3,$$

and the number with momenta between p and $p + \delta p$ is, by differentiation,

$$g(p)\delta p = \frac{4\pi V}{h^3} p^2 \delta p.$$

In terms of the energy ϵ this means that the number of states whose translational kinetic energy lies between ϵ and $\epsilon + \delta\epsilon$ is

$$g(\epsilon)\delta\epsilon = \frac{4\pi V}{h^3} (2m^3\epsilon)^{\frac{1}{2}}\delta\epsilon.$$

Substituting this for g in (8.14) gives the number of gas molecules with energies between ϵ and $\epsilon + \delta\epsilon$ as

$$\delta N_\epsilon = \frac{4\pi V}{h^3} \frac{(2m^3)^{\frac{1}{2}}\epsilon^{\frac{1}{2}}\delta\epsilon}{\varepsilon^{\lambda + \epsilon/kT} - 1}. \tag{8.15}$$

This has to be compared with the classical result derived from (8.7) which is (see e.g. Kennard, *Kinetic Theory of Gases*, McGraw-Hill, 1938, p. 47, eqn. 61b)

$$\delta N_\epsilon = \frac{2}{\pi^{\frac{1}{2}}} \frac{N}{(kT)^{\frac{3}{2}}} \, \varepsilon^{-\epsilon/kT} \, \epsilon^{\frac{1}{2}} \delta\epsilon. \tag{8.16}$$

The energy-dependent parts of these expressions differ in that the quantum result contains the quantity $\varepsilon^{\lambda+\epsilon/kT} - 1$ where the classical result has $\varepsilon^{-\epsilon/kT}$. Writing $\varepsilon^{-\lambda} = A$, these become similar if

$$\frac{\varepsilon^{\epsilon/kT}}{A} \gg 1$$

i.e. if A is very small. When this is so, (8.15) becomes

$$\delta N_\epsilon = \frac{4\pi V}{h^3} (2m^3)^{\frac{1}{2}} A\varepsilon^{-\epsilon/kT} \epsilon^{\frac{1}{2}} \delta\epsilon$$

which is the same as (8.16) provided

$$A = \frac{Nh^3}{V(2\pi mkT)^{\frac{3}{2}}}.$$

(This expression for A is not a general one; it is valid only for small A.)

In a gas at N.T.P. in which N/V is of the order of 10^{19} per c.c., A is indeed small – for hydrogen it is about 3×10^{-3}, and for gases of higher molecular weight it is smaller still.

A will tend to increase if N/V increases, or if T decreases. A therefore becomes larger when the low energy levels are more densely populated; it is when this happens that the difference between the classical and quantal methods of representing and counting degenerate states becomes important. A is called the 'degeneracy parameter', and increases towards unity as the energy levels become densely populated. (If A became greater than 1, δN_ϵ might become negative, which would be absurd.) The condition that A is small can be pictured as meaning that the volume per particle is large compared with the cube of the de Broglie wavelength of particles of mass m and kinetic energy kT, so that the distance between the particles is large compared with their de Broglie wavelength.

(iii) *'Anti-symmetric' case – Fermi-Dirac statistics*

The second form of quantum statistics – the statistics of systems whose state-functions are anti-symmetric, and which obey the Pauli principle – is the statistics of assemblies of elementary particles and of all systems whose spin is half-integral, as is the case with some atoms and nuclei. In fact any 'unit' which contains an odd number of elementary particles has half-integral spin and obeys Fermi-Dirac statistics; photons and units containing an even number of elementary particles have integral spin and obey Bose-Einstein statistics.

The Fermi-Dirac statistics refer to those indistinguishable particles of which only one may be put into each cell. In view of the assumption of indistinguishability the various arrangements counted by (8.1) for the classical case are now counted as one, and we merely have to compute the number of ways of choosing n_s cells for occupation out of g_s; this number is of course

$$_{g_s}C_{n_s} = \frac{g_s!}{n_s!(g_s - n_s)!}$$

and so

$$W_{FD} = \prod_s \frac{g_s!}{n_s!\,(g_s - n_s)!}. \tag{8.17}$$

We then find, using Stirling's Theorem,

$$\log W_{FD} = \sum_s \left(\log g_s! - \log n_s! - \log(g_s - n_s)!\right)$$

$$= \sum_s \left(g_s \log g_s - n_s \log n_s - (g_s - n_s)\log(g_s - n_s)\right).$$

If we want to find the equilibrium distribution for an 'electron gas' – for instance, the conduction electrons in a metal – we use the subsidiary equations

$$E = \sum_s n_s \epsilon_s\,,$$

$$N = \sum_s n_s\,,$$

and the equilibrium is then defined by

$$\delta \log W_{FD} = \sum_s \log \frac{g_s - n_s}{n_s} \delta n_s = 0$$

$$\delta E = \sum_s \epsilon_s\,\delta n_s = 0$$

$$\delta N = \sum_s \delta n_s = 0.$$

Combining these with the aid of undetermined multipliers μ and λ gives

$$\sum_s \left(\log \frac{g_s - n_s}{n_s} - \mu \epsilon_s - \lambda \right) \delta n_s = 0.$$

As before it follows that for any r

$$\log \frac{g_r - n_r}{n_r} = \mu \epsilon_r + \lambda$$

and, with $\mu = 1/kT$,

$$n = \frac{g}{\varepsilon^{\lambda + \epsilon/kT} + 1} = \frac{g}{A^{-1} \varepsilon^{\epsilon/kT} + 1}. \tag{8.18}$$

Substituting (cf. p. 174)

$$g(\epsilon) \delta \epsilon = 2 \frac{4\pi V}{h^3} (2m^3 \epsilon)^{\frac{1}{2}} \delta \epsilon \tag{8.19}$$

in which the factor 2 allows for the two opposite directions of the electron spin, we find for the number of electrons with energies between ϵ and $\epsilon + \delta \epsilon$

$$\delta N_\epsilon = \frac{8\pi V}{h^3} \frac{(2m^3)^{\frac{1}{2}} \epsilon^{\frac{1}{2}} \delta \epsilon}{A^{-1} \varepsilon^{\epsilon/kT} + 1}. \tag{8.20}$$

In this case the degeneracy parameter may range from very small to very large values. If it is small (8.20) tends to the classical form (8.16) with

$$A = \frac{1}{2} \frac{Nh^3}{V(2\pi mkT)^{\frac{3}{2}}}.$$

If A is large, at low temperatures δN_ϵ varies as $\epsilon^{\frac{1}{2}}$; this dependence comes from the expression (8.19) for the density of the energy levels. In fact we can write

$$\delta N_\epsilon = F(\epsilon) \epsilon^{\frac{1}{2}} \delta \epsilon$$

where the *Fermi function* $F(\epsilon)$ is the probability that a level of energy ϵ is occupied and states a general property of systems obeying the exclusion principle, while the factor $\epsilon^{\frac{1}{2}}$ represents the density distribution of the energy levels in the specific physical system whose properties are under discussion. For large A and low temperatures *all* the low-lying levels are occupied, so the distribution-in-energy of the electrons coincides with the distribution-in-energy of the energy levels.

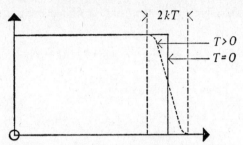

FIG. 8.1. The Fermi function for $T=0$ and $T>0$.

The electron gas in a metal

We shall now consider in a little more detail the application of (8.20) to an electron gas in thermal equilibrium; the conduction electrons in a metal can be thought of, in first approximation at any rate, as forming such a gas. The ratio of the degeneracy parameter for an electron to that for the hydrogen molecule, in the limit when A is small, is

$$\frac{A_e}{A_{H_2}} = \tfrac{1}{2}(2 \times 1837)^{\frac{3}{2}} \qquad \therefore \ A_e = A_{H_2} \times 1 \cdot 1 \times 10^5.$$

Since for hydrogen gas at N.T.P., with $N/V \approx 10^{19}$ per c.c., we saw that $A_{H_2} = 3 \times 10^{-3}$, it would appear that the electron gas in a metal, where $N/V \approx 10^{23}$, must be highly degenerate, so $A \gg 1$. This means that the distribution will differ little from that at $0°$ K, at which temperature the N lowest levels will be occupied by the N electrons, and all the higher levels will be vacant. $F(\epsilon)$ must then be rectangular as shown in Fig. 8.1, terminating at some limiting energy ϵ_0 which we shall now determine.

The number of energy levels up to the one with energy $\epsilon_0 = p_0^2/2m$ is from the argument following (8.14)

$$N = 2\frac{4\pi V}{3h^3} p_0^{\,3},$$

N being also the number of electrons in the completely degenerate system. If we put $N/V = n =$ the density of electrons, we have

$$\epsilon_0 = \frac{h^2}{2m}\left(\frac{3n}{8\pi}\right)^{\frac{2}{3}} \tag{8.21}$$

$$= 3 \cdot 6 \times 10^{-15} \times n^{\frac{2}{3}} \ \text{eV}.$$

If $n = 10^{23}$ per c.c., $\epsilon_0 = 7 \cdot 8$ eV. This is very much greater than kT at the temperatures at which metals are solid.

We can now relate ϵ_0 to the degeneracy parameter. Reverting to (8.18),

$$\frac{n}{g} = \frac{1}{\varepsilon^{\lambda + \epsilon/kT} + 1}$$

is the probability that a level of energy ϵ is occupied at temperature T. This probability should be independent of the origin of the energy scale – since the addition of any arbitrary potential energy should not affect the distribution – and we can make this so by putting $\lambda = -\epsilon'/kT$ so that

$$\frac{n}{g} = \frac{1}{\varepsilon^{(\epsilon - \epsilon')/kT} + 1}.$$

Then

$$\delta N_\epsilon = \frac{8\pi V}{h^3} \frac{(2m^3)^{\frac{1}{2}} \epsilon^{\frac{1}{2}} \, \delta\epsilon}{\varepsilon^{(\epsilon - \epsilon')/kT} + 1}.$$

At a temperature very little above the absolute zero, and for energies such that

$$\epsilon < \epsilon' \quad \text{and} \quad \left| \frac{\epsilon - \epsilon'}{kT} \right| \gg 1,$$

$$\delta N_\epsilon \to \frac{8\pi V}{h^3} (2m^3)^{\frac{1}{2}} \epsilon^{\frac{1}{2}} \delta\epsilon.$$

At the same temperature and for energies ϵ such that

$$\epsilon > \epsilon' \quad \text{and} \quad \left| \frac{\epsilon - \epsilon'}{kT} \right| \gg 1, \qquad \delta N_\epsilon \to 0.$$

It follows that ϵ' must be the same as ϵ_0, and so

$$\delta N_\epsilon = \frac{8\pi V}{h^3} \frac{(2m^3)^{\frac{1}{2}} \epsilon^{\frac{1}{2}} \delta\epsilon}{\varepsilon^{(\epsilon - \epsilon_0)/kT} + 1}.$$

For a highly degenerate system the degeneracy parameter and the Fermi energy are therefore related through

$$A = \varepsilon^{\epsilon_0/kT}$$

or

$$\log A = \frac{h^2}{2mkT} \left(\frac{3n}{8\pi} \right)^{\frac{2}{3}}.$$

This is a limiting form, appropriate for large A. For a metal at room temperature $A = \varepsilon^{7\cdot8/0\cdot025} = \varepsilon^{312}$ which is indeed large.

The Fermi function varies rapidly only in the range between $\epsilon_0 - kT$ and $\epsilon_0 + kT$. This means that the only electrons affected by thermal agitation are the relatively small number in this energy range. Those much lower in energy cannot be excited for there are no vacant levels into which they can be raised by an energy increment of kT. Hence, although there are 'free electrons' to take part in thermal and electrical conduction, there are very few, *relative to the number of atoms*, to contribute to the specific heat by sharing in the exchange of thermal energy. The specific heat of metals is therefore very close to the classical value of Dulong and Petit, which was calculated on the assumption that only the atoms share in the thermal agitation.

The Fermi-Dirac statistics was first applied to the study of the electronic properties of metals by Pauli and Sommerfeld in 1927.

The Thomas-Fermi model of the atom

Fermi-Dirac statistics may be applied to the problem of finding an approximation to the charge-distribution in a many-electron atom. The method is much simpler than that of Hartree and Fock, and though it reproduces none of the fine detail which the Hartree method shows – the shell-structure, for instance – the results of this statistical calculation which is due to Thomas and Fermi are frequently useful.

Rather as in the Hartree method the electrons are supposed to move in the potential due to the nucleus and the averaged charge-distribution of the electrons, but there is an important difference of detail in the way this assumption is framed. In the Hartree method each electron is supposed to move in the potential due to the nucleus and the *other* electrons, whereas in the Thomas-Fermi model the potential which is calculated is that due to the nucleus and *all* the electrons: it is therefore the potential experienced by an infinitesimal test charge, rather than that experienced by an electron. If the number of electrons is enormously large this distinction is negligible.

It is supposed that the electrons are grouped as densely as possible, so that they have the greatest degeneracy allowed by Fermi-Dirac statistics, and that the potential energy $V(r)$ varies so slowly that many electrons can be localized within a volume over which $V(r)$ is sensibly constant. The greatest possible kinetic energy of a bound electron at a distance r from the nucleus is $-V(r)$. From (8.21) it follows that the maximum density of electrons in this region is

$$n(r) = \frac{\{-2mV(r)\}^{\frac{3}{2}}}{3\pi^2\hbar^3}. \qquad (8.22)$$

Now the charge density $\rho(r) = en(r)$ is related to the electrostatic potential $V(r)/e$ by Poisson's equation

$$\frac{1}{e}\nabla^2 V = -\frac{\rho}{\varepsilon_0}$$

(where ε_0 is again the electric constant of free space) so that

$$\nabla^2 V = -\frac{e^2}{\varepsilon_0} n(r) = -\frac{e^2\{-2mV(r)\}^{\frac{3}{2}}}{3\pi^2\varepsilon_0\hbar^3}. \qquad (8.23)$$

This equation for $V(r)$ has to be solved subject to two boundary conditions: firstly, for small values of r the potential is that due to the unscreened nucleus, so if the atomic number is Z

$$\lim_{r \to 0} V(r) = -\frac{Ze^2}{4\pi\varepsilon_0 r} \qquad (8.24a)$$

or

$$\lim_{r \to 0} rV(r) = -\frac{Ze^2}{4\pi\varepsilon_0};$$

secondly, for a neutral atom the net charge within a sphere of very large radius tends to zero, so the potential tends to zero more rapidly than $1/r$ and

$$\lim_{r \to \infty} rV(r) = 0. \qquad (8.24b)$$

Assuming that the charge-distribution is spherically symmetric we write (8.23) as

$$\frac{1}{r^2}\frac{d}{dr} r^2 \frac{d}{dr}(-V(r)) = \frac{e^2\{-2mV(r)\}^{\frac{3}{2}}}{3\pi^2\varepsilon_0\hbar^3}. \qquad (8.25)$$

The form of the boundary conditions suggests that we might proceed by putting

$$V(r) = -\frac{Ze^2}{4\pi\varepsilon_0 r}\chi(r)$$

where $\chi = 1$ at $r = 0$ and $\chi \to 0$ when $r \to \infty$. A change of variable to $x = r/b$ with

$$b = \tfrac{1}{2}\left(\frac{3\pi}{4}\right)^{\frac{2}{3}} \frac{4\pi\varepsilon_0\hbar^2}{me^2 Z^{\frac{1}{3}}} = \frac{0\cdot 885\, a_0}{Z^{\frac{1}{3}}} \qquad (8.26)$$

puts (8.25) into the dimensionless form

$$\frac{d^2\chi}{dx^2} = \left(\frac{\chi^3}{x}\right)^{\frac{1}{2}}$$

with $\chi = 1$ when $x = 0$ and $\chi \to 0$ as $x \to \infty$.

When this equation is solved, either graphically or numerically, $n(r)$ is computed from (8.22). The resulting distribution is shown in Fig. 7.3; it is a good 'smoothed out' approximation to the distribution given by the self-consistent field calculation, and is sometimes used as a first trial solution in the Hartree method.

One result of the Thomas-Fermi calculation which is frequently employed can be extracted from (8.26). This equation shows that the charge-distribution is similar for all Z, but that the linear scale depends on Z, the radius of an atom of atomic number Z varying inversely as $Z^{\frac{1}{3}}$. In fact, since for the hydrogen atom the expectation value of the radius is $\tfrac{3}{2}a_0$, we may expect that for an atom of atomic number Z the mean radius will be about

$$\frac{3a_0}{2Z^{\frac{1}{3}}} = \frac{0\cdot 79}{Z^{\frac{1}{3}}}\,\text{Å}.$$

Problems

(1) By constructing a table analogous to that on p. 168 or otherwise, find, for each of the three types of statistics, the probability that when three particles are distributed over three cells, all three particles will be in the same cell.

The conclusion that this 'bunching' is most probable for particles obeying Bose-Einstein statistics, and least probable for particles obeying Fermi-Dirac statistics, is generally true. Show that this is so.

(2) Show that in an electron gas at $0°$ K the mean electron energy is $3\epsilon_0/5$. Show also that at $0°$ K the electron gas exerts a pressure

$$P = \frac{2}{5}n\epsilon_0$$

where n and ϵ_0 have the meanings they have in (8.21). Check that for the electron gas in a metal this pressure is about 10^6 atmospheres.

(3) The compressibility of a substance is defined as

$$K = -\frac{1}{V}\frac{dV}{dP}.$$

Writing the expression for P in problem (2) in the more explicit form

$$P = \frac{\hbar^2}{5m}(3\pi^2)^{\frac{2}{3}}\left(\frac{N}{V}\right)^{5/3}$$

show that the compressibility of the electron gas is given by

$$K^{-1} = \frac{\hbar^2}{3m}(3\pi^2)^{\frac{2}{3}}\left(\frac{N}{V}\right)^{5/3} = \tfrac{5}{3}P.$$

Is this compatible with observed values for the compressibilities of metals?

(4) From the expression for the energy distribution of conduction electrons in a metal (p. 179) show that the mean energy of a conduction electron increases by only a few per cent above the value $3\varepsilon_0/5$ as the temperature is raised from $0°$ K to the melting point (which may be assumed to be in the region of 10^3 °K).

(5) Show that (8.24b) is equivalent to the assertion that the total charge due to the electrons within a sphere of very large radius tends to Ze; show also that the radius of a sphere which encloses a fixed fraction of the electrons in a 'Thomas-Fermi atom' is proportional to $1/Z^{\frac{1}{3}}$.

CHAPTER NINE

THE MOTION OF A PARTICLE IN WAVE-MECHANICS

Representation of a particle by a wave-packet

It follows from the uncertainty principle that we cannot have precise knowledge of the simultaneous values of the position and momentum coordinates of a particle. The values of x and p can be thought of as being represented by probability distribution functions $|\psi(x)|^2$ and $|\phi(p)|^2$ whose minimum spreads are related. Thus the derivation preceding (2.17) shows that if the function $|\psi(x)|^2$ is Gaussian with standard deviation Δx the uncertainty attaching to our simultaneous knowledge of the momentum cannot be less than $\Delta p = \hbar/2\Delta x$.

The state-function $\psi(x)$, which defines the probability of observing the particle between x and $x + \delta x$ as $|\psi(x)|^2 \delta x$, may be represented by a superposition of the functions $\varepsilon^{ipx/\hbar}$ which are eigenfunctions of the momentum – since

$$\frac{\hbar}{i} \frac{\partial}{\partial x} \varepsilon^{ipx/\hbar} = p \, \varepsilon^{ipx/\hbar}$$

– for all real values of p. The momentum eigenfunctions form a continuous set, and a superposition of them will generally be represented by an integral, rather than by a sum of discrete terms. The momentum eigenfunction $\varepsilon^{ipx/\hbar}$ represents a state in which x is completely indeterminate, for $|\varepsilon^{ipx/\hbar}|^2 \delta x = 1 \times \delta x$, so the position probability density is independent of position. The expansion of $\psi(x)$ in terms of momentum eigenfunctions is

$$\psi(x) = \int_{-\infty}^{+\infty} \phi(p) \, \varepsilon^{ipx/\hbar} \, dp \tag{9.1}$$

where $|\phi(p)|^2$ is proportional to the probability that a measurement of the momentum of a particle in the state $\psi(x)$ will yield a value close to p. The form of (9.1) shows that $\psi(x)$ and $\phi(p)$ are related as Fourier Transform and Inverse, so that

$$\phi(p) = \frac{1}{2\pi} \int_{-\infty}^{+\infty} \psi(x) \, \varepsilon^{-ipx/\hbar} \, dx \tag{9.2}$$

184

in which the $\varepsilon^{ipx/\hbar}$ are regarded as position eigenfunctions, with associated probability amplitudes $\psi(x)$. In this context the uncertainty principle affirms – what is well known in Fourier analysis – that a function $\psi(x)$ which is vanishingly small except in the range Δx must contain components whose p-values have a spectrum whose breadth varies inversely as Δx, and in fact $\Delta x \cdot \dfrac{\Delta p}{\hbar} \approx 1$.

The momentum eigenfunction $\varepsilon^{ipx/\hbar}$ represents a travelling wave whose wavelength is, by inspection, $\lambda = \dfrac{2\pi\hbar}{p} = \dfrac{h}{p}$; this is called the 'de Broglie wavelength'. The superposition of momentum eigenfunctions which constitutes $\psi(x)$ is called a *wave-packet*. If the momentum distribution function $\phi(p)$ is symmetric about some value p_0, for that packet $\langle p \rangle_\psi = p_0$, and the spread or uncertainty in p can be derived from $\phi(p)$.

A wave-packet whose form is specified at a certain time $t=0$ spreads with the passage of time. The one-dimensional Schrödinger equation for a particle of mass m moving in a field-free region is

$$-\frac{\hbar^2}{2m}\frac{\partial^2 \psi}{\partial x^2} = i\hbar \frac{\partial \psi}{\partial t} \tag{9.3}$$

which can be written

$$\frac{\partial \psi}{\partial t} = D \frac{\partial^2 \psi}{\partial x^2} \quad \text{if} \quad D = \frac{i\hbar}{2m}.$$

This is like the equation of diffusion, or of heat conduction, and it is easy to verify that a solution is

$$\psi(x, t) = \frac{C}{\{D(t+\tau)\}^{\frac{1}{2}}}\, \varepsilon^{-x^2/4D(t+\tau)}. \tag{9.4}$$

If we write $2D\tau$ as a real positive quantity a^2,

$$\psi(x, t) = \frac{2^{\frac{1}{2}}C}{\left\{a^2 + \dfrac{i\hbar t}{m}\right\}^{\frac{1}{2}}}\, \varepsilon^{-x^2/2(a^2 + i\hbar t/m)}$$

and therefore

$$\psi^* \psi = \frac{2C^2}{a\left\{a^2 + \left(\dfrac{\hbar t}{ma}\right)^2\right\}^{\frac{1}{2}}}\, \varepsilon^{-x^2/(a^2 + (\hbar t/ma)^2)}. \tag{9.5}$$

Comparison with (2.17) shows that (9.5) represents a packet whose maximum is stationary at $x=0$ and whose standard deviation is

$$\Delta x = \left\{ \left(\frac{a}{2}\right)^2 + \left(\frac{\hbar t}{2ma}\right)^2 \right\}^{\frac{1}{2}}.$$

Now this resembles the expression, familiar in statistical theory, for the standard deviation in the sum of two independently fluctuating variables whose standard deviations are respectively $\frac{a}{2}$ and $\frac{\hbar t}{2ma}$.

When $t=0$, $\Delta x=\frac{a}{2}$; also when $t=0$, $\Delta p\,\Delta x=\frac{\hbar}{2}$, so $\Delta p=\frac{\hbar}{a}$, and

$\frac{\hbar t}{2ma}=\frac{\Delta p}{2m}t$. The rate of spreading of the packet is therefore represented by $\Delta p/2m$ – a conclusion whose physical interpretation is obvious. In the absence of forces there is no reason for Δp to change, and a packet which is initially a minimal packet – one for which $\Delta p\,\Delta x=\hbar/2$ when $t=0$ – will at any later or earlier time have a greater uncertainty product. For large enough times $\Delta p\,\Delta x$ is in fact proportional to $|t|$. See also problem (6) on p. 217.

Oscillating wave-packet

While the wave-packet representing a free particle spreads with time this will not happen with the wave-packet which represents a bound particle. This is strikingly exemplified by a wave-packet formed by superposing solutions of the Schrödinger equation for a one-dimensional harmonic oscillator. This packet can be written as

$$\psi(x,t) = \sum_0^\infty a_n u_n(x)\, \varepsilon^{-iE_n t/\hbar} = \varepsilon^{-i\omega t/2} \sum_0^\infty a_n u_n(x)\, \varepsilon^{-in\omega t}$$

where ω is the classical oscillator frequency. Apart from the phase factor $\varepsilon^{-i\omega t/2}$ this represents a function which is periodic in time with period $2\pi/\omega$, for the summation represents a harmonic series.

The functions $u_n(x)$ in the summation are the normalized one-dimensional oscillator energy eigen-functions

$$u_n(x) = N_n H_n(\alpha x)\, \varepsilon^{-\frac{1}{2}\alpha^2 x^2}$$

where $\alpha = (m\omega/\hbar)^{\frac{1}{2}}$, and the normalizing constant is $N_n = (\alpha/\pi^{\frac{1}{2}}2^n n!)^{\frac{1}{2}}$ It was shown by Schrödinger† that if the coefficients a_n are

$$a_n = (\alpha a)^n\, \varepsilon^{-\alpha^2 a^2/4}/(2^n n!)^{\frac{1}{2}}$$

† *Collected Papers on Wave Mechanics*, pp. 41-44.

then

$$| \psi(x, t) |^2 = (\alpha/\pi^{\frac{1}{2}}) \, \varepsilon^{-\alpha^2(x - a \cos \omega t)^2}.$$

This is a distribution of Gaussian profile and constant width, which performs an oscillation of amplitude a and angular frequency ω. The most probable result of a measurement of the energy is the value of $(n+\frac{1}{2})\hbar\omega$ corresponding to the largest a_n, which is the one associated with the energy eigenstate u_n for which $(n+\frac{1}{2})\hbar\omega = \frac{1}{2}m\omega^2 a^2$; thus the main contribution to $\psi(x)$ comes from energy eigenstates whose energies are in the neighbourhood of the energy of the classical oscillator whose amplitude is a.

By referring to eqn. (3.13), and to the discussion of the minimum-uncertainty property of the wave-function $\varepsilon^{-m\omega x^2/2\hbar} = \varepsilon^{-\frac{1}{2}\alpha^2 x^2}$ on pp. 38 and 39, it is easy to verify that the oscillating wave-packet we are discussing here is one which has at all times the same profile as the minimum-uncertainty wave-function of (2.17) or (3.13); when $a \to 0$ the oscillating packet tends to the form (3.13) precisely, in which case there is only one term in the superposition, but for non-zero a, although the breadth of the packet is the same, the number of terms contributing appreciably to the summation increases with increase of a.

When this type of wave-packet was first studied, it was of interest mainly because of the close correspondence between the properties of these oscillating wave-packets for very large (i.e. macroscopic) values of a, and the classical harmonic oscillator. Much more recently interest in these superpositions has again become keen as a result of their introduction into quantum optics by Glauber (1963) to represent 'coherent states' of optical radiation fields.

Motion of a wave-packet in a field of force

It was shown by Ehrenfest (1926) that a wave-packet moves in accordance with Newton's Laws in the sense that the expectation values of x and p, averaged over the wave-packet, satisfy the equations

$$\frac{d}{dt} \langle x \rangle = \frac{1}{m} \langle p \rangle$$

$$\frac{d}{dt} \langle p \rangle = \left\langle -\frac{\partial V}{\partial x} \right\rangle.$$

Provided then the expectation values give a good representation of the corresponding classical variables – which they will do if V does not vary much across the packet – the packet behaves in a field of force like a classical particle. This result is known as *Ehrenfest's Theorem*.

We first show that the packet as a whole travels with velocity $\langle p \rangle / m$. We consider a three-dimensional packet $\psi(r)$, and calculate the x-component of its velocity. This is

$$\frac{d}{dt} \langle x \rangle = \frac{d}{dt} \int \psi^* x \psi \, d\tau = \int \frac{\partial \psi^*}{\partial t} x \psi \, d\tau + \int \psi^* x \frac{\partial \psi}{\partial t} d\tau$$

where the integration is over all space. Substituting for $\dfrac{\partial \psi}{\partial t}$ and $\dfrac{\partial \psi^*}{\partial t}$ from the time-dependent equation

$$-\frac{\hbar^2}{2m} \nabla^2 \psi + V(r) \psi = i\hbar \frac{\partial \psi}{\partial t}$$

and its complex conjugate, we find

$$\frac{d}{dt} \langle x \rangle = -\frac{i\hbar}{2m} \{ \int (\nabla^2 \psi^*) x \psi \, d\tau - \int \psi^* x \nabla^2 \psi \, d\tau \}. \tag{9.6}$$

Now by Green's theorem

$$\int \{ (\nabla^2 \psi^*) x \psi - \psi^* (\nabla^2 x \psi) \} d\tau$$
$$= \int \{ (\nabla \psi^*) x \psi - \psi^* (\nabla x \psi) \} dS$$

where the surface integral is over an infinitely distant bounding surface; the wave-packet must vanish all over this surface, since it represents a localized particle, so the surface integral vanishes. Hence

$$\int (\nabla^2 \psi^*) x \psi \, d\tau = \int \psi^* (\nabla^2 x \psi) \, d\tau.$$

Substitution of this in (9.6) gives

$$\frac{d}{dt} \langle x \rangle = -\frac{i\hbar}{2m} \int \{ \psi^* (\nabla^2 x \psi) - \psi^* x \nabla^2 \psi \} \, d\tau$$

$$= -\frac{i\hbar}{2m} \int \psi^* \left\{ x \nabla^2 \psi + 2 \frac{\partial \psi}{\partial x} - x \nabla^2 \psi \right\} d\tau$$

$$= \frac{1}{m} \int \psi^* \frac{\hbar}{i} \frac{\partial \psi}{\partial x} \, d\tau$$

$$\therefore \frac{d}{dt} \langle x \rangle = \frac{1}{m} \langle p_x \rangle. \tag{9.7}$$

In the same kind of way we can show that the rate of change of $\langle p_x \rangle$ is proportional to $\left\langle -\dfrac{\partial V}{\partial x} \right\rangle$. For

$$\frac{d}{dt}\langle p_x \rangle = \frac{\hbar}{i}\frac{d}{dt}\int \psi^* \frac{\partial \psi}{\partial x}\,d\tau$$

$$= \frac{\hbar}{i}\left\{ \int \frac{\partial \psi^*}{\partial t}\frac{\partial \psi}{\partial x}\,d\tau + \int \psi^* \frac{\partial}{\partial x}\frac{\partial \psi}{\partial t}\,d\tau \right\}$$

$$= \int \left(-\frac{\hbar^2}{2m}\nabla^2 \psi^* + V\psi^* \right)\frac{\partial \psi}{\partial x}\,d\tau + \int \psi^* \frac{\partial}{\partial x}\left(\frac{\hbar^2}{2m}\nabla^2 \psi - V\psi \right)d\tau$$

$$= \int \psi^* \left(V\frac{\partial \psi}{\partial x} - \frac{\partial}{\partial x}(V\psi) \right)d\tau$$

$$= \int \psi^* \left(-\frac{\partial V}{\partial x} \right)\psi\,d\tau$$

$$\therefore \frac{d}{dt}\langle p_x \rangle = \left\langle -\frac{\partial V}{\partial x} \right\rangle. \tag{9.8}$$

This establishes Ehrenfest's Theorem.

Expectation velocity and group velocity of a wave-packet

It has been shown above (equation (9.7)) that, for a wave-packet representing a particle moving in a potential field, the relationship between the expectation values of a cartesian position coordinate and the associated momentum is the same as the corresponding relationship in classical mechanics. A different method of estimating the velocity of a wave-packet, using the concept of *group velocity*, pre-dated Ehrenfest's discussion of the problem. Later in this chapter it will be convenient to make use of the group velocity, so the justification for its use will now be explained, and its connection with the expectation values appearing in (9.7) will be established.

First, we generalize (9.1) and represent the state-function for a particle moving in one dimension by the time-dependent super-position

$$\Psi(x, t) = \int_{-\infty}^{+\infty} \phi(p, t)\,\varepsilon^{i(px - Et)/\hbar}\,dp \tag{9.9}$$

where

$$E = \frac{p^2}{2m} + V(x). \tag{9.10}$$

To find the value of the state-function at any point $x = x_0$ and time $t = t_0$ we put these values for x and t in (9.9) and perform the integration with respect to p. Let us for the moment denote $(px - Et)/\hbar$ by $\alpha(p)$. Then the exponential factor in the integrand is an oscillatory function of $\alpha(p)$: the real and imaginary parts of the exponential function will oscillate between the limits ± 1 and $\pm i$ respectively as the value of p is swept through the range of integration. These oscillations will be rapid in any part of that range in which $\alpha(p)$ is a rapidly varying function of p, which is to say, when $\frac{\partial}{\partial p} \alpha(p)$ differs markedly from zero. In any part of the range of integration in which the oscillations of the exponential function are rapid compared with the variation of $\phi(p, t)$, neighbouring positive and negative contributions to the integral will very largely balance one another, and such regions will contribute little to the integral. On the other hand, there will be substantial contributions to the integral from ranges of p in which $\phi(p, t)$ is appreciable and $\frac{\partial}{\partial p} \alpha(p) = 0$. This condition on $\alpha(p)$ is called the *condition of stationary phase*, and was introduced in the discussion of hydrodynamic waves by Lord Rayleigh.

Since $\alpha(p) = (px - Et)/\hbar$, the stationary-phase condition can be written as

$$x - \frac{\partial E}{\partial p} \cdot t = 0 \qquad (9.11)$$

where $\frac{\partial E}{\partial p}$ clearly has the dimensions of a velocity, and we shall denote it by v_g. Then the equation

$$v_g = \frac{\partial E}{\partial p} \qquad (9.12)$$

recalls Hamilton's equation

$$\dot{q} = \frac{\partial H}{\partial p},$$

and shows that v_g is just the velocity with which a classical particle would move in the field of force in which the wave-packet is moving. Differentiation of (9.10) then shows that

$$v_g = p/m. \qquad (9.13)$$

It follows that, if the distribution-in-p represented by $\phi(p, t)$ at time t is concentrated in a narrow range around p_0, the superposition of these components of the wave-packet can result in an appreciable amplitude $\Psi(x, t)$ only in a region of space in the neighbourhood of a point whose coordinate x varies with time according to the kinematic relation (9.11), i.e.

$$\frac{x}{t} = \left(\frac{\partial E}{\partial p}\right)_{p = p_0} = \frac{p_0}{m}$$

$$\therefore \quad x = (p_0/m)t \quad \text{from (9.12) and (9.13).}$$

The velocity v_g, called the group velocity, is thus the velocity with which the peak region of the probability density $\left|\Psi(x, t)\right|^2$ travels through space. We know, from the discussion following (9.5), that when the distribution-in-p is narrow and p is well-defined, the distribution-in-x will be broad, and the wave-packet will spread only slowly. Also, if the distribution-in-p is narrow and concentrated around a value p_0, the expectation value of p will be close to p_0, and will coincide with p_0 if the distribution is symmetrical about that value. Then (9.13) agrees with (9.7).

The situation is more complicated if the distribution-in-p is broad. Then, if p_0 is the value of p for which $\phi(p, t)$ is a maximum, and p_1 is any other value of p for which $\phi(p_1, t)/\phi(p_0, t)$ is not very far from unity, the components of the wave-packet whose momenta lie close to p_1 will make an appreciable contribution to $\Psi(x, t)$ in a region which moves so that its coordinate x satisfies the equation

$$\frac{x}{t} = \left(\frac{\partial E}{\partial p}\right)_{p = p_1} = \frac{p_1}{m} \tag{9.14}$$

and the amplitude resulting from the superposition of these components travels with velocity p_1/m. Hence there is a range of propagation velocities, that range being $\Delta p/m$; and the wave-packet will spread, its breadth increasing at a rate proportional to $\Delta p/m$ (cf. p. 186). Assigning the appropriate statistical weight $\left|\phi(p, t)\right|^2$ to each of the velocities (9.14) associated with the wave-packet, we find that the expectation value of the group velocity is

$$\langle v_g \rangle = \frac{1}{m} \int_{-\infty}^{+\infty} \left|\phi(p, t)\right|^2 p \cdot dp = \langle p \rangle/m$$

which is consistent with (9.7).

Probability current density

If we multiply the time-dependent Schrödinger equation

$$i \frac{\partial \psi}{\partial t} = -\frac{\hbar^2}{2m} \nabla^2 \psi + V\psi$$

from the left by ψ^*, multiply the complex conjugate of this equation from the right by ψ, and subtract, we get

$$i\hbar \left\{ \psi^* \frac{\partial \psi}{\partial t} + \frac{\partial \psi^*}{\partial t} \psi \right\} = -\frac{\hbar^2}{2m} \{\psi^* \nabla^2 \psi - (\nabla^2 \psi^*)\psi\}$$

$$\therefore \frac{\partial}{\partial t} (\psi^* \psi) = \frac{i\hbar}{2m} \nabla \{\psi^* \nabla \psi - (\nabla \psi^*)\psi\}$$

$$= -\frac{\hbar}{2im} \operatorname{div} \{\psi^* \operatorname{grad} \psi - (\operatorname{grad} \psi^*)\psi\}. \qquad (9.15)$$

When we put $\psi^* \psi = \rho(\mathbf{r}, t)$ and

$$\frac{\hbar}{2im} \{\psi^* \operatorname{grad} \psi - (\operatorname{grad} \psi^*)\psi\} = \mathbf{S}(\mathbf{r}, t), \qquad (9.16)$$

(9.15) is seen to resemble the continuity equation of hydrodynamics:

$$\frac{\partial \rho}{\partial t} + \operatorname{div} \mathbf{S} = 0.$$

Since ρ is a probability density $\mathbf{S}$ may be called a *probability current density* or *probability flux*. Then, just as in hydrodynamics the equation of continuity ensures the conservation of mass in space and time, so here equation (9.15) ensures the conservation of total probability in space and time.

To illustrate the utility of the concept of probability current density we shall calculate the magnetic moment of the state represented by the hydrogen-like wave-function ψ_{nlm}, on the assumption that the vector $e\mathbf{S}$ can represent an electric current density.

We first note from (9.16) that

$$\mathbf{S} = \frac{\hbar}{im} \times (\text{imaginary part of } \psi^* \operatorname{grad} \psi).$$

This means that there is no component of $\mathbf{S}$ for any coordinate on which ψ depends in a *real* way. The only coordinate on which

$$\psi_{nlm} = R_{nl}(r) P_l^{|m|} (\cos \theta) \varepsilon^{im\phi}$$

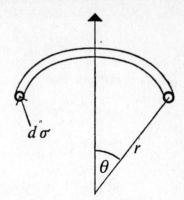

FIG. 9.1.

depends in an imaginary way is ϕ, so we need to calculate only the ϕ-component of grad ψ. Now

$$\text{grad}_\phi = \frac{1}{r \sin \theta} \frac{\partial}{\partial \phi}$$

$$\therefore \psi^* \text{grad}_\phi \psi = \{R_{nl}(r) P_l^{|m|}(\cos \theta)\}^2 \, \varepsilon^{-im\phi} \frac{im}{r \sin \theta} \, \varepsilon^{im\phi}$$

$$= \frac{im}{r \sin \theta} |\psi|^2$$

so

$$S_\phi = \frac{\hbar}{m_e} \frac{m}{r \sin \theta} |\psi|^2.$$

Here we again have to write the electronic mass as m_e to differentiate it from the quantum number m. The corresponding electric current density is

$$j_\phi = eS_\phi = \frac{e\hbar}{m_e} \frac{m}{r \sin \theta} |\psi|^2,$$

circulating about the z-axis. The current in an annulus of cross-section $d\sigma$ and radius $r \sin \theta$ (Fig. 9.1) generates a magnetic moment

$$dM = \frac{\mu_0 e\hbar}{m_e} \frac{m}{r \sin \theta} |\psi|^2 \, \pi r^2 \sin^2 \theta \, d\sigma$$

$$= \frac{\mu_0 e\hbar}{m_e} m |\psi|^2 \, \pi r \sin \theta \, d\sigma.$$

The volume of this annulus is $2\pi r \sin \theta \, d\sigma = d\tau$, say, so

$$dM = \frac{\mu_0 e\hbar}{2m_e} \, m \, | \, \psi \, |^2 \, d\tau.$$

The total magnetic moment is therefore

$$M = \frac{\mu_0 e\hbar}{2m_e} \, m \int | \, \psi \, |^2 \, d\tau$$

$$= \frac{\mu_0 e\hbar}{2m_e} \, m \text{ (since } \psi \text{ is normalized to unity)}$$

$$\therefore \ M = m \text{ Bohr magnetons.}$$

Penetration of potential barriers

We have seen in chapter 5 that the wave-function of a particle need not be zero in a region in which its total energy is less than its potential energy. In classical mechanics a particle cannot enter such a region. In classical wave-optics, on the other hand, light waves may enter and pass through regions in which, because of refractive index changes, their velocity of propagation becomes imaginary (see Sommerfeld, *Optics*, Academic Press, 1954, pp. 32-33). There is an analogous effect in the quantum mechanics of particles, where as we shall see a beam of particles may be partially transmitted by a thin potential barrier even when the kinetic energy of the incident particles is less than the height of the barrier, Fig. 9.2.

Let us suppose that a beam of particles of mass m and momentum p_1 parallel to the x-axis is incident from the left on the potential barrier of Fig. 9.2; for the present the kinetic energy $p_1{}^2/2m$ will be assumed to be greater than V_2. For negative x the solution of the Schrödinger equation will represent a right-going (incident) and a left-going (reflected) wave:

$$\underline{x < 0:} \qquad -\frac{\hbar^2}{2m} \frac{d^2\psi_1}{dx^2} = E\psi_1$$

$$\therefore \ \psi_1(x) = A\,\varepsilon^{ik_1 x} + B\,\varepsilon^{-ik_1 x}$$

where

$$E = \frac{p_1{}^2}{2m} = \frac{\hbar^2 k_1{}^2}{2m}$$

$$\therefore \ v_1 = \frac{\hbar k_1}{m}.$$

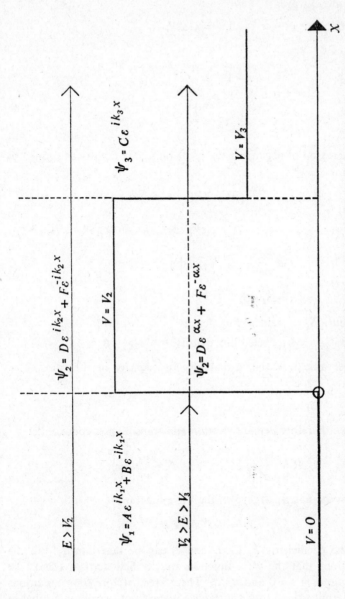

$$\psi_1 = A\epsilon^{ik_1x} + B\epsilon^{-ik_1x}$$

$$\psi_2 = D\epsilon^{ik_2x} + F\epsilon^{-ik_2x}$$

$$\psi_2 = D\epsilon^{\alpha x} + F\epsilon^{-\alpha x}$$

$$\psi_3 = C\epsilon^{ik_3x}$$

$E > V_2$

$V_2 > E > V_3$

$V = V_2$

$V = V_3$

$V = 0$

Fig. 9.2. Diagram for discussion of penetration of rectangular potential barrier by corpuscular stream.

For large positive x (i.e. for $x > a$) the solution should represent a transmitted wave,

$$\underline{x > a:} \qquad\qquad \psi_3 = C\varepsilon^{ik_3 x}$$

where

$$E - V_3 = \frac{\hbar^2 k_3{}^2}{2m}$$

$$\therefore \; v_3 = \frac{\hbar k_3}{m}.$$

In the region of negative x the probability flux density as defined by (9.16) is

$$S_1 = \frac{\hbar}{2im}\{(A^* \varepsilon^{-ik_1 x} + B^* \varepsilon^{ik_1 x})ik_1(A\varepsilon^{ik_1 x} - B\varepsilon^{-ik_1 x})$$

$$- ik_1(-A^* \varepsilon^{-ik_1 x} + B^* \varepsilon^{ik_1 x})(A\varepsilon^{ik_1 x} + B\varepsilon^{-ik_1 x})\}$$

$$= \frac{\hbar k_1}{m}(|A|^2 - |B|^2)$$

$$= S_i + S_r$$

where $\quad S_i$ = incident flux density $\quad = \; v_1|A|^2$

and $\quad S_r$ = reflected flux density $\quad = \; -v_1|B|^2.$

In the same way the probability flux density in the transmitted beam is

$$S_t = v_3|C|^2.$$

We can therefore define reflection and transmission coefficients:

$$R = \frac{|B|^2}{|A|^2}, \qquad\qquad T = \frac{v_3|C|^2}{v_1|A|^2}. \qquad (9.17)$$

Within the barrier $(0 \leqq x \leqq a)$ the wave-function is

$$\psi_2 = D\varepsilon^{ik_2 x} + F\varepsilon^{-ik_2 x}$$

and the coefficients B, C, D and F can be determined from the conditions that the wave-function and its first derivative must be continuous at $x = 0$ and $x = a$. There are therefore four conditions to determine these four constants. We are not usually interested in the coefficients D and F; instead we eliminate these and determine

B and C, from which we can find the (observable) reflection and transmission coefficients. It turns out that

$$\frac{B}{A} = \frac{(k_1-k_2)(k_1+k_2)(1+\varepsilon^{2ik_2a})}{(k_1+k_2)(k_2+k_3)+(k_1-k_2)(k_2-k_3)\,\varepsilon^{2ik_2a}}$$

$$\left(\frac{v_3}{v_1}\right)^{\tfrac{1}{2}}\frac{C}{A} = \frac{4k_1^{\tfrac{1}{2}}k_2k_3^{\tfrac{1}{2}}\,\varepsilon^{i(k_2-k_3)a}}{(k_1+k_2)(k_2+k_3)+(k_1-k_2)(k_2-k_3)\,\varepsilon^{2ik_2a}}.$$

In the special case $V_1 = V_3 = 0$, $k_1 = k_3$, and the above expressions simplify, so that eventually

$$R = \frac{|B|^2}{|A|^2} = \left\{1+\frac{4E(E-V_2)}{V_2^2\sin^2 k_2a}\right\}^{-1} \tag{9.18a}$$

$$T = \frac{|C|^2}{|A|^2} = \left\{1+\frac{V_2^2\sin^2 k_2a}{4E(E-V_2)}\right\}^{-1}. \tag{9.18b}$$

According to classical mechanics the reflection coefficient would be zero as long as $E = p_1^2/2m > V_2$, but (9.18a) shows that this will not be the case. We find instead that perfect transmission occurs only when $E/V_2 \to \infty$, or when $\sin k_2a = 0$; the latter means that $k_2a = \pi$, $2\pi, 3\pi \ldots$ etc., so the barrier contains a whole number of half wave-lengths of the wave-function (cf. the interference filter in physical optics). As V_2 increases towards E the transmission factor decreases in the way shown in Fig. 9.3, until when $E = V_2$ the value of T is

$$\left(1+\frac{mV_2a^2}{2\hbar^2}\right)^{-1}.$$

When $E < V_2$ the reflection and transmission coefficients are found by putting $k_2 = i\alpha$ in (9.18), whereupon the transmission coefficient is found to be

$$T = \left\{1+\frac{V_2^2\sinh^2\alpha a}{4E(V_2-E)}\right\}^{-1} \tag{9.19}$$

which is greater than zero, but decreases rapidly as V_2 increases. When $\alpha a \gg 1$

$$T \approx \frac{16E(V_2-E)}{V_2^2}\,\varepsilon^{-2\alpha a}.$$

The penetration of particles through potential barriers even when $E < V_2$ has been called the 'tunnel effect'; it provides an explanation of such phenomena as the spontaneous emission of α-particles by

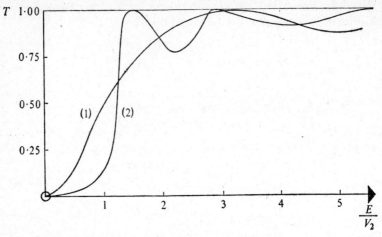

FIG. 9.3. Transmissivity of a barrier for which $V_1 = V_3 = 0$, for (1) a 'thin' barrier with $\frac{mV_2a^2}{2\hbar^2} = 1$, (2) a 'thick' barrier with $\frac{mV_2a^2}{2\hbar^2} = 10$.

atomic nuclei and the cold emission of electrons from metals in the presence of strong electric fields.

The WKB method

In physical problems potentials do not usually vary discontinuously, like that of Fig. 9.2; instead the potential varies smoothly over a finite range of the position variable. The methods used in the preceding section are not then applicable, for when the particle momentum $p = \{2m(E-V)\}^{\frac{1}{2}}$ varies continuously we can no longer find a solution of the Schrödinger equation by fitting together a small number of distinct wave-functions. In this case the wave-equation may be solved by a method of approximation which was introduced into quantum mechanics separately by Wentzel, Kramers and Brillouin, and is known as the WKB method. It will be presented here only as far as is necessary to indicate a relationship between the classical and wave-mechanical descriptions of particle motion; a very full account of it is given in Kemble's *The Fundamental Principles of Quantum Mechanics*, McGraw-Hill, 1937, § 21.

The wave-function $\psi(x) = \varepsilon^{ipx/\hbar}$ refers to the motion, in a one-dimensional region of constant potential, of a particle whose momentum is p. If the potential varies 'slowly' – and later we must consider what that means – the momentum will vary as $p =$

$\{2m(E-V(x))\}^{\frac{1}{2}}$, and we might hope to be able to use a wavefunction like $\psi = \varepsilon^{iS(x)/\hbar}$ where $S(x)$ is a (possibly) complex function of x determined by the Schrödinger equation. In fact if we write

$$\psi(x,t) = \varepsilon^{i(S(x)-Et)/\hbar}$$

and substitute in

$$i\hbar \frac{\partial \psi}{\partial t} = -\frac{\hbar^2}{2m}\frac{\partial^2 \psi}{\partial x^2} + V(x)\psi$$

we have

$$\frac{1}{2m}\left(\frac{\partial S}{\partial x}\right)^2 - (E-V) - \frac{i\hbar}{2m}\frac{\partial^2 S}{\partial x^2} = 0. \qquad (9.20)$$

In the classical limit, when $\hbar = 0$, (9.20) becomes

$$\frac{1}{2m}\left(\frac{\partial S}{\partial x}\right)^2 = E-V.$$

Now

$$\frac{p^2}{2m} = E-V \quad \text{so} \quad p = \frac{\partial S}{\partial x}$$

or, more generally, $\mathbf{p} = \text{grad } S$. This shows that the momentum is orthogonal to the surfaces of constant phase, $S(x) = $ constant. The function $S(x)$ is then Hamilton's Principal Function of classical mechanics (see Leech, *Classical Mechanics*, chapter 7).

Let us expand $S(x)$ as a power series in $\hbar$:

$$S(x) = S_0(x) + \hbar S_1(x) + \frac{\hbar^2}{2}S_2(x) + \ldots \qquad (9.21)$$

so that S becomes Hamilton's Principal Function in the limit when $\hbar$ is so small that only the first term of this expansion has to be retained. The quantal aspects of the motion will be contained in the later terms; this expansion will be useful mainly when only one or two of the terms involving $\hbar$ are appreciably greater than zero. Inserting (9.21) into (9.20) we find that

$$0 = \frac{1}{2m}\left(\frac{\partial S_0}{\partial x}\right)^2 - (E-V) + \frac{\hbar}{m}\left(\frac{\partial S_0}{\partial x}\frac{\partial S_1}{\partial x} - \frac{i}{2}\frac{\partial^2 S_0}{\partial x^2}\right)$$

$$+ \frac{\hbar^2}{2m}\left(\frac{\partial S_0}{\partial x}\frac{\partial S_2}{\partial x} + \left(\frac{\partial S_1}{\partial x}\right)^2 - i\frac{\partial^2 S_1}{\partial x^2}\right)$$

$$+ \text{ terms in higher powers of } \hbar.$$

For this equation to be true regardless of the magnitude of $\hbar$ the coefficient of each power of $\hbar$ must vanish separately, so

$$\frac{1}{2m}\left(\frac{\partial S_0}{\partial x}\right)^2 = E - V \tag{9.22a}$$

$$\frac{\partial S_0}{\partial x}\frac{\partial S_1}{\partial x} = \frac{i}{2}\frac{\partial^2 S_0}{\partial x^2} \tag{9.22b}$$

$$\frac{\partial S_0}{\partial x}\frac{\partial S_2}{\partial x} = i\frac{\partial^2 S_1}{\partial x^2} - \left(\frac{\partial S_1}{\partial x}\right)^2. \tag{9.22c}$$

From (9.22a)

$$\frac{\partial S_0}{\partial x} = \pm\{2m(E-V)\}^{\frac{1}{2}}$$

$$\therefore\ S_0(x) = \pm\int_{x_0}^{x}\{2m(E-V)\}^{\frac{1}{2}}\,dx. \tag{9.23a}$$

Substituting this in (9.22b) we can show that

$$\frac{\partial S_1}{\partial x} = \frac{i}{2}\left(\frac{\partial S_0}{\partial x}\right)^{-1}\frac{\partial^2 S_0}{\partial x^2} = \frac{i}{2}\frac{\partial}{\partial x}\log\frac{\partial S_0}{\partial x}$$

$$\therefore\ S_1 = \frac{i}{2}\log\frac{\partial S_0}{\partial x}$$

$$\therefore\ \varepsilon^{iS_1} = \left(\frac{\partial S_0}{\partial x}\right)^{-\frac{1}{2}} = \frac{1}{\{2m(E-V)\}^{\frac{1}{4}}}. \tag{9.23b}$$

Similarly, from (9.22c)

$$S_2 = \tfrac{1}{2}\frac{m\,\partial V/\partial x}{\{2m(E-V)\}^{\frac{3}{2}}} - \tfrac{1}{4}\int_{x_0}^{x}\frac{m^2\,(\partial V/\partial x)^2}{\{2m(E-V)\}^{\frac{5}{2}}}\,dx. \tag{9.23c}$$

Being proportional to the logarithm of $\partial S_0/\partial x$, S_1 may not be small compared with S_0 even when $\partial S_0/\partial x$ is small. On the other hand S_2 will be small whenever $\partial V/\partial x$ is small and $E - V$ is not too small; the term in S_2 in (9.21) is in fact small whenever

$$\left|\frac{\hbar m\,\partial V/\partial x}{\{2m(E-V)\}^{\frac{3}{2}}}\right| \ll 1. \tag{9.24}$$

The later terms in the expansion of S can be shown to be negligible provided the higher derivatives of V are small.

The meaning of (9.24) may be visualized with the help of the following argument:

We know that

$$-\frac{\partial V}{\partial x} = m\frac{d^2x}{dt^2} = mv\frac{\partial v}{\partial x} = \frac{p}{m}\frac{\partial p}{\partial x}$$

or, putting $p = \dfrac{2\pi\hbar}{\lambda}$, $\qquad -\dfrac{\partial V}{\partial x} = -\dfrac{(2\pi\hbar)^2}{m\lambda^3}\dfrac{\partial\lambda}{\partial x}.$

Hence

$$\frac{\hbar m\, \partial V/\partial x}{\{2m(E-V)\}^{\frac{3}{2}}} = \frac{(2\pi)^2\hbar^3\,\partial\lambda/\partial x}{\lambda^3}\frac{\lambda^3}{(2\pi\hbar)^3}$$

$$= \frac{1}{2\pi}\frac{\partial\lambda}{\partial x}$$

$$= \frac{1}{2\pi}\frac{\delta\lambda/\lambda}{\delta x/\lambda}.$$

The criterion (9.24) is satisfied, therefore, if the fractional change in wavelength of the wave-function $\varepsilon^{iS(x)}$ is small in a distance of one wavelength, and the potential may be said to vary slowly when this is so. This will also ensure the validity of the representation of a particle by a wave-packet in the sense of Ehrenfest's theorem.

When the above criterion is satisfied we can write

$$\psi(x) = \varepsilon^{i(S_0 + \hbar S_1)/\hbar}$$

$$= \frac{A}{\{E-V(x)\}^{\frac{1}{4}}}\varepsilon^{i/\hbar\int_{x_0}^x\{2m(E-V)\}^{\frac{1}{2}}dx} + \frac{B}{\{E-V(x)\}^{\frac{1}{4}}}\varepsilon^{-i/\hbar\int_{x_0}^x\{2m(E-V)\}^{\frac{1}{2}}dx}.$$

$$\tag{9.25}$$

Each term is of the form

$$\frac{\text{const}}{p^{\frac{1}{2}}}\varepsilon^{\pm i\,S_0(x,\,E)/\hbar},$$

and the time-dependent form is

$$\frac{\text{const}}{p^{\frac{1}{2}}}\varepsilon^{\pm i\{S_0(x,\,E)-Et\}/\hbar}.\tag{9.26}$$

A superposition of such functions will constitute a wave-packet. Let us write

$$\psi(x,t) = \int_E \varepsilon^{i\,S(x,\,t,\,E)/\hbar}f(E-E_0)\frac{dE}{p^{\frac{1}{2}}}$$

for a wave-packet whose mean energy is E_0. The phase of each component is $S(x, t, E)$, and the packet will propagate with the group velocity found by applying the condition of stationary phase, which here is most conveniently written as

$$\frac{\partial}{\partial E} S(x, t, E) = 0.$$

But

$$\frac{\partial}{\partial E} S(x, t, E) = \frac{\partial S_0}{\partial E} - t$$

so, extracting the form of $S_0(x, E)$ from (9.26) and (9.25), we see that the time-dependence of the location of the packet is expressed by

$$t(x) = \frac{\partial S_0}{\partial E} = \frac{\partial}{\partial E} \int_{x_0}^{x} \{2m(E - V)\}^{\frac{1}{2}} dx$$

$$= \int_{x_0}^{x} \left\{ \frac{m}{2(E - V)} \right\}^{\frac{1}{2}} dx$$

$$= \int_{x_0}^{x} \frac{dx}{v(x)} \quad \text{(for } V \text{ is a function of } x\text{)}.$$

The wave-packet therefore travels from x_0 to x in the time

$$t = \int_{x_0}^{x} \frac{dx}{v(x)},$$

which is the time a classical particle would take to travel the same distance, so the wave-packet moves in the field of force specified by $V(x)$ with the same velocity as a classical particle with the same total energy E.

When $E < V(x)$ the WKB solution (9.25) becomes

$$\psi = \frac{1}{\{V(x) - E\}^{\frac{1}{4}}} \left\{ A\varepsilon^{1/\hbar \int_{x_0}^{x} \{2m(V - E)\}^{\frac{1}{2}} dx} + B\varepsilon^{-1/\hbar \int_{x_0}^{x} \{2m(V - E)\}^{\frac{1}{2}} dx} \right\}.$$

$$(9.27)$$

There is then a non-vanishing solution of the wave-equation in the classically forbidden region of imaginary momenta, and this treatment is suitable for the discussion of barrier penetration. Unfortunately, although $\partial V/\partial x$ may be small throughout the whole space

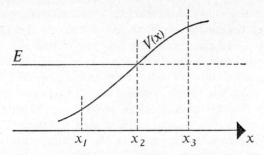

FIG. 9.4.   The WKB solutions apply to the left of x_1 and to the right of x_3, but not in the region near x_2 where the de Broglie wavelength is very large.

the value of $E-V$ becomes zero at the point x_2 (Fig. 9.4) at which a classical particle of energy E would be reflected. In the neighbourhood of x_2, then, the condition (9.24) is not satisfied. A solution like (9.25) may be found which is valid to the left of x_1, and a solution like (9.27) may be found which is valid to the right of x_3, but the joining up of the wave-function at x_2 cannot be done using the WKB solutions. In practice it may be legitimate to assume that $V(x)$ is linear in the region $x_1 x_3$, so that $V-E=C(x-x_2)$; then an accurate solution of the Schrödinger equation

$$-\frac{\hbar^2}{2m}\frac{d^2\psi(x)}{dx^2}+C(x-x_2)\psi(x) = 0$$

is found in this region and is joined to the WKB solutions which are valid beyond x_1 and x_3.

The discussion of this aspect of the WKB method would go beyond the scope of this book; Gamow and Critchfield give a complete discussion of the penetration of the nuclear potential barrier by an escaping α-particle in *Theory of Atomic Nucleus and Nuclear Energy Sources* (O.U.P., 1949, pp. 157-69), and Bohm quotes the 'connection formulae' which link the oscillatory and real exponential solutions on either side of x_2 in his *Quantum Theory*, chapter 12. The object of the more restricted discussion here has been to show how the WKB method illuminates the transition from classical to wave-mechanics.

State-functions for a conduction electron in a metal

As has already been mentioned in chapter 8, Sommerfeld originated a theory of the behaviour of conduction electrons in metals in which the metallic crystal is regarded as a rectangular potential well inside which the conduction electrons – usually one per atom – can move freely. The electronic state-functions within the crystal are then 'free-particle state-functions' of the type $\exp(\pm ikr)$, where the momentum is $\hbar k$ and the kinetic energy is $\hbar^2 k^2 / 2m$. The number of electronic states within any specified energy range is found by calculating the distribution-in-k^2 of the solutions of the wave-equation which satisfy periodic boundary conditions at the edges of the well – or (as in chapter 8) which represent the standing-wave within the well – and allowing for the association of two spin orientations with each spatial configuration.

This rectangular-well model of the metal ignores both the interactions between the electrons and the atomic structure of the crystal. Since the depth of the well is treated as a parameter to be deduced from the comparison of theoretical predictions with experimental results, the *average* contribution of the fields of all the other conduction electrons to the potential experienced by a particular conduction electron is simply one of the many factors which is subsumed in the statement of the effective well-depth; with this go the very sweeping assumptions that all temporal and spatial fluctuations in the field of the conduction electrons can be ignored, and that each conduction electron experiences *the same* average field. In this section we shall be describing a theory of a one-dimensional crystal in which the potential experienced by a single conduction electron is regarded as periodic, and we may if we wish regard this periodicity as representing, partly the potential variation due to the regularly spaced atoms in the crystal, and partly the average of the static self-consistent fields of all the conduction electrons. We shall not, however, regard the detailed form of this potential as being known or predictable *a priori*, and shall discuss its general characteristics solely in terms of its dependence on the lattice atoms.

For the interaction between a single valence electron and the core of a single atom (consisting of the nucleus and the more tightly bound electrons) the interaction potential is represented by the pair of dotted curves AA of Fig. 9.5. When a regular array of atoms is formed up on either side of this the resultant potential is as shown by the continuous lines. Low-lying levels in the individual atoms, at energy E_1, say, are hardly affected by the neighbouring atoms, and a material in which no higher levels were populated would be an insulator. Levels at E_2, on the other hand, would be lowered by the

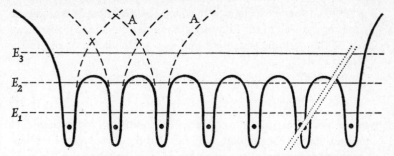

FIG. 9.5. The potential within a 'one-dimensional lattice' is periodic except at the extremities of the lattice. Electrons with energies E_1, E_2 or E_3 are all bound to the lattice, but an electron with energy E_3 is more free to move through the lattice than one with energy E_1.

widening of the individual wells due to the neighbouring atoms, and if the potential peaks above this level, separating neighbouring atoms, were low enough, an electron in such an energy state would be able to migrate fairly easily through the crystal by the tunnelling process discussed earlier in this chapter. Finally, the highest bound states within the individual atom might be well above the resultant lattice potential, except at the edge of the crystal, and an electron in such a state – with energy E_3, for example – would be virtually free within the crystal. Such electrons can no longer be associated with individual atoms: they are 'collectivized' and belong to the lattice as a whole. These are the conduction electrons.

In Sommerfeld's model it is assumed that the conduction electrons are in states sufficiently above the peaks of the effective potential to be unaffected by its periodic variations. A better description can be constructed by using the free-particle state-functions of the Sommerfeld model as zero-order state-functions in a perturbation calculation, and finding the modifications produced in these state-functions and their energies by the oscillations of the actual potential about its mean value.

Suppose, for simplicity, the crystal contains only one kind of atom, and is one-dimensional and very extensive in the positive and negative x-directions. Then the lattice constant is the same as the interatomic spacing a, and except near the edges of the crystal the potential can be expressed as a Fourier series:

$$V(x) = \sum_{q=-\infty}^{q=+\infty} v_q \exp\left(-2\pi i q x / a\right) \quad \text{for integral } q. \quad (9.28)$$

It will be convenient to set $v_0=0$, which has the effect of making the bottom of the well in the Sommerfeld model coincide with the mean value of the periodic potential, and a suitable choice of origin for x makes $v_q=v_{-q}$.

Now consider a normalized electron state-function

$$\psi_k = L^{-\frac{1}{2}}\,\varepsilon^{ikx} \qquad (9.29)$$

where L is the length of the crystal. The imposition of the boundary condition that ψ_k be periodic in L, i.e. that $\psi_k(x) = \psi_k(x+L)$, quantizes the energy since it requires that $kL=\pm 2r\pi$ where r is integral, and hence $k=\pm 2r\pi/L$ and

$$E_k = \hbar^2 k^2/2m = 2r^2\pi^2\hbar^2/mL^2. \qquad (9.30)$$

Note that there is two-fold degeneracy, since k (and therefore r) may be positive or negative without affecting E_k.

The matrix element of the perturbation between states represented by state-functions like (9.29), and corresponding to allowed wave vectors k and k', is

$$V_{k'k} = L^{-1}\int_L \varepsilon^{-i(k'-k)x}\sum_q v_q\,\varepsilon^{-2\pi iqx/a}\,dx$$

$$= L^{-1}\sum_q v_q\int_L \varepsilon^{-i(k'-k+2\pi q/a)x}\,dx.$$

The only non-vanishing term in this summation is that for which

$$k'-k+2\pi q/a = 0, \qquad (9.31a)$$

and for that term

$$V_{k'k} = v_q. \qquad (9.31b)$$

Since $v_0=0$, the term with $k'=k$, and q therefore zero, is zero for all k, i.e.,

$$V_{kk} = 0 \quad \text{for all } k. \qquad (9.31c)$$

This does not mean that there are no first-order energy changes due to the periodic potential, for we have not yet taken account of the fact, which was pointed out, following (9.30), that the zero-order state-functions are doubly degenerate. Suppose that k_1 and k_2 are a pair of k-values corresponding to a single energy. From (9.30) it is clear that $k_1 = -k_2$. We now know that of the elements in the matrix

$$\begin{bmatrix} V_{k_1k_1} & V_{k_1k_2} \\ V_{k_2k_1} & V_{k_2k_2} \end{bmatrix}$$

$V_{k_1k_1} = V_{k_2k_2} = 0$ from (9.31c), and $V_{k_1k_2} = V_{k_2k_1} = 0$ unless

$$k_1 - k_2 = 2\pi q/a$$

in which case $\qquad\qquad 2k_1 = 2\pi q/a$

$$\therefore \quad k_1 = \pi q/a.$$

Thus $V_{-k,\,k} = 0$ except for those k for which

$$q = ka/\pi = 2a/\lambda,$$

where q is, by definition, an integer.

The matrix of V between the states $L^{-\frac{1}{2}} \exp(i\pi q x/a)$ and $L^{-\frac{1}{2}} \exp(-i\pi q x/a)$ is therefore

$$V = \begin{bmatrix} 0 & v_q \\ v_q & 0 \end{bmatrix}.$$

The eigenvalues are v_q and $-v_q$, and the corresponding state-functions are

$$(\Psi_q)_+ = (2L)^{-\frac{1}{2}}(\varepsilon^{i\pi q x/a} + \varepsilon^{-i\pi q x/a})$$

$$= (2/L)^{\frac{1}{2}} \cos \pi q x/a \qquad (9.32a)$$

and $\qquad (\Psi_q)_- = (2L)^{-\frac{1}{2}}(\varepsilon^{i\pi q x/a} - \varepsilon^{-i\pi q x/a})$

$$= i(2/L)^{\frac{1}{2}} \sin \pi q x/a. \qquad (9.32b)$$

These are standing-wave state-functions whose wavelengths are integral sub-multiples of twice the lattice constant. The energies of the two solutions for any q differ because the corresponding probability densities are respectively in phase and in antiphase with the qth component of the lattice potential.

To first-order, therefore, the only states whose energies are modified by the periodic potential are those for which $k = \pi q/a$; and for these states the appropriate zero-order state-functions are those given at (9.32), and the corresponding energies are $(\hbar^2 \pi^2 q^2/2ma^2) \pm v_q$, correct to first order. For other states there is no first-order energy shift, but the state-function, for any state ψ_k for which $k\pi \neq q/a$, becomes (cf. (6.7a)):

$$(\psi)_k = L^{-\frac{1}{2}} \varepsilon^{ikx} + L^{-\frac{1}{2}} \sum_{k'} \frac{V_{k'k}}{E_k^q - E_{k'}} \varepsilon^{ik'x}$$

where $k' = k - 2\pi q/a$, from (9.31a),

$$\therefore \quad (\psi)_k = L^{-\frac{1}{2}} \varepsilon^{ikx} \left\{ 1 + \sum_q v_q \varepsilon^{-2\pi i q x/a} \bigg/ \frac{2\pi q \hbar^2}{ma} \left(k - \frac{\pi q}{a} \right) \right\}. \quad (9.33)$$

Such state-functions are used extensively in solid state physics where – with a slightly different notation – they are known as *Bloch eigenfunctions*.

(9.33) shows that the perturbed state-functions are spatially modulated, with period a. The precise form of the potential function $V(x)$ in (9.28) is not known, but the usefulness of this treatment depends on the assumption that a fairly good approximation is obtained with only a few terms in the Fourier series for $V(x)$. It will then be the case that a useful approximation to $(\psi)_k$ is obtained with only a few terms in (9.33). In particular, if k is close to one of the values $\pi q/a$ at which degeneracy occurs, *one* term in the summation is dominant, and (9.33) then approaches one of the forms (9.32).

Fig. 9.6 shows the variation with k of the kinetic energy of the unperturbed (free-particle) state-functions; this is shown as a continuous curve because the values of k, though discrete and regularly spaced, effectively form a continuum if the crystal contains a very large number of atoms. The separation-in-k between adjacent k-values is $2\pi/L$ (see the discussion preceding (9.30)); the spacing between the k-values for which the periodic lattice potential removes the degeneracy of the unperturbed states, corresponding to the various integral values of q, is π/a (see the discussion following (9.31)). The number of allowed k-values within the range bounded by two adjacent integers q is therefore $(\pi/a)/(2\pi/L) = L/2a = n/2$, say, where n is the number of atoms along the direction of k in the crystal. We shall speak of the corresponding range of energies – between $\hbar^2 \pi^2 q^2/2ma^2$ and $\hbar^2 \pi^2 (q+1)^2/2ma^2$, for any integer q – as an *energy band*. Because of the two-fold degeneracy of the state-functions $L^{-\frac{1}{2}} \exp(i|k|x)$, and the further two-fold spin degeneracy, each energy band contains $2n$ electronic energy-states. It follows from the exclusion principle that in this one-dimensional lattice each energy band can 'accommodate' $2n$ electrons, i.e. 2 electrons per atom.

Effective mass of a conduction electron

Although there is no first-order perturbation of the energies of states other than those for which $k = \pi q/a$, we shall see that there are higher-order contributions to the energy of those states for which $k \neq \pi q/a$. These contributions produce appreciable effects only for states whose k-values are in the neighbourhood of one or other of the values specified by an integer q.

The behaviour of the energy in the immediate vicinity of these critical k-values is of such interest that it is worth investigating it by a method which allows us to obtain an expansion for the energy in powers of the difference between k and the nearest value of $\pi q/a$. This method, using the variation technique, stems from the remark following (9.33), that as $k \to \pi q/a$ one term in the summation in (9.33) predominates over the others, and the state-function approaches one of the forms (9.32).

When k is close to $\pi q/a$ only one term in the summation in (9.33) has an appreciable amplitude, and we may approximate to $(\psi)_k$ by writing

$$(\psi)_k = L^{-\frac{1}{2}} \varepsilon^{ikx} (c_0 + c_q \varepsilon^{-2\pi iqx/a})/(c_0^2 + c_q^2)^{\frac{1}{2}} \qquad (9.34)$$

where the best values for c_0 and c_q are to be found by the variational method. Then, with

$$H = \frac{p^2}{2m} + V(x)$$

we have, after making use of (9.19), and the orthogonality relations for the complex exponentials,

$$(c_0^2 + c_q^2)\langle H \rangle = \left\{ \frac{\hbar^2 k^2}{2m} c_0^2 + \frac{\hbar^2}{2m} \left(k - \frac{2\pi q}{a} \right)^2 c_q^2 + 2v_q c_0 c_q \right\}.$$

The conditions for minimum $\langle H \rangle$ – that $\dfrac{\partial}{\partial c_0} \langle H \rangle$ and $\dfrac{\partial}{\partial c_q} \langle H \rangle$ are zero – give us the equations

$$\left. \begin{aligned} 2c_0 \left(\langle H \rangle - \frac{\hbar^2 k^2}{2m} \right) - 2c_q v_q &= 0 \\ -2c_0 v_q + 2c_q \left(\langle H \rangle - \frac{\hbar^2}{2m} \left(k - \frac{2\pi q}{a} \right)^2 \right) &= 0. \end{aligned} \right\} \qquad (9.35)$$

The condition that these equations for c_0 and c_q have non-trivial solutions is that the determinant of their coefficients vanishes, i.e.

$$\left(\langle H \rangle - \frac{\hbar^2 k^2}{2m} \right) \left(\langle H \rangle - \frac{\hbar^2}{2m} \left(k - \frac{2\pi q}{a} \right)^2 \right) - v_q^2 = 0.$$

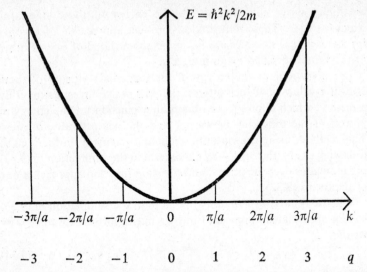

FIG. 9.6. The variation with k of the kinetic energy for the unperturbed (free-particle) state functions. The values of k corresponding to integral q are those for which the lattice potential removes the two-fold degeneracy of the unperturbed states.

Solving this to find the minimum $\langle H \rangle$ we get

$$\langle H \rangle =$$

$$\tfrac{1}{2}\left\{ \frac{\hbar^2 k^2}{2m} + \frac{\hbar^2}{2m}\left(k - \frac{2\pi q}{a}\right)^2 \pm \left[\left(\frac{\hbar^2 k^2}{2m} - \frac{\hbar^2}{2m}\left(k - \frac{2\pi q}{a}\right)^2\right)^2 + 4v_q^{\,2}\right]^{\frac{1}{2}} \right\}.$$

We have not yet made use of the fact that the trial function (9.34) was chosen for its appropriateness in the regions $k \approx \pi q/a$, but we can very quickly see that if $k = \pi q/a$

$$\langle H \rangle_q = \frac{\hbar^2 \pi^2 q^2}{2ma^2} \pm v_q, \text{ and } c_0/c_q = \pm 1,$$

which agrees with (9.32). Now let us put $k = \pi q/a + \delta$, where δ is very small, and retain in the expression for $\langle H \rangle$ only terms as far as the second order in δ. We get

$$\langle H \rangle_{q,\,\delta} = \frac{\hbar^2}{2m}\left(\frac{\pi^2 q^2}{a^2} + \delta^2\right) \pm v_q \left[1 + \left(\frac{\pi \hbar^2 \delta q}{mav_q}\right)^2\right]^{\frac{1}{2}}$$

$$\approx \frac{\hbar^2}{2m}\left(\frac{\pi^2 q^2}{a^2} + \delta^2\right) \pm v_q \pm \frac{\hbar^2 \delta^2}{m} \cdot \frac{1}{v_q} \cdot \frac{\hbar^2 \pi^2 q^2}{2ma^2}.$$

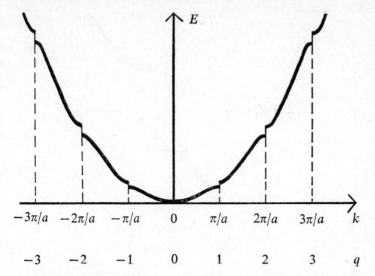

FIG. 9.7(*a*) The effect of the lattice potential perturbations is to break up the *E* vs. *k* curve of Fig. 9.6 into separate segments, with an energy gap as in Fig. 9.7(*b*) at each integral *q*.

If we write $\hbar^2 \pi^2 q^2 / 2ma^2$ as H_q, this can be rearranged as

$$\Delta H_q = \langle H \rangle_{q,\delta} - H_q = \pm v_q + \frac{\hbar^2 \delta^2}{2m}\left(1 \pm \frac{2H_q}{v_q}\right). \quad (9.36a)$$

If, as our previous use of perturbation theory has assumed, $H_q \gg v_q$, this can be further simplified and becomes

$$\Delta H_q = \langle H \rangle_{q,\delta} - H_q = \pm v_q \pm \frac{\hbar^2 \delta^2}{2m} \cdot \frac{2H_q}{v_q}. \quad (9.36b)$$

It follows from the mode of deriving this result that the two plus signs belong to one solution, and the two minus signs to the other. In the vicinity of the point on the curve of Fig. 9.6 which corresponds to $k = \pi/a$, $E = H_q$, the information presented in (9.36) is displayed on Fig. 9.7(*b*). The inclined dashed line represents a portion of the curve $E = \hbar^2 k^2 / 2m$; v_q is assumed to be negative. Then (9.36) shows that the curve of energy *vs.* δ (or *k*) – known as a *dispersion curve* – has two branches, each of which has zero slope where $\delta = 0$, and these branches must merge smoothly into the dashed curve when $|\delta|$ is no longer small. The complete dispersion curve is therefore as shown in Fig. 9.7(*a*).

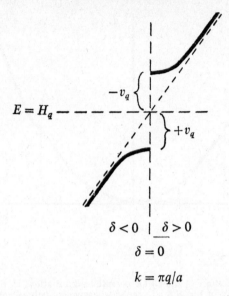

FIG. 9.7(b).   Detail of dispersion curve in the neighbourhood of an energy gap.

The quantity $m^* = m/(1 \pm 2H_q/v_q)$ whose reciprocal appears in (9.36a) is called the *effective mass* of an electron in a state characterized by the wave-vector $\pi q/a + \delta$; the negative and positive signs apply, one on either side of the 'zone-boundary' at $\delta = 0$, so the effective mass has quite different values on either side of the zone-boundary.

Momentum, kinetic energy and effective mass

The justification for the use of the name 'effective mass' for m^* appears if we consider the dynamical behaviour of an electron as the magnitude of its wave-vector k approaches one of the values $\pi q/a$. For simplicity, let us suppose the electron is in a state such that $0 < k < \pi/a$, and let us assume – as seems plausible – that an electric field applied to the crystal in such a direction as to accelerate the electron to the right causes the value of k to increase, so that Newton's second law of motion takes the form $\hbar \dot{k} = e\mathscr{E}$. We know from Ehrenfest's Theorem that this would lead to a valid statement about the time-dependence of k for a wave-packet representing a free particle. However, the state-functions we are using here represent stationary states of a system for which k is a *good quantum number*, and is not a continuous variable. When the electric field is applied k is no longer a good quantum number, but physical intuition encourages us to believe that the physical behaviour will not be *very* different in the presence of the field, so long as the field is weak. We therefore hope that we shall not be led astray by making two assumptions which, in strict logic, must seem inconsistent – that we may use state-functions labelled by values of k to represent electron states in the applied electric field, and that we may represent the dynamical behaviour of packets formed from such components by means of the foregoing transcription of Newton's second law. Then, if the value of k is initially far enough from π/a, the spatial part of the state-function is initially $L^{-\frac{1}{2}} \exp(ikx)$, the expectation value of the momentum is $\hbar k$, and the energy is $\hbar^2 k^2/2m$. Under the influence of the applied electric field the value of k will approach π/a, and the state-function then begins to assume the form of (9.34) with $q=1$. This can be pictured as a superposition of a right-going wave with momentum $\hbar k$ and statistical weight $c_0^2/(c_0^2 + c_1^2)$, and a left-going wave with momentum $\hbar(k - 2\pi/a)$ and statistical weight $c_1^2/(c_0^2 + c_1^2)$. As k becomes nearly equal to π/a, the statistical weight associated with the left-ward momentum of the left-going component grows very rapidly, and this outweighs the increase of right-ward momentum associated with the increase of k; the expectation value of the momentum of the electron consequently decreases, becoming zero when $k=\pi/a$, for then $c_1 = c_0$ and the state-function is (9.32a).

This does not imply the break-down of any conservation principle. An impulse is applied to the electron by the electric field, and momentum is imparted to the system of electron-plus-lattice. If k is remote from one of the critical values the momentum is transferred entirely to the electron, but as k nears any of the values $\pi q/a$ the interaction between lattice and electron becomes effective in transferring momentum from the electron to the lattice. In picturesque terms, the electron wave-function is strongly reflected by the periodic lattice potential, and the conservation of momentum in this Bragg-like reflection implies a transfer of momentum to the lattice.

If however we look merely at the interaction of the electron with the applied electric field, we can formally interpret the paradox that the change of momentum of the electron is in the direction opposite to the applied force by assigning to the electron a negative 'effective mass'.

Let us consider in more detail the behaviour for small δ ($= k - \pi/a$)

of the state-function (9.34). The equations (9.35) can be solved for the ratio c_0/c_q, and give

$$\frac{c_0}{c_q} = \left\{ \langle H \rangle - \frac{\hbar^2}{2m} \left(k - \frac{2\pi q}{a} \right)^2 \right\} \bigg/ v_q.$$

In the region $k \lesssim \pi/a$ this becomes

$$\frac{c_0}{c_1} = \left\{ \langle H \rangle_1 - \frac{\hbar^2}{2m} \left(k - \frac{2\pi}{a} \right)^2 \right\} \bigg/ v_1$$

$$\therefore \ \frac{c_0}{c_1} v_1 = H_1 + v_1 + \frac{\hbar^2 \delta^2}{2m} \cdot \frac{2H_1}{v_1} - \frac{\hbar^2}{2m} \left(\delta - \frac{\pi}{a} \right)^2 \qquad \text{from} \quad (9.36a)$$

$$= H_1 + v_1 - \frac{\hbar^2 \delta^2}{2m} \left(1 - \frac{2H_1}{v_1} \right) + \frac{\hbar^2}{2m} \cdot \frac{2\pi \delta}{a} - H_1$$

$$\therefore \ \frac{c_0}{c_1} = 1 + \frac{\hbar^2}{2m} \cdot \frac{2\pi \delta}{a} \cdot \frac{1}{v_1} - \frac{\hbar^2 \delta^2}{2m} \left(1 - \frac{2H_1}{v_1} \right) \frac{1}{v_1}$$

$$\approx 1 + \frac{\hbar^2}{2m} \cdot \frac{2\pi \delta}{a} \cdot \frac{1}{v_1} \qquad \text{for very small } \delta.$$

With $\delta = 0$, $c_0/c_1 = 1$; and with k just less than π/a, δ is negative so that, with negative v_1, $c_0 > c_1$ as we expected.

Thus the state-function is

$$\psi_{k = \frac{\pi}{a} + \delta} = L^{-\frac{1}{2}} \varepsilon^{i(\frac{\pi}{a} + \delta)x} (c_0 + c_1 \varepsilon^{-2\pi i x/a})/(c_0{}^2 + c_1{}^2)^{\frac{1}{2}}$$

$$= L^{-\frac{1}{2}} \varepsilon^{i\delta x} (c_0 \varepsilon^{i\pi x/a} + c_1 \varepsilon^{-i\pi x/a})/(c_0{}^2 + c_1{}^2)^{\frac{1}{2}}.$$

Hence

$$\langle p \rangle = \int_0^L \psi^* \frac{\hbar}{i} \frac{\partial}{\partial x} \psi \, dx$$

$$= \frac{c_0{}^2}{c_0{}^2 + c_1{}^2} \hbar \left(\delta + \frac{\pi}{a} \right) + \frac{c_1{}^2}{c_0{}^2 + c_1{}^2} \hbar \left(\delta - \frac{\pi}{a} \right)$$

$$= \frac{c_0{}^2 - c_1{}^2}{c_0{}^2 + c_1{}^2} \cdot \frac{\hbar \pi}{a} + \frac{c_0{}^2 + c_1{}^2}{c_0{}^2 + c_1{}^2} \cdot \hbar \delta.$$

From this, many interesting results follow. When k is not close to π/a, $c_0 = 1$ and $c_1 = 0$, and $\langle p \rangle = \hbar(\pi/a + \delta) = \hbar k$. When k is exactly equal to π/a, $c_1 = c_0$, $\delta = 0$, and $\langle p \rangle = 0$. When k is just less than π/a,

$$\frac{c_0{}^2 - c_1{}^2}{c_0{}^2 + c_1{}^2} \approx c_0 - c_1.$$

Now suppose $c_0 = 1+s$, $c_1 = 1-s$, where s is small, which gives $c_0^2 + c_1^2 = 1$ apart from terms in s^2. Then $c_0/c_1 = (1+s)/(1-s) \approx 1 + 2s \approx 1 + c_0 - c_1$, hence $c_0 - c_1 \approx c_0/c_1 - 1$. For small δ this means that

$$c_0 - c_1 = \frac{\hbar^2}{2m} \cdot \frac{2\pi\delta}{a} \cdot \frac{1}{v_1}$$

and so

$$\langle p \rangle_{\text{small }\delta} = (c_0 - c_1)\frac{\hbar\pi}{a} + \hbar\delta$$

$$= \frac{\hbar^2}{2m} \cdot \frac{2\pi\delta}{a} \cdot \frac{1}{v_1} \cdot \frac{\hbar\pi}{a} + \hbar\delta$$

$$= \hbar\delta\left(1 + 2 \cdot \frac{\hbar^2\pi^2}{2ma^2} \cdot \frac{1}{v_1}\right)$$

$$\therefore \ \langle p \rangle_{\text{small }\delta} = \hbar\delta\left(1 + \frac{2H_1}{v_1}\right) = \hbar\delta \cdot \frac{m}{m^*}. \tag{9.37}$$

Abbreviating $\langle p \rangle_{\text{small }\delta}$ as p_δ, we now invoke (9.7) and write the corresponding velocity as

$$v_\delta = p_\delta/m = \hbar\delta/m^*. \tag{9.38}$$

If we now associate kinetic energy with v_δ through the expression

$$T_\delta = \tfrac{1}{2}m^*v_\delta^2 = \frac{\hbar^2\delta^2}{2m^*},$$

this is just the last term of (9.36a), and the expectation value of the total energy of a state for which $k = \pi/a + \delta$ is

$$\langle H \rangle_{1,\delta} = H_1 \pm v_1 + T_\delta$$

where H_1 and v_1 are specific to the lattice and T_δ is the kinetic energy associated with the expectation value of the electron velocity, or – by a derivation which is not given here, but can easily be shown to be equivalent to the one we have given – with the electron probability current deduced from (9.16) and (9.34). If k is just less than π/a, T_δ is negative because m^* is negative; for if k decreases from the value π/a the energy of the state decreases even as the *magnitude* of the expectation value of the momentum increases from its limiting value zero. If k is just greater than π/a, T_δ is positive because m^* is positive – and because m^* is large compared with m the momentum expectation value increases very rapidly as k grows from π/a. At the

QM P

other band edges, i.e. for other values of q, analogous results apply.

The way in which the effective mass arises and is defined, shows that its application is restricted to discussions of effects associated with electrons in states near the edge of an energy-band. There is in fact a considerable number of such phenomena, arising from the properties of electrons in energy bands which are nearly full or nearly empty. In either case, the effective mass of the electrons which take part in energy-transfer processes may be very different from the mass of free electrons, depending on the curvature of the relevant portion of the dispersion curve. The effective mass of the electrons, and consequently the shape of the dispersion curve, may be deduced from measurements of these phenomena, which include the electronic heat capacity, the diamagnetic susceptibility, the spin magnetic susceptibility, and the electrical conductivity. The *utility* of the concept of effective mass derives from the fact that throughout such a large range of electronic phenomena the effect of the interaction of the electrons with the lattice is represented by the same effective mass parameters – though it should be mentioned here that in the case of a real three-dimensional lattice the effective mass is a tensor rather than a scalar.

Problems

(1) Show that if the position probability density $|\psi(x)|^2$ is Gaussian, so is the associated momentum probability density $|\phi(p)|^2$, and hence find the relation between Δx and Δp.

(Hint: Find the Fourier transform of the Gauss function, or refer to equations (2.15) et seq.)

(2) Show that equation (9.3) has a solution representing a wave-packet with mean momentum p_0, and show that the conclusions reached in the text concerning the rate of spreading of the packet (9.4) are valid also for this solution.

(3) Show that the quantum equation of motion $i(HF-FH)=\hbar\dot{F}$ may be used to establish (9.7) and (9.8), by putting $F=x$ and $F=p$ respectively.

(4) Show that, for the barrier of Fig. 9.2 and an incident particle beam of energy E such that $V_2-E=E-V_3$, the fraction of incident particles which penetrate the barrier is

$$4\left\{\left(1+\frac{k_2}{k_1}\right)^2 \cosh^2 k_2 a + \left(1-\frac{k_2}{k_1}\right)^2 \sinh^2 k_2 a\right\}^{-1}.$$

Hence find the transmission and reflection coefficients.

(5) Compare the transmission factors of the barrier of Fig. 9.2 for particles incident from the right and from the left with total energy E.

(6) Show that the wave-packet representing a free particle of mass 1.7×10^{-24} gm. localized within 10^{-8} cm. doubles its width in about 10^{-12} sec., while if the particle has mass 1 gm. and is localized within 10^{-3} cm. the corresponding time is 10^{22} sec. (Ehrenfest, *Zeits. für Physik*, **45**, p. 455, 1927.)

CHAPTER TEN

TIME-DEPENDENT PERTURBATIONS: COLLISION THEORY

The previous chapters have been concerned almost exclusively with the properties of stationary states, that is, with quantum statics. In these last chapters we turn to quantum dynamics, to find the probability that the application of a perturbation will cause a system to undergo a transition from one state to another.

General expression for the transition probability

We shall consider the following problem:

A system is initially in an eigenstate u_n of a Hamiltonian H_0, for which $H_0 u_n(r) = E_n u_n(r)$ where H_0, u_n and E_n are known. A perturbation H', which need not depend on time explicitly, is switched on at time $t = 0$, and switched off at time $t = t$. We seek a description of the state of the system at time t by an expansion

$$\sum_m a_m(t)\, u_m(r)$$

in which the functions u_m are the eigenfunctions of H_0 and $|a_m(t)|^2$ is the probability of finding the system in the state u_m at the time t – or subsequently, since the u_m represent stationary states. If these probabilities vary linearly with time, we call the constants of proportionality 'transition probabilities per unit time' and write them as w_m, so that

$$w_m = \frac{|a_m(t)|^2}{t}.$$

We shall find that the only states for which appreciable probability amplitudes develop are those for which energy is conserved between the initial and final states u_n and u_m.

We start from the time-dependent form of Schrödinger's equation (2.16) with the Hamiltonian $H_0 + H'$:

$$(H_0 + H')\Psi = i\hbar \frac{\partial \Psi}{\partial t}$$

and we write

$$\Psi = \sum_n a_n(t) u_n(r) \varepsilon^{-i E_n t/\hbar}$$

where the $u_n(r)$ are functions of the space – and if necessary the spin – coordinates, but not of time, while the $a_n(t)$ are functions of time only. Then

$$\sum_n (a_n H_0 u_n + a_n H' u_n) \varepsilon^{-i E_n t/\hbar} = \sum_n (i\hbar \dot{a}_n u_n + a_n E_n u_n) \varepsilon^{-i E_n t/\hbar}$$

$$\therefore \sum_n a_n H' u_n \varepsilon^{-i E_n t/\hbar} = i\hbar \sum_n \dot{a}_n u_n \varepsilon^{-i E_n t/\hbar}.$$

This is an 'equation of motion', defining the rates of change of the amplitudes of the states in terms of the applied perturbation.

To solve this equation, we multiply through from the left by u_m* and integrate over all the space and spin coordinates. Because of the orthogonality of the u_n this gives

$$\sum_n a_n H'_{mn} \varepsilon^{-i E_n t/\hbar} = i\hbar \dot{a}_m \varepsilon^{-i E_m t/\hbar}$$

where, as before,

$$H'_{mn} = \int u_m* H' u_n \, d\tau.$$

We therefore have a set of differential equations for the amplitudes $a_m(t)$.

If the system was initially in the state u_n, $a_n(0) = 1$ and $a_m(0) = 0$ for all $m \neq n$. Then

$$a_m(t) = \frac{1}{i\hbar} \int_0^t H'_{mn} \varepsilon^{i\omega_{mn}t} dt \qquad (10.1a)$$

where we have put $\omega_{mn} = (E_m - E_n)/\hbar$. It is assumed here that a_n remains constant throughout the time for which the perturbation is applied and that the growth of the amplitudes other than a_m can be neglected; this is the *first-order approximation*. The quantity on the right is the Fourier Transform of the perturbation, since the perturbation is zero except between 0 and t. If H' is not explicitly dependent on time the expression for $a_m(t)$ is

$$a_m(t) = \frac{1}{i\hbar} H'_{mn} \int_0^t \varepsilon^{i\omega_{mn}t} dt. \qquad (10.1b)$$

Provided $E_m \neq E_n$ integration of (10.1b) gives

$$a_m(t) = -H'_{mn} \frac{\varepsilon^{i\omega_{mn}t} - 1}{\hbar \omega_{mn}}$$

and the probability of finding the system in the state u_m after the perturbation is switched off at time t is

$$|a_m(t)|^2 = \frac{2|H'_{mn}|^2}{(\hbar\omega_{mn})^2}(1-\cos\omega_{mn}t)$$

$$= \frac{|H'_{mn}|^2}{\hbar^2}\frac{\sin^2(\omega_{mn}t/2)}{(\omega_{mn}/2)^2}. \qquad (10.2)$$

If H'_{mn} vanishes this does not mean that the transition cannot occur, but that it cannot occur by a first-order process. There may be other states u_k for which $H'_{kn}\neq 0$ and $H'_{mk}\neq 0$. The transition can then occur in two stages, $u_n \to u_k \to u_m$, in which case we call it a *second-order process*. The second and higher order approximations are best found by a calculation in which the perturbation is presented as a power series in a parameter λ, as was done for the stationary case in chapter 6. It then appears, as we should expect, that

$$\dot{a}_m(t) \propto \sum H'_{mk}H'_{kn}\times(\text{time factors}) \propto H'^2.$$

Important examples of second-order processes are the Raman and Compton effects.

The function

$$\frac{\sin^2(\omega_{mn}t/2)}{(\omega_{mn}/2)^2}$$

of (10.2) is well known in diffraction optics; it is shown in Fig. 10.1 as a function of ω_{mn} for a fixed value of t. The maximum occurs when $\omega_{mn}=0$. The most likely product of the perturbation process is therefore a state having the same energy as the initial one, so that energy is conserved. This is not a trivial statement and does not imply that nothing has happened; it asserts, for example, that in the elastic scattering of α-particles by massive nuclei the only probable processes are those in which the α-particles have the same energy after scattering as they had before it, although their momenta may be changed – that is, their *directions* of motion may change.

In a collision or scattering experiment the initial and final states are not uniquely determined. The direction of travel of the incident α-particle (say) is specified only approximately by the finite size of the source and scatterer and of whatever diaphragms are placed between them, and the direction of the scattered α-particles which enter the detector is, similarly, only approximately specified. Also,

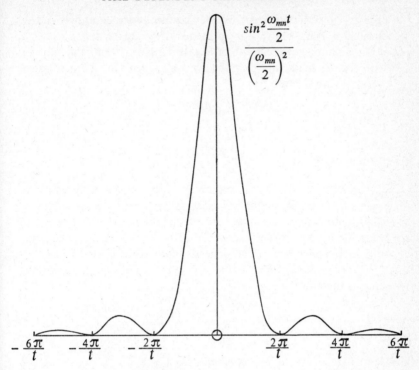

FIG. 10.1. The function $\dfrac{\sin^2 \dfrac{\omega_{mn}t}{2}}{\left(\dfrac{\omega_{mn}}{2}\right)^2}$ plotted as a function of ω_{mn} for constant t.

the energies of the scattered particles are to some extent indefinite, because the scattering centres have some random thermal motion. We can allow for such effects by calculating the probability of finding the scattered particle, not in a unique final state, but in any one of a group of final states whose energy lies in a small range ΔE. Let the density-in-energy of the final states be $\rho(E)$. Then this probability is

$$\frac{|H'_{mn}|^2}{\hbar^2} \int_{\Delta E} \rho(E) \frac{\sin^2(\omega_{mn}t/2)}{(\omega_{mn}/2)^2} \, dE.$$

If $\rho(E)$ varies with E more slowly than the other factor in the integrand, we can without serious error ignore its variation and take it outside the integral with $E = E_0$, this being the energy for which the factor remaining under the integral has its maximum. Further, since this maximum is sharp we may replace the integral over ΔE by an integral from $-\infty$ to $+\infty$, provided ΔE is greater than the width of the main lobe of the graph of Fig. 10.1. This is justifiable, for the width of the main lobe is given by $\frac{1}{2}\Delta\omega \cdot t = \pi$ and the associated energy spread is given by

$$\frac{1}{2}\Delta E \cdot t = \pi\hbar$$

$$\therefore \quad \Delta E \cdot t = 2\pi\hbar$$

$$\text{or} \quad \Delta E = \frac{2\pi\hbar}{t}.$$

This is of the order of the minimum energy uncertainty which is inevitable in a measurement occupying a time t, because of the operation of the uncertainty principle for the conjugate variables E and t. It follows that conservation of energy can be verified with only limited accuracy, which depends on the time available.

The probability of finding the system in one of the group of final states is therefore

$$|a_m(t)|^2 = \frac{|H'_{mn}|^2}{\hbar^2}\rho(E_0)\,\hbar \int_{-\infty}^{+\infty} \frac{\sin^2(\omega t/2)}{(\omega/2)^2}\,d\omega$$

$$= \frac{2\pi}{\hbar}\rho(E_0)\,|H'_{mn}|^2\,t. \tag{10.3}$$

(Without doing the integration we might have noted that the height of the main lobe of the graph of Fig. 10.1 is proportional to t^2 and its width to $1/t$, so that the area is proportional to t.) Hence the transition probability per unit time is

$$w = \frac{2\pi}{\hbar}\rho(E_0)\,|H'_{mn}|^2. \tag{10.4}$$

The cross-section for elastic scattering

The experimental study of collision processes has provided a great deal of information about atomic and nuclear structure, and about the nature of the forces which act between elementary particles. Classical physics provided a satisfactory basis for interpreting experiments on the scattering of α-particles by nuclei, in which there was no excitation of the nuclei. Born's successful application of wave-mechanics to the same process was the first step in the development of elegant and powerful methods of analysing experiments in which the bombardment of target atoms and nuclei produces transitions in the target, accompanied by inelastic scattering of the incident particles.

The results of experiments on the scattering of beams of particles are usually stated as a set of values for the *differential cross-section* or *total cross-section* for the interaction between incident particle and scatterer. Suppose that a parallel flux of N particles per unit area per second bombards a target containing n particles. The number of particles scattered into an element of solid angle $d\Omega$ whose polar coordinates relative to the direction of the incident flux are θ and ϕ will usually be proportional to $Nn\, d\Omega$. (This may not be the case if the incident beam is so intense that there is appreciable interference between the particles in it, or if the target is so thick that incident particles may make more than one collision inside the target.) The number of particles entering $d\Omega$ in unit time can then be written as

$$N_s\, d\Omega = Nn\, \sigma(\theta, \phi)\, d\Omega. \qquad (10.5)$$

$\sigma(\theta, \phi)$ has the dimensions of an area, and is called the differential cross-section. It can be regarded as the cross-sectional area in the incident beam that contains the particles scattered into $d\Omega$ by a single scattering centre in the target, or as the probability per second of observing a particle scattered into unit solid angle when unit flux is incident on a single scatterer. If the direction of the incident beam is $\theta = 0$, and if the incident beam and the target are unpolarized, the differential cross-section is independent of ϕ and may be written as $\sigma(\theta)$. The integral $\int \sigma(\theta, \phi) d\Omega$ taken over a sphere is called the total cross-section.

In what follows we shall assume that we are concerned with the motion of the incident and scattered particles in the coordinate system in which the centre of mass of the scattering centre and incident particle is at rest. The mass which then appears in our equations is the reduced mass of the incident particle, and the angles which specify $\sigma(\theta, \phi)$ are angles in the centre-of-mass coordinate system.

As an incident particle approaches and passes a scattering centre it experiences a force which varies from point to point. There is thus an interaction between scatterer and incident particle which varies in time, and will produce transitions of the incident particle from an initial state characterized by a momentum vector $\mathbf{k}$ to a final state characterized by a momentum vector $\mathbf{k}'$. The interaction potential is not, however, an *explicit* function of time in this case, since it is expressed as a function of **r**, the position vector of the incident particle relative to the scatterer. So we can use (10.4), which gives the transition probability when the perturbation is not an explicit function of time. The matrix elements H'_{mn} in equation (10.4) will now be the matrix elements of the interaction potential evaluated between the initial and final states characterized by **k** and **k'**, and the function $\rho(E_0)$ will be the density of final states whose momentum vectors are directed within the solid angle $d\Omega$ and satisfy the mechanical conservation requirements and whatever boundary conditions or normalization conditions are imposed. It is convenient to choose initial and final state-functions which represent a particle moving in regions at such a great distance from the scatterer that the interaction is effectively zero. This ensures, by implication, that the integral in (10.1b) has been evaluated over a finite but sufficient range of time. It remains then to determine the form of $\rho(E_0)$, and to evaluate the matrix elements of the interaction potential between an initial state represented by $L^{-3/2} \varepsilon^{i\mathbf{k_0} \cdot \mathbf{r}}$, and a final state represented by $L^{-3/2} \varepsilon^{i\mathbf{k} \cdot \mathbf{r}}$. The first of these functions, which are normalized within a very large but finite cube of side L, represents a plane wave – i.e. a parallel incident beam, travelling in the direction of $\mathbf{k_0}$ with energy $E_0 = \hbar^2 k_0^2/2m$. The second represents a plane wave travelling in the direction of **k** with energy $\hbar^2 k^2/2m$. If there is no internal excitation of the particles involved the collision is said to be elastic, and

$$\frac{\hbar^2 k_0^2}{2m} = \frac{\hbar^2 k^2}{2m} \quad \text{so that} \quad |\,\mathbf{k_0}\,| = |\,\mathbf{k}\,|.$$

The change in the momentum of the scattered particle is $\hbar(\mathbf{k} - \mathbf{k_0})$ and will be written as $\hbar\mathbf{K}$. The number of final states whose wave-vectors lie in a solid angle $d\Omega$ and whose energies lie in the range between E and $E + dE$ is

$$\left(\frac{L}{2\pi\hbar}\right)^3 (2m^3 E)^{\frac{1}{2}} d\Omega dE = \rho(E)dE$$

$$\therefore \quad \rho(E) = \left(\frac{L}{2\pi\hbar}\right)^3 mp d\Omega.$$

Hence if the interaction between the incident particle and scatterer is represented by a potential $V(r)$, (10.4) becomes

$$w_{k_0 \to k} = \frac{2\pi}{\hbar} \left(\frac{L}{2\pi\hbar}\right)^3 mp d\Omega \left|\frac{1}{L^3} \int V(r) \varepsilon^{i\mathbf{K} \cdot \mathbf{r}} d\tau\right|^2.$$

The wave-function for the initial state is normalized in the volume L^3 and so represents a particle density of L^{-3}. Further, the velocity of the particles is $v = p/m$. The flux in the incident beam is therefore v/L^3 particles per unit area per second. The differential scattering cross-section must then be given by

$$\sigma(\theta)d\Omega = \left(\frac{v}{L^3}\right)^{-1} w_{k_0 \to k}$$

and so

$$\sigma(\theta) = \left(\frac{m}{2\pi\hbar^2}\right)^2 \left| \int V(r)\varepsilon^{i\mathbf{K}\cdot\mathbf{r}}d\tau \right|^2. \tag{10.6}$$

The integral is reduced by taking polar angles α, β about the direction of $\mathbf{K}$:

$$\int V(r)\varepsilon^{i\mathbf{K}\cdot\mathbf{r}}d\tau = \int_{r=0}^{\infty}\int_{\alpha=0}^{\pi}\int_{\beta=0}^{2\pi} V(r)\varepsilon^{iKr\cos\alpha}d\beta\,\sin\alpha\,d\alpha\,r^2dr$$

$$= -2\pi\int_{r=0}^{\infty}\int_{\cos\alpha=1}^{-1} V(r)\varepsilon^{iKr\cos\alpha}d(\cos\alpha)\,r^2dr$$

$$= -\frac{2\pi}{iK}\int_0^{\infty} V(r)\{\varepsilon^{-iKr}-\varepsilon^{iKr}\}r\,dr$$

$$= \frac{4\pi}{K}\int_0^{\infty} V(r)\sin Kr\,rdr.$$

Then

$$\sigma(\theta) = \left| \frac{2m}{\hbar^2 K}\int_0^{\infty} V(r)\sin Kr\,rdr \right|^2. \tag{10.7}$$

The dependence on θ is implicit in K, for $K = 2k_0\sin\theta/2$ from Fig. 10.2.

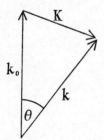

FIG. 10.2. Momentum change in an elastic collision.
$K = k - k_0, \quad K = 2k_0\sin\frac{\theta}{2}.$

Rutherford's law of scattering

We shall find the differential scattering cross-section when $V(r)$ is the screened Coulomb potential

$$V(r) = \frac{Zze^2}{4\pi\varepsilon_0 r} \varepsilon^{-r/r_0}. \qquad (10.8)$$

Ze and ze are the charges of the scattering and scattered particle respectively, and r_0 will be called the *screening radius*. We shall see that when $r_0 \to \infty$ the angular dependence of the differential cross-section is

$$\sigma(\theta) \propto \operatorname{cosec}^4 \frac{\theta}{2}.$$

This angular dependence was deduced from classical mechanics by Rutherford for the scattering of charged particles in a Coulomb field, and one of the early triumphs of wave-mechanics was the derivation of this same law by Born and Wentzel in 1926.

Combining (10.8) and (10.7) we see that $\sigma(\theta)$ is proportional to the square of the integral

$$\int_0^\infty \varepsilon^{-r/r_0} \sin Kr \, dr.$$

Integrating by parts, we get

$$-K^{-1} \varepsilon^{-r/r_0} \cos Kr \bigg|_0^\infty + (Kr_0)^{-1} \int_0^\infty \varepsilon^{-r/r_0} \cos Kr \, dr$$

$$= \frac{1}{K} - \frac{\varepsilon^{-r/r_0}}{K^2 r_0} \sin Kr \bigg|_0^\infty - \frac{1}{K^2 r_0{}^2} \int_0^\infty \varepsilon^{-r/r_0} \sin Kr \, dr.$$

Hence

$$\int_0^\infty \varepsilon^{-r/r_0} \sin Kr \, dr = \frac{1}{K} - \frac{1}{K^2 r_0{}^2} \int_0^\infty \varepsilon^{-r/r_0} \sin Kr \, dr$$

$$\therefore \left(1 + \frac{1}{K^2 r_0{}^2}\right) \int_0^\infty \varepsilon^{-r/r_0} \sin Kr \, dr = \frac{1}{K}$$

$$\therefore \int_0^\infty V(r) \sin Kr \, . \, r \, dr = \frac{Zze^2}{4\pi\varepsilon_0} \frac{Kr_0{}^2}{K^2 r_0{}^2 + 1}.$$

Putting this in (10.7) we find

$$\sigma(\theta) = \left(\frac{2mzZe^2}{4\pi\varepsilon_0 \hbar^2}\right)^2 \frac{r_0{}^4}{(K^2 r_0{}^2 + 1)^2}.$$

Since $K = 2k_0 \sin \theta/2$ this is equivalent to

$$\sigma(\theta) = \left(\frac{2mzZe^2}{4\pi\varepsilon_0\hbar^2}\right)^2 \frac{r_0^4}{(4k_0^2r_0^2\sin^2\theta/2+1)^2} \qquad (10.9a)$$

and as $r_0 \to \infty$, $V(r)$ becomes the ordinary Coulomb potential

$$\frac{zZe^2}{4\pi\varepsilon_0 r}$$

and (10.9a) becomes

$$\sigma(\theta) = \left(\frac{2mzZe^2}{4\pi\varepsilon_0\hbar^2}\right)^2 \frac{1}{(4k_0^2\sin^2\theta/2)^2}$$

$$= \left(\frac{zZe^2}{4\pi\varepsilon_0}\right)^2 \left(\frac{1}{2mv^2}\right)^2 \operatorname{cosec}^4 \theta/2. \qquad (10.9b)$$

(10.9b) tends to infinity as θ tends to zero. Such small-angle scattering is due to the deflection of particles which pass at great distances from the scattering centre; in practice there will always be some modification of the Coulomb field – screening, in fact – which keeps the cross-section finite. (For example, neutral atoms appear uncharged from distances greater than about 10^{-8} cm., due to the screening of the nucleus by the electrons.) The difference between the differential cross-sections (10.9a) and (10.9b) will be negligible as long as

$$4k_0^2r_0^2\sin^2\frac{\theta}{2} \gg 1.$$

Putting

$$r_0 = \frac{a_0}{Z^{\frac{1}{3}}}$$

– the radius of the atom according to the Thomas-Fermi statistical model, see eqn. (8.26) – and

$$k_0 = \frac{2\pi}{\lambda} = \frac{mv}{\hbar},$$

this becomes

$$\sin\frac{\theta}{2} \gg \frac{1}{4\pi}\frac{\lambda}{r_0} = \frac{\hbar Z^{\frac{1}{3}}}{2\,mv\,a_0}. \qquad (10.10)$$

For the collision between an α-particle of, say, 2 MeV energy and the nucleus of an atom of gold, for which $Z=79$,

$$\theta \gg 30 \text{ min. of arc.}$$

The effect of screening is significant, then, only for very small angles indeed, and would be difficult to demonstrate experimentally.

The total cross-section calculated from (10.9a) by integrating over all angles is

$$\sigma_{\text{tot}} = \int \sigma(\theta)\, 2\pi \sin\theta\, d\theta = \left(\frac{2mzZe^2}{4\pi\varepsilon_0\hbar^2}\right)^2 \frac{4\pi\, r_0{}^4}{4k_0{}^2 r_0{}^2 + 1}.$$

(10.9b) leads to an infinite total cross-section, because of the slow fall-off with distance of the Coulomb potential.

Scattering by a spherical potential well

Experimentally much of the importance of scattering measurements stems from the information that the differential cross-section gives about the law of force between the scatterer and the scattered particles. For example, the differential cross-section for scattering in a Coulomb field is quite different from that for the scattering due to a spherical well represented by the potential function $V(r) = -V_0$ when $r < a$, $V(r) = 0$ when $r > a$. For this case the integral in (10.7) is

$$-V_0 \int_0^a \sin Kr \cdot r\, dr = V_0\left(\frac{a}{K}\cos Ka - \frac{1}{K^2}\sin Ka\right)$$

and the differential scattering cross-section is

$$\sigma(\theta) = \left(\frac{2mV_0 a^3}{\hbar^2}\right)^2 \left(\frac{\sin x - x\cos x}{x^3}\right)^2$$

where

$$x = Ka = 2k_0 a \sin\frac{\theta}{2}.$$

The angular dependence is contained in the function of x, which is sketched in Fig. 10.3. When $x = 0$ this function has the value $\frac{1}{9}$, it falls to zero when $x = \tan x$, i.e. when $x = 4\cdot49$, and rises to a very weak maximum when $x \approx 6$. In terms of the de Broglie wavelength $\lambda = h/p$ of the incident particle the first zero of the scattering cross-section occurs when

$$\sin\frac{\theta}{2} = 0\cdot36\frac{\lambda}{a};$$

for larger angles the scattering is negligible.

It is interesting to notice that for both the screened Coulomb potential and the spherical well the differential cross-section for small values of $2k_0 a \sin \theta/2$ varies as

$$\sigma(\theta) \propto a - b\,(2k_0 a \sin \theta/2)^2 \,;$$

this is found for other potentials, and shows that a marked dependence of $\sigma(\theta)$ on the detailed form of the potential appears only at higher angles and higher momenta. The reason for this is easily seen.

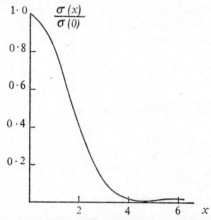

FIG. 10.3. The variation of the differential scattering cross-section for a rectangular potential well, as a function of $x = 2k_0 \sin \dfrac{\theta}{2}$ (Born approximation).

Equation (10.6) shows that the differential cross-section depends on the Fourier transform of the potential function, and information about the detailed variations of $V(r)$ will be contained mainly in the shorter wavelength components which correspond to the larger momentum changes, and so to larger deflections.

The Born approximation and the classical description

Our treatment of the scattering problem has not given us an expression for the total scattered wave-function. The general treatment in the first section of this chapter represents the final state as a superposition of orthogonal eigenfunctions u_m, and derives the transition probability from the corresponding amplitudes a_m. In the scattering problem the final state is represented as a superposition of the plane waves $L^{-3/2}\,\varepsilon^{i\mathbf{k}\cdot\mathbf{r}}$, but rather than calculate the individual amplitudes and then construct the total wave-function we proceeded directly to calculate the observable differential cross-section. We readily see, however, that the total state-function would have the form

$$\psi = \varepsilon^{ikz} + \frac{f(\theta, \phi)}{r} \varepsilon^{ikr} \qquad (10.11)$$

for it must represent a plane wave incident on the scatterer and a spherical (scattered) wave spreading out from it, the amplitude of the scattered wave being a function of direction. And further, from this function ψ we can derive expressions for the incident and scattered flux, and so deduce the relationship between $f(\theta, \phi)$ and the differential cross-section $\sigma(\theta, \phi)$. Using (9.16) we find that the incident flux is proportional to

$$S_i = \frac{k\hbar}{m}$$

and the scattered flux is proportional to

$$S_s = \frac{k\hbar}{m} \frac{|f(\theta, \phi)|^2}{r^2}.$$

The probability of scattering into unit solid angle for unit incident flux is therefore

$$\sigma(\theta, \phi) = |f(\theta, \phi)|^2. \qquad (10.12)$$

By using the first-order perturbation theory – the Born approximation – we have excluded from consideration the possibility of multiple scattering in the potential field. In fact, since the potential field occupies a finite volume the momentum change may be the result of a series of transitions, but if the amplitudes of the once-scattered wave are small enough, the probability of these multiple scatterings will be negligibly small. Thus the Born approximation represents scattering as a single-stage process. This is the antithesis of the classical description in terms of trajectories. The classical description represents the motion adequately if the potential does not vary rapidly within the region occupied by the wave-packet which represents a localized particle. This means that the forces on the particle are small. On the other hand the initial direction of motion of the particle must be imprecise, for the definition of the trajectory by slits or apertures produces an uncertainty in the transverse components of momentum, which appears as an uncertainty in the direction of motion of the incident particle. The classical description will be useful only if the deflection of the particle in the collision is considerably greater than this inherent uncertainty. If this argument is followed out quantitatively it emerges that the classical description is applicable when the scattering potential produces a gradual, but in the end considerable deflection, so that the scattering process is effectively continuous.

Validity of the Born approximation

The Born approximation will be valid whenever the total wave-function of (10.11) is not greatly different from the incident wave-function $\varepsilon^{i\mathbf{k_0 \cdot r}}$. It is a good deal more difficult to set up *necessary* conditions for its validity than it is to set up *sufficient* conditions; here we shall consider only a sufficient condition which is, in fact, rather stringent.

We saw in chapter 9 that a change of potential produces a change in the phase of the wave-function. The total wave-function will not differ greatly from the initial wave-function if the phase of the incident wave is not much altered as it passes through the region in which it is influenced by the perturbing potential. At great distances the magnitude of the wave-vector is $k_0 = (2mE)^{\frac{1}{2}}\hbar^{-1}$, and near the centre of force it is $\{2m(E-V)\}^{\frac{1}{2}}\hbar^{-1}$. The change of phase due to the potential is then

$$\Delta\phi = \left(\frac{2m}{\hbar^2}\right)^{\frac{1}{2}} \int_0^\infty \left\{(E-V)^{\frac{1}{2}} - E^{\frac{1}{2}}\right\} dr$$

and we can ensure the validity of the first-order theory by requiring that

$$|\Delta\phi| = \left|\left(\frac{2m}{\hbar^2}\right)^{\frac{1}{2}} \int_0^\infty \left\{(E-V)^{\frac{1}{2}} - E^{\frac{1}{2}}\right\} dr\right| \ll 1. \qquad (10.13)$$

(In fact this condition may be unnecessarily stringent, for if certain relations exist between the phase-shifts of the different components of a wave-packet quite large phase-shifts may occur without any scattering.)

If $V \ll E$, when we express (10.13) as a function of the ratio V/E the criterion becomes

$$\left(\frac{2mE}{\hbar^2}\right)^{\frac{1}{2}} \left|\int_0^\infty \left\{\left(1 - \frac{V}{E}\right)^{\frac{1}{2}} - 1\right\} dr\right| \ll 1$$

$$\therefore \left(\frac{m}{2\hbar^2 E}\right)^{\frac{1}{2}} \left|\int_0^\infty V \, dr\right| \ll 1 \qquad (10.14)$$

$$\text{or} \quad \left(\frac{m}{2\hbar^2 E}\right)^{\frac{1}{2}} |\bar{V}\bar{a}| \ll 1$$

where $\bar{V}$ is the average potential and $\bar{a}$ is the mean range.

In the case of the scattering of high-energy particles by the spherical potential well this condition can be used at once, and becomes

$$\left(\frac{m}{2\hbar^2 E}\right)^{\frac{1}{2}} V_0 a \ll 1$$

or

$$\frac{mV_0 a}{\hbar^2 k} \ll 1. \tag{10.15a}$$

If the well is strong enough to bind a particle of mass m we know from chapter 5 that

$$\frac{mV_0 a^2}{\hbar^2} \gtrsim 1$$

so for such a well the Born approximation is useful only if

$$ka \gg 1. \tag{10.15b}$$

If low-energy particles are scattered by this potential well we find a different criterion by putting $V = -V_0$ in (10.13) and expanding

$$\left(\frac{2m}{\hbar^2}\right)^{\frac{1}{2}} \{(E+V_0)^{\frac{1}{2}} - E^{\frac{1}{2}}\} a$$

in powers of E/V_0. In place of (10.15a) we find

$$\frac{mV_0 a^2}{\hbar^2} \ll 1$$

which shows that the Born approximation will be valid in the low-energy limit only if the well is very weak.

For the screened Coulomb potential the criterion (10.13) is, in full,

$$\left(\frac{2m}{\hbar^2}\right)^{\frac{1}{2}} \left| \int_0^\infty \left\{ \left(\frac{\hbar^2 k_0^2}{2m} + \frac{zZe^2}{4\pi\varepsilon_0 r} \varepsilon^{-r/r_0}\right)^{\frac{1}{2}} - \left(\frac{\hbar^2 k_0^2}{2m}\right)^{\frac{1}{2}} \right\} dr \right| \ll 1.$$

The greatest contribution to the integral will come from the region near the origin where ε^{-r/r_0} is nearly unity, so to get an approximate idea of the value of the integral we shall set ε^{-r/r_0} equal to unity and confine the integration to the range from 0 to r_1, where

$$\frac{zZe^2}{4\pi\varepsilon_0 r_1} = \frac{\hbar^2 k_0^2}{2m},$$

that is, to the range in which $|V| \gtrsim E$. If in addition we neglect the terms in $\hbar^2 k_0^2/2m$ the effect will be to increase the value of the integral, and so to tighten up, rather than relax, the condition. Doing this we get

$$\left(\frac{2m}{\hbar^2}\right)^{\frac{1}{2}} \left| \int_0^{r_1} \left(\frac{zZe^2}{4\pi\varepsilon_0 r}\right)^{\frac{1}{2}} dr \right| \ll 1$$

whence
$$2\frac{2m}{\hbar^2}\frac{zZe^2}{4\pi\varepsilon_0 k_0} \ll 1$$

or
$$\frac{4zZe^2}{4\pi\varepsilon_0 \hbar v} \ll 1. \tag{10.16}$$

In experiments on secondary electron emission bound atomic electrons may be bombarded by electrons of energy 1 keV, with $v = 2 \times 10^9$ cm. sec.$^{-1}$; then

$$\frac{4zZe^2}{4\pi\varepsilon_0 \hbar v} \approx 0.6$$

and the validity of the Born approximation in this context would be questionable. In an α-particle scattering experiment using gold foil scatterers we should have $z=2$, $Z=79$, and the particle velocity would apparently have to be increased to about 3.2×10^{11} cm./sec. to give the same value to this numeric! This must mean *either* that for heavy particles and scatterers of large atomic number the Born approximation is inapplicable below relativistic velocities *or* that the criterion developed here is too stringent. Since the cross-section found experimentally in α-particle scattering experiments agrees well with (10.9) we must suspect the latter. In fact the Coulomb force is unique; the Born approximation works surprisingly well for the Coulomb field, even though the general criteria for its validity are not satisfied. For other fields – the rectangular well, for example – the criterion may be applied with a fair degree of confidence.

The method of partial waves

The working-out of the higher-order perturbation theory is very tedious, and when the Born approximation breaks down it is usual to tackle collision problems by a quite different method, known as the *method of partial waves*. We shall illustrate this method in its simplest form, applicable only at very low energies.

The total wave-function

$$\psi(\mathbf{r}) \propto \varepsilon^{ikz} + f(\theta)\frac{\varepsilon^{ikr}}{r}$$

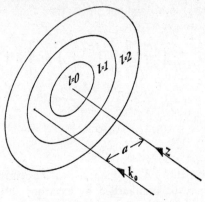

FIG. 10.4.   The angular momentum of the incident particle about the scattering centre is $pa = \hbar ka = l\hbar$.

must be a solution of the three-dimensional Schrödinger equation and can be written as

$$\psi(\mathbf{r}) = \sum_{l=0}^{\infty} \psi_l(r)\, Y_{l0}(\theta)$$

(there is no angular momentum about the z-axis) whence

$$\psi_l(r) = \int_{\theta,\,\phi} \psi(\mathbf{r})\, Y_{l0}(\theta) \sin\theta\, d\theta\, d\phi$$

(because of the orthogonality of the Y_{l0}).

If the range of the scattering potential is limited, and if the energy of the incident particle is low, only small values of l need be considered. A wave-packet constructed so as to approach the scatterer along a line distant a from the z-axis would correspond to a particle having an angular momentum $pa = \hbar ka$ about the scatterer (Fig. 10.4). If the maximum range of the scattering potential is r_0, and the incident particle has energy $E = \hbar^2 k^2 / 2m$, there will be no scattering if the packet passes at a distance greater than r_0, so the highest angular momentum that needs to be represented in the components of the packet $\psi(r)$ is that for which

$$l\hbar \approx \hbar k r_0$$
or $\qquad l \approx k r_0.$

The limiting case in which

$$\varepsilon^{ikz}+f(\theta)\frac{\varepsilon^{ikr}}{r} \propto \psi(\mathbf{r}) = \psi_0(r)\,Y_{00}(\theta)$$

will give isotropic scattering, since $Y_{00}(\theta)$ is a constant. Putting $Y_{00} = (4\pi)^{-\frac{1}{2}}$ we find

$$\psi_0(r) = (4\pi)^{-\frac{1}{2}}\int_{\phi=0}^{2\pi}\int_{\theta=0}^{\pi}\left(\varepsilon^{ikr\cos\theta}+f(\theta)\frac{\varepsilon^{ikr}}{r}\right)\sin\theta\, d\theta\, d\phi$$

$$= -\pi^{\frac{1}{2}}\int_{\cos\theta=1}^{-1}\varepsilon^{ikr\cos\theta}\,d(\cos\theta)+2\pi^{\frac{1}{2}}\overline{f(\theta)}\frac{\varepsilon^{ikr}}{r}$$

where $\overline{f(\theta)}$ is the mean value of $f(\theta)$.

Thus $\psi_0(r) = \dfrac{i\pi^{\frac{1}{2}}}{kr}(\varepsilon^{-ikr}-\varepsilon^{ikr})+2\pi^{\frac{1}{2}}\overline{f(\theta)}\dfrac{\varepsilon^{ikr}}{r}$. \qquad (10.17)

Now $r\psi_0(r)=\chi(r)$ must satisfy the radial wave-equation

$$-\frac{\hbar^2}{2m}\frac{d^2\chi(r)}{dr^2}+V(r)\chi(r) = E\chi(r)$$

with $\chi(0)=0$; as $r\to\infty$ $V(r)\to 0$ and the solution takes the asymptotic form

$$\chi(r) = c\sin(kr+\delta).$$

If this solution is normalized so that

$$\chi(r) = \frac{\sin(kr+\delta)}{\sin\delta} = \frac{1}{2i\sin\delta}\{\varepsilon^{i(kr+\delta)}-\varepsilon^{-i(kr+\delta)}\}\qquad (10.18)$$

a comparison of the ingoing-wave terms – those in ε^{-ikr} – in (10.17) and (10.18) shows that

$$2i\sin\delta\;\varepsilon^{i\delta}\chi(r) = ikr\,\pi^{-\frac{1}{2}}\psi_0(r)$$

$$\therefore\; \psi_0(r) = 2\pi^{\frac{1}{2}}\varepsilon^{i\delta}\sin\delta\,\frac{\chi(r)}{kr}.$$

The solution at great distances is therefore

$$\psi_0(r) = \frac{2\pi^{\frac{1}{2}}}{kr}\varepsilon^{i\delta}\sin\delta\,\frac{\sin(kr+\delta)}{\sin\delta}$$

$$= \frac{\pi^{\frac{1}{2}}}{ikr}\{\varepsilon^{i(kr+2\delta)}-\varepsilon^{-ikr}\}.$$

Comparison of the outgoing-wave terms – those in ε^{ikr} – in this equation and in (10.17) gives

$$\frac{i}{k}\varepsilon^{2i\delta} = \frac{i}{k} - 2\overline{f(\theta)}$$

so that

$$\frac{1}{k}(\varepsilon^{2i\delta}-1) = 2i\overline{f(\theta)}$$

or

$$\frac{1}{2i}(\varepsilon^{i\delta}-\varepsilon^{-i\delta}) = k\overline{f(\theta)}\,\varepsilon^{-i\delta}$$

$$\therefore\ \overline{f(\theta)} = \frac{\sin\delta\,\varepsilon^{i\delta}}{k}.$$

Now

$$\sigma(\theta) = |f(\theta)|^2$$

so

$$\sigma(\theta) = \frac{\sin^2\delta}{k^2}.$$

The partial-wave method for the spherical potential well

We shall apply this result to the scattering by a spherical potential well, for which the Born approximation result was obtained earlier in this chapter. The use of a single term in the expansion of the wave-function will be valid if $ka \ll 1$. (10.19)
Inside the sphere the wave-equation is

$$-\frac{\hbar^2}{2m}\frac{d^2\chi}{dr^2} = (E+V_0)\chi;$$

the solution must vanish at the origin, so it must be

$$\chi = A\sin k_1 r$$

where

$$k_1{}^2 = \frac{2m}{\hbar^2}(E+V_0).$$

Outside the sphere the solution is

$$\chi = B\sin(kr+\delta)$$

where

$$k^2 = \frac{2m}{\hbar^2}E.$$

The solution must be continuous, and have a continuous derivative, at $r=a$. These conditions can be written as

$$A \sin k_1 a = B \sin (ka+\delta)$$
$$Ak_1 \cos k_1 a = Bk \cos (ka+\delta).$$

Dividing, we have

$$k \cot (ka+\delta) = k_1 \cot k_1 a,$$

whence, after some work,

$$\tan \delta = \frac{k \tan k_1 a - k_1 \tan ka}{k \tan ka \tan k_1 a + 1}.$$

The differential cross-section $\sigma(\theta) = (\sin^2 \delta)/k^2$ is independent of θ in this low-energy limit so the total cross-section is

$$\sigma_{\text{tot}} = 4\pi\sigma(\theta) = \frac{4\pi}{k^2 \operatorname{cosec}^2 \delta} = \frac{4\pi}{k^2(1+\cot^2 \delta)}.$$

The cross-section can be computed, but without embarking on this we can see that whenever $\tan \delta = 0$ the cross-section is zero; this happens when

$$\frac{\tan ka}{k} = \frac{\tan k_1 a}{k_1}.$$

This condition may be satisfied for a number of values of the bombarding energy. Since ka is small, we have $ka \approx \tan ka$ so that $\tan k_1 a = k_1 a$ whence $k_1 a = 4.49, 7.72, 10.9 \ldots$ etc. The vanishing of the scattering cross-section at certain low values of the energy is found in a number of wave-processes. For example helium or other noble gas atoms are practically transparent to slow electrons of about 0·7 eV energy, while smokes consisting of particles homogeneous in size are virtually transparent to light in a narrow wavelength region.

If the sphere is impenetrable the wave-function vanishes over the surface of the sphere and there is no interior wave, so the phase in the exterior solution $\chi = \sin (kr+\delta)$ must be $\delta = -ka$. The total cross-section is then

$$\sigma_{\text{tot}} = 4\pi \frac{\sin^2 ka}{k^2}$$

and for small ka this becomes

$$\sigma_{\text{tot}} = 4\pi a^2.$$

This result is four times the classical (geometrical) value, because of wave-diffraction effects.

At higher energies partial waves of higher angular momenta need to be included in the solution, and it is shown in, e.g. Bohm's *Quantum Theory*, chapter 21, that the differential cross-section in the general case is

$$\sigma(\theta) = \frac{1}{k^2} \left| \sum_l \frac{2l+1}{2} P_l(\cos\theta)(\varepsilon^{2i\delta_l} - 1) \right|^2 \tag{10.20}$$

and that the total cross-section is

$$\sigma_{tot} = \sum_l \frac{4\pi}{k^2}(2l+1)\sin^2\delta_l.$$

If a differential cross-section is determined experimentally, and the experimental curve is fitted by a polynomial in $\cos\theta$, the highest term of that polynomial identifies the highest term required in the expansion (10.20). It usually turns out that the number of terms required is quite small, and this makes the partial-wave treatment a very useful tool for the analysis of experimental results.

Equations (10.15b) and (10.19) state the conditions for the validity of the Born approximation and the partial-wave treatment respectively in the case of scattering by the rectangular potential well. Comparison of these conditions shows that the partial-wave treatment with only a few terms is useful just when the Born approximation is inapplicable, so these methods supplement one another.

Problems

(1) At sufficiently low energies the neutron-proton scattering is isotropic in the centre-of-mass coordinate system. How does the differential cross-section depend on angles measured in the 'laboratory coordinate system' in which the scatterer is initially stationary?

(2) The neutron-proton force can be represented approximately by a spherical potential well of depth 25 MeV and radius 2×10^{-13} cm. (see problem 6, chapter 5). How many terms would be required in a partial-wave analysis of a neutron-proton scattering experiment if the energy of the incident protons is 5 MeV; or 10 MeV? Above what energy would this scattering be susceptible to analysis by the Born approximation? (Remember that the neutron and proton have equal masses.)

(3) How does the total cross-section for neutron-proton scattering depend on energy in the range in which only *s*-waves need to be

considered? What is the magnitude of the cross-section at vanishingly low energies?

(4) Verify that for both the screened Coulomb potential and the spherical well, the differential scattering cross-section for small values of momentum and scattering angle has the limiting form stated on page 229.

(5) Find the differential and total scattering cross-sections, using the Born approximation (equation (10.7) etc.), for a scattering potential represented by $V(r) = V_0 \exp(-r^2/a_0^2)$. With the help of tables of the Gauss function find a range of pairs of values of V_0 and a_0 for which the total cross-section has a constant value, and find how this simultaneous variation affects the shape of the differential cross-section curve.

(6) Show that in the Born approximation the scattering at high energies is concentrated into small angles, and that the differential scattering cross-section takes the form $\sigma(\theta) = |f(v\theta)|^2$ where v is the velocity of the incident particle. Hence show that in these circumstances the total scattering cross-section varies inversely as the energy.

CHAPTER ELEVEN

TIME-DEPENDENT PERTURBATIONS: SEMI-CLASSICAL TREATMENT OF RADIATION PROBLEMS

Most of our knowledge of the structure of the atom has come from the study of the interaction between matter and radiation, and a crucial test of theories of atomic structure has been the extent to which they give satisfactory answers to questions about this inter-action. The present chapter deals with the interaction between atoms, regarded as quantized systems, and the electromagnetic field, described classically and represented by a continuous vector poten-tial. This semi-classical treatment follows closely that given by Schrödinger in 1926. From it we can derive selection rules which agree with those inferred from spectroscopic evidence; we can predict the relative intensities in line spectra, and we can show the connection between the theories of line spectra and optical dispersion. The representation of the quantal properties of the electromagnetic field is deferred until chapter 12; that treatment naturally gives a deeper insight into the properties of the electromagnetic field and its interactions, but it will appear that the quantitative predictions of the semi-classical method are in many respects the same as those of the more rigorous theory.

Interaction of atomic electron with electromagnetic radiation

We start by using time-dependent perturbation theory to calculate the probabilities of the emission and absorption of radiation by an atom. The treatment differs from that in the previous chapter in that, since we are here concerned with the interaction of an atom and an oscillatory electromagnetic field, the perturbation will have to be represented by a function which depends explicitly on time. Consequently, whereas (10.1a) is again our starting point, (10.1b) and what followed from it specifically is not applicable.

The classical Hamiltonian for a particle in an electromagnetic field superposed on a central field is

$$H = \frac{1}{2m}(\mathbf{p}-e\mathbf{A})^2 + e\phi + V(r), \tag{11.1}$$

where $\mathbf{A}$ and ϕ are the vector and scalar potentials of the field. Thus

$$H = \frac{p^2}{2m} - \frac{e}{2m}(\mathbf{p}.\mathbf{A}+\mathbf{A}.\mathbf{p}) + \frac{e^2}{2m}A^2 + e\phi + V(r).$$

If $\mathbf{A}$ can be expressed as a function of x, y, z this can be simplified. We know that

$$i(\mathbf{p}.\mathbf{f}(r)-\mathbf{f}(r).\mathbf{p}) = \hbar\{\mathbf{p},\mathbf{f}(r)\}$$

$$= \hbar\sum_i\left(\frac{\partial\mathbf{p}}{\partial p_i}\cdot\frac{\partial\mathbf{f}}{\partial q_i} - \frac{\partial\mathbf{p}}{\partial q_i}\cdot\frac{\partial\mathbf{f}}{\partial p_i}\right)$$

$$= \hbar\sum_i\frac{\partial\mathbf{p}}{\partial p_i}\cdot\frac{\partial\mathbf{f}}{\partial q_i}$$

$$= \hbar\,\mathrm{div}\,\mathbf{f}(r)$$

and so

$$i(\mathbf{p}.\mathbf{A}-\mathbf{A}.\mathbf{p}) = \hbar\,\mathrm{div}\,\mathbf{A}$$

$$\therefore \quad \mathbf{p}.\mathbf{A} = \mathbf{A}.\mathbf{p} - i\hbar\,\mathrm{div}\,\mathbf{A}. \tag{11.2}$$

The Hamiltonian can therefore be written

$$H = \frac{p^2}{2m} - \frac{e}{m}\mathbf{A}.\mathbf{p} - \frac{e\hbar}{2im}\,\mathrm{div}\,\mathbf{A} + \frac{e^2}{2m}A^2 + e\phi + V(r).$$

By means of a suitable gauge transformation we can make div $\mathbf{A}=0$ and $\phi=0$ for the radiation field, and if the field is weak we may neglect the term in A^2, so that we arrive at

$$H = \frac{p^2}{2m} + V(r) - \frac{e}{m}\mathbf{A}.\mathbf{p} \tag{11.3}$$

$$= H_0 + H'.$$

H_0 is the Hamiltonian for a particle moving in a central field, which has been discussed in chapters 4 and 5. The familiar substitution of differential operators for the components of the vector $\mathbf{p}$ gives for H' an operator

$$H' \rightarrow -\frac{e}{m}\frac{\hbar}{i}\mathbf{A}.\mathrm{grad}. \tag{11.4}$$

Over the volume of the atom we shall treat the incident electromagnetic wave as a plane wave, and we neglect any scattering that may occur, so for $\mathbf{A}$ we write

$$\mathbf{A}(\mathbf{r}, t) = \mathbf{A}_0 \, \varepsilon^{i\alpha} \varepsilon^{i(\mathbf{k} \cdot \mathbf{r} - \omega t)} + \mathbf{A}_0 \, \varepsilon^{-i\alpha} \varepsilon^{-i(\mathbf{k} \cdot \mathbf{r} - \omega t)}. \tag{11.5}$$

From (10.1a) we now have

$$i\hbar a_m(t) = \int_0^t \left[H'_{mn} \, \varepsilon^{i(\omega_{mn} - \omega)t} + H''_{mn} \, \varepsilon^{i(\omega_{mn} + \omega)t} \right] dt$$

$$= H'_{mn} \frac{\varepsilon^{i(\omega_{mn} - \omega)t} - 1}{i(\omega_{mn} - \omega)} + H''_{mn} \cdot \frac{\varepsilon^{i(\omega_{mn} + \omega)t} - 1}{i(\omega_{mn} + \omega)} \tag{11.6}$$

where

$$-H'_{mn} = \frac{e\hbar}{im} \varepsilon^{i\alpha} \int u_m{}^* \, \varepsilon^{i\mathbf{k} \cdot \mathbf{r}} \, \mathbf{A}_0 \cdot \operatorname{grad} u_n \, d\tau$$

and

$$-H''_{mn} = \frac{e\hbar}{im} \varepsilon^{-i\alpha} \int u_m{}^* \varepsilon^{-i\mathbf{k} \cdot \mathbf{r}} \, \mathbf{A}_0 \cdot \operatorname{grad} u_n \, d\tau.$$

Only one of these terms need concern us at one time. If $\omega_{mn} \approx \omega$ the first term will be very large compared with the second; if $\omega_{mn} \approx -\omega$ the second term will predominate over the first, while if neither of these conditions is satisfied we see from the discussion of Fig. 10.1, leading to equation (10.4), that the probability of a transition is vanishingly small. This means that transitions are probable only if

$$E_m - E_n \approx \pm \hbar \omega$$

which is Bohr's frequency condition – appearing here, not as a postulate as it did in the early Bohr theory, but as a deduction. Of these two possibilities one corresponds to an absorption of radiation from the field, the other to an emission induced by the field:

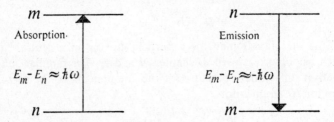

We shall consider the term in H'_{mn}, which represents an upward transition, that is, an absorption of radiation by the atom. We have then to integrate the first term in (11.6) over a range of frequencies ω around the frequency ω_{mn} for which it has its maximum value, to take account of the fact that the initial state of the system [atom + radiation] is not unique. The random motions of the emitting and absorbing atoms produce a Doppler broadening of the spectral lines, and the radiation which is present in the initial state has a continuum of frequencies. Suppose then that the radiation has a spectrum which is continuous over a small but finite frequency range, the components of different frequencies having random relative phases. The intensity in a radiation field is represented by the mean value of the Poynting vector $\mathbf{N}$, defined as

$$\mathbf{N} = \mathscr{E} \wedge \mathscr{H}.$$

Now (11.5) can be written as

$$\mathbf{A}(\mathbf{r}, t) = 2\mathbf{A}_0 \cos (\mathbf{k} \cdot \mathbf{r} - \omega t + \alpha)$$

and since

$$\mathscr{E} = -\dot{\mathbf{A}}, \ \mathscr{B} = \mu_0 \mathscr{H} = \operatorname{curl} \mathbf{A},$$

we have

$$\mathscr{E} = -2\omega \mathbf{A}_0 \sin (\mathbf{k} \cdot \mathbf{r} - \omega t + \alpha)$$

$$\mathscr{H} = -\frac{2\omega}{\mu_0 c} (\hat{\mathbf{k}} \wedge \mathbf{A}_0) \sin (\mathbf{k} \cdot \mathbf{r} - \omega t + \alpha)$$

where $\hat{\mathbf{k}}$ is a unit vector with the same direction as $\mathbf{k}$. Then the intensity is

$$\left| \overline{\mathbf{N}} \right| = \left| \overline{\mathscr{E} \wedge \mathscr{H}} \right| = \tfrac{1}{2} \cdot \frac{4\omega^2}{\mu_0 c} A_0{}^2 = \frac{2\omega^2}{\mu_0 c} A_0{}^2.$$

If we express this as $I(\omega)\Delta\omega$, where $\Delta\omega$ is the effective bandwidth of the radiation and $I(\omega)$ is the magnitude of the average intensity per unit bandwidth within this band, we get for $A_0{}^2$ the expression

$$A_0{}^2 = \frac{\mu_0 c}{2\omega^2} I(\omega) \Delta\omega.$$

Now, from (11.6), neglecting the second term on the right, and summing over the components of the incident radiation, we have (by a process similar to that which gave (10.2)):

$$\left| a_m(t) \right|^2 = \sum_\omega \frac{\left| H'_{mn} \right|^2}{\hbar^2} \frac{\sin^2 (\omega_{mn} - \omega) t/2}{(\omega_{mn} - \omega)^2 / 4}.$$

To evaluate this summation we proceed by the following stages:

We substitute for H'_{mn} from the equation following (11.6), and introduce an operator grad_A which finds the rate of change of the operand along the direction of $\mathbf{A}$, so that $\mathbf{A}_0 \cdot \text{grad} = A_0 \, \text{grad}_A$. Then we can substitute for A_0^2 in terms of $I(\omega)\Delta\omega$, and get $\left| a_m(t) \right|^2 =$

$$\sum_\omega \frac{\mu_0 ce^2}{2m^2\omega^2} I(\omega) \Delta\omega \left| \int u_m^* \varepsilon^{i\mathbf{k} \cdot \mathbf{r}} \text{grad}_A u_n \, d\tau \right|^2 \frac{\sin^2(\omega_{mn} - \omega)t/2}{(\omega_{mn} - \omega)^2/4}.$$

Now we take advantage of the fact that $I(\omega)$ can be assumed constant over the sharp maximum of the other frequency-dependent factor, with the value $I(\omega_{mn})$; this constant quantity is brought outside the summation, and the summation over ω is replaced by an integration over ω from $-\infty$ to $+\infty$, which is legitimate if the true breadth of the absorption line is less than the effective breadth of the spectrum of the incident radiation. This gives

$$|a_{mn}(t)|^2 = \frac{\mu_0 ce^2}{2m^2\omega^2} I(\omega_{mn}) \left| \int u_m^* \varepsilon^{i\mathbf{k} \cdot \mathbf{r}} \text{grad}_A u_n \, d\tau \right|^2 \int_{-\infty}^{+\infty} \frac{\sin^2(\omega_{mn} - \omega)t/2}{(\omega_{mn} - \omega)^2/4} d\omega$$

$$\therefore \ |a_{mn}(t)|^2 = \frac{\pi\mu_0 ce^2}{m^2\omega^2} I(\omega_{mn}) \left| \int u_m^* \varepsilon^{i\mathbf{k} \cdot \mathbf{r}} \text{grad}_A u_n \, d\tau \right|^2 t. \qquad (11.7)$$

The coefficient of t on the right is the transition probability.

For the downward transition there is a similar result with $\varepsilon^{i\mathbf{k}.\mathbf{r}}$ replaced by $\varepsilon^{-i\mathbf{k}.\mathbf{r}}$; the probabilities for absorption and induced emission are therefore the same.

The dipole approximation

The integral in (11.7) is usually evaluated by expanding the exponential term by term:

$$\varepsilon^{i\mathbf{k} \cdot \mathbf{r}} = 1 + i\mathbf{k}.\mathbf{r} - \frac{(\mathbf{k}.\mathbf{r})^2}{2!} - \cdots$$

The magnitudes of successive terms are as

$$1 : \frac{2\pi r}{\lambda} : \tfrac{1}{2}\left(\frac{2\pi r}{\lambda}\right)^2 : \cdots$$

that is, they decrease by factors of the order of magnitude of r/λ. Now the integral is to be taken over the space occupied by the atom, and the integrand is virtually zero at distances from the origin which are greater than about 10^{-8} cm. For visible and ultra-violet radiation $\lambda = 10^{-5}$ cm. The factor r/λ is therefore, in this case, of the order of 10^{-3}, and to start with we may put $\varepsilon^{i\mathbf{k}.\mathbf{r}} = 1$.

We then have to evaluate

$$\int u_m^* \operatorname{grad}_A u_n \, d\tau = \int u_m^* \left(\frac{\partial}{\partial r}\right)_A u_n \, d\tau$$

$$= \frac{i}{\hbar} \int u_m^* p_A u_n \, d\tau$$

$$= \frac{i}{\hbar} \langle p_A \rangle_{mn}$$

$$\therefore \int u_m^* \operatorname{grad}_A u_n \, d\tau = -\frac{m\omega_{mn}}{\hbar} \langle r_A \rangle_{mn}$$

since $\quad p = m\dot{q} = im\omega q$.

$e\langle r_A \rangle_{mn}$ is the component parallel to A of the electric dipole moment associated with the transition $u_n \to u_m$; this justifies the association between dipole moments and transition probabilities which was suggested in chapter 3. The transition probability can now be written

$$w_{mn} = \frac{\pi \mu_0 c e^2}{\hbar^2} I(\omega_{mn}) \left| \langle r_A \rangle_{mn} \right|^2.$$

If there is no static field applied to line up the angular momentum axes (the z-axes) of the atoms, we must calculate the x, y and z components of the dipole moment and average over all orientations; the result is

$$w_{mn} = \frac{\pi \mu_0 c e^2}{3\hbar^2} I(\omega_{mn}) \left| r_{mn} \right|^2. \tag{11.8}$$

This transition probability is that for induced transitions; we cannot use the methods of this chapter for a rigorous discussion of spontaneous emission, but, pending the more thorough discussion in chapter 12, we shall provisionally estimate the rate of spontaneous emission of radiation by considering the energy distribution of the radiation in equilibrium with the walls of a uniform temperature enclosure, i.e. the 'black-body radiation'.

Suppose the mean energy density of the radiation in unit bandwidth within the range $\Delta\omega$ around ω_{mn} is $\rho(\omega_{mn})$, so that

$$\rho(\omega)\Delta\omega = I(\omega)\Delta\omega/c$$

$$\therefore \quad \rho(\omega) = I(\omega)/c.$$

When the radiation in the enclosure is in thermal equilibrium with the walls, the number of atoms present in states u_n and u_m with energies E_n and E_m are proportional to $\varepsilon^{-E_n/kT}$ and $\varepsilon^{-E_m/kT}$ respectively. We have seen that the probabilities per atom of upward and downward transitions under the influence of radiation of frequency ω_{mn} are equal, and are proportional to the intensity of this radiation. Then the numbers of upward and downward transitions per second must be proportional to the number of atoms in the lower and upper states respectively, and to $\rho(\omega_{mn})$. Let these numbers per second of upward and downward transitions be

$$B_{mn}\rho(\omega_{mn})\varepsilon^{-E_n/kT} \quad \text{and} \quad B_{mn}\rho(\omega_{mn})\varepsilon^{-E_m/kT}.$$

B_{mn} must be proportional to the quantity w_{mn} of (11.8). In fact

$$B_{mn}\rho(\omega_{mn}) = w_{mn}$$

$$\therefore \quad B_{mn} = w_{mn}/\rho(\omega_{mn}) = w_{mn}c/I(\omega_{mn})$$

$$\therefore \quad B_{mn} = \frac{\pi\mu_0 c^2 e^2}{3\hbar^2}|r_{mn}|^2. \tag{11.9}$$

Since the exponential factors in the expression for the rates of the upward and downward transitions are not equal, the processes of stimulated absorption and emission cannot by themselves produce and maintain thermal equilibrium. The maintenance of equilibrium requires the further process of spontaneous emission – the occurrence of emissive transitions whose probability is independent of $\rho(\omega)$. If the number of spontaneous transitions per second is taken to be $A_{mn}\varepsilon^{-E_m/kT}$, equilibrium between the states m and n exists when

$$A_{mn}\varepsilon^{-E_m/kT} = B_{mn}\rho(\omega_{mn})(\varepsilon^{-E_n/kT}-\varepsilon^{-E_m/kT})$$

which is equivalent to

$$\rho(\omega_{mn}) = \frac{A_{mn}}{B_{mn}} \cdot \frac{1}{\varepsilon^{(E_m-E_n)/kT}-1}.$$

Since this specifies the spectral energy density of radiation in thermal equilibrium with matter in a uniform temperature enclosure, it must agree with the black-body radiation law found in chapter 8, and expressed by (8.13), which we now recall:

$$u_\nu\delta\nu = \frac{8\pi h}{c^3} \cdot \frac{\nu^3\delta\nu}{\varepsilon^{h\nu/kT}-1}. \tag{8.13}$$

Writing $\rho(\omega)\Delta\omega$ in place of $u_v\delta v$, and replacing h and v on the right by $2\pi\hbar$ and $\omega/2\pi$, we have

$$\rho(\omega) = \frac{\hbar}{\pi^2 c^3} \cdot \frac{\omega^3}{\varepsilon^{\hbar\omega/kT}-1}.$$

Comparing this with the expression above for $\rho(\omega_{mn})$, we see that A_{mn} and B_{mn} must satisfy the relation

$$\frac{A_{mn}}{B_{mn}} = \frac{\hbar\omega_{mn}{}^3}{\pi^2 c^3},$$

and combining this with (11.9) we get for the probability per second of a spontaneous decay from the state u_m to the state u_n,

$$A_{mn} = \frac{\mu_0 e^2 \omega_{mn}{}^3}{3\pi\hbar c}|r_{mn}|^2. \tag{11.10}$$

Since in each decay a quantum of energy $\hbar\omega_{mn}$ is emitted, the mean rate of spontaneous radiation of energy is

$$\bar{S} = A_{mn}\hbar\omega_{mn} = \frac{\mu_0 e^2 \omega_{mn}{}^4}{3\pi c}|r_{mn}|^2. \tag{11.11}$$

This result is independent of $\hbar$, and has the same form as the classical result for the rate of radiation from an oscillating electric dipole whose (angular) frequency is ω_{mn}.

The frequency dependence of the ratio A_{mn}/B_{mn} has an interesting technological consequence – that processes depending on induced or stimulated emission are more difficult to exhibit at very high – say optical – frequencies than at lower – say microwave – frequencies. The higher the frequency the more probable is the 'noise'-generating random process of spontaneous emission compared with the stimulated emission which can give rise to coherent radiation. Indeed A_{mn}/B_{mn} is approximately 10^{-28} at centimetric-wave frequencies, and approximately 10^{-14} in the visible spectrum, and this increase by 10^{14} in the relative probability of spontaneous emission or 'noise' is one of the fundamental reasons why the microwave maser was found easier to develop and utilize than the optical laser. (In this connection see problem (9) on p. 262.)

Dipole moments for circularly polarized radiation

(11.5) specifies the vector potential of a plane-polarized plane electromagnetic wave, and we have seen that the intensity of such radiation is proportional to, *inter alia*, the square of the component of the atomic electric dipole moment in the direction of A_0. It is important to find out what are the corresponding dipole moments for circularly polarized radiation, because it is well known from observations of the Zeeman effect that atoms may emit circularly polarized light and that there are selection rules which refer specifically to this possibility, and also because the formal decomposition of plane-polarized light into oppositely rotating circularly polarized components gives added insight into interaction processes in fields as separate as crystal optics and radio frequency spectroscopy.

It will simplify matters if we consider the case of a plane wave propagating along the z-axis. Then, if the phase angle α of (11.5) is zero for the x-polarized component of the wave we have

$$A_x(z, t) = A_{0,x}(\varepsilon^{i(kz-\omega t)} + \varepsilon^{-i(kz-\omega t)})$$

$$= 2A_{0,x} \cos (kz - \omega t).$$

If $\alpha = \pi/2$ for the y-component of A, since $\exp (i\pi/2) = i$ we have

$$A_y(z, t) = iA_{0,y}(\varepsilon^{i(kz-\omega t)} - \varepsilon^{-i(kz-\omega t)})$$

$$= -2A_{0,y} \sin (kz - \omega t).$$

Then if

$$A_{0,x} = A_{0,y} = A_0/2^{\frac{1}{2}},$$

$$\left.\begin{array}{c} A_x(z, t) = 2^{\frac{1}{2}}A_0 \cos (kz - \omega t) \\ A_y(z, t) = -2^{\frac{1}{2}}A_0 \sin (kz - \omega t) \end{array}\right\}$$

are the components of a circularly polarized wave whose field vector A appears to rotate clockwise in any plane $z = $ constant, when viewed by an observer looking along the z-axis in the direction in which the wave is travelling. If we had chosen to put $\alpha = -\pi/2$ for the y-component, the sign of A_y would have been reversed, and we should have had

$$\left.\begin{array}{c} A_x(z, t) = 2^{\frac{1}{2}}A_0 \cos (kz - \omega t) \\ A_y(z, t) = 2^{\frac{1}{2}}A_0 \sin (kz - \omega t) \end{array}\right\}$$

which are the components of a circularly polarized wave with an anticlockwise sense of rotation.

The expressions for H'_{mn} in (11.6) for the perturbation of an atom by the circularly polarized radiation field are clearly given by

$$-(H'_{mn})_x = \frac{e\hbar}{im} \int u_m^* \varepsilon^{ikz} A_0 \, (\mathrm{grad})_x \, u_n \, d\tau$$

$$-(H'_{mn})_y = \frac{e\hbar}{im} \exp(\pm i\pi/2) \int u_m^* \varepsilon^{ikz} A_0 \, (\mathrm{grad})_y \, u_n \, d\tau$$

and in the dipole approximation these would become

$$-(H'_{mn})_x = \frac{e\hbar}{im} \cdot \frac{i}{\hbar} \cdot im\omega_{mn}\langle x\rangle_{mn} = ie\omega_{mn}\langle x\rangle_{mn}$$

$$-(H'_{mn})_y = \frac{e\hbar}{im} \cdot \frac{i}{\hbar} \cdot im\omega_{mn} \exp(\pm i\pi/2)\langle y\rangle_{mn} = ie\omega_{mn}\langle \pm iy\rangle_{mn}.$$

The dipole matrix element associated with the absorption of the circularly polarized radiation is therefore

$$(H'_{mn})_{\text{circular pol.}} = -ie\omega_{mn}\langle x\pm iy\rangle_{mn}$$

the two signs corresponding to the two possible directions of rotation. Comparison of the definitions of H'_{mn} and H''_{mn} following (11.6) shows that, for the same direction of propagation and sense of rotation, H''_{mn} – which is the matrix element for emission – is the complex conjugate of H'_{mn}. The significance of this in relation to angular momentum conservation will emerge from the discussion of selection rules, in the following section.

Dipole selection rules

To calculate the intensity – or probability – of a specified transition by evaluating the dipole moment we need a complete knowledge of the corresponding state-functions. On the other hand we can sometimes assert that if the state-functions are of a certain type – for example, and most importantly, if l and m are 'good quantum numbers', which means that $m_1{}^2 + m_2{}^2 + m_3{}^2$ and m_3 are constants of the motion – then the transition probability is identically zero unless the values of l and m for the initial and final states differ by specific amounts. Such a statement is called a *selection rule*. The simplest selection rule for electric dipole transitions involves the concept of the 'parity' of a state-function, or of the state which that function represents.

If a state-function is a function of both space and spin coordinates, say $\psi(\mathbf{r}, \boldsymbol{\sigma})$, then if

$$\psi(\mathbf{r}, \boldsymbol{\sigma}) = \begin{cases} +\psi(-\mathbf{r}, \boldsymbol{\sigma}) \\ -\psi(-\mathbf{r}, \boldsymbol{\sigma}) \end{cases}$$

the state is said to have $\begin{cases} even \\ odd \end{cases}$ parity.† We shall first show that
eigenfunctions of a Hamiltonian in which the potential is such that
$V(-\mathbf{r}) = V(\mathbf{r})$ do possess a definite parity.

Let $\psi(\mathbf{r}, \sigma)$ be a non-degenerate eigenfunction of H with energy E,
so that

$$H\psi = E\psi.$$

Now replace $\mathbf{r}$ by $-\mathbf{r}$ which alters neither H nor E; then

$$H\psi(-\mathbf{r}, \sigma) = E\psi(-\mathbf{r}, \sigma).$$

Since the state represented by ψ is non-degenerate, $\psi(-\mathbf{r}, \sigma)$ and
$\psi(\mathbf{r}, \sigma)$ can differ at most only by a constant multiplier, so that

$$\psi(\mathbf{r}, \sigma) = C\psi(-\mathbf{r}, \sigma).$$

If we again replace $\mathbf{r}$ by $-\mathbf{r}$ we get

$$\psi(-\mathbf{r}, \sigma) = C\psi(\mathbf{r}, \sigma) = C^2\psi(-\mathbf{r}, \sigma)$$
$$\therefore C = \pm 1,$$

which shows that ψ must have a definite parity, either even or odd.

For the one-dimensional oscillator the parity alternates from one
eigenstate to the next up the level-scheme. For the eigenstates in the
central field problem, since $R(r)$ depends only on r which is essentially
positive, the parity depends on the angle-functions $Y_l(\theta, \phi)$ and is
even for even l, odd for odd l (see problem 11, p. 92).

Now for an electric dipole transition the probability of the transition between states ψ_{nlm} and $\psi_{n'l'm'}$ depends on quantities like

$$\int \psi_{n'l'm'}{}^* z\, \psi_{nlm}\, d\tau$$

which will vanish if the integrand is odd. Since z is odd, the integrand
is even – and therefore non-vanishing – only if one of the ψ's is even
and the other odd, so for electric dipole transitions the parities of the
initial and final states must differ.

A less general dipole selection rule was found, in quite a different
context, in the course of the discussion of the first order Stark effect
in chapter 6. It was shown there that the matrix element representing
the z-component of the electric dipole moment vanishes between all

† The replacement of $(\mathbf{r}, \sigma)$ by $(-\mathbf{r}, \sigma)$ represents a reflection of the state-
function through the origin. This reflection changes the sign of the position
vector $\mathbf{r}$, but the angular momentum vector, being an axial vector (and behaving
like $\mathbf{r} \wedge \mathbf{p}$), is unaltered.

pairs of states with different values of the quantum number m. We shall now see how such selection rules can be obtained systematically.

A selection rule is usually stated in the form: the transitions which can or cannot occur are those in which the value of a named quantum number changes by specified amounts. This is a useful type of statement since the initial and final stationary states are usually specified by the quantum numbers associated with a set of compatible variables. Since the stationary states are eigenstates of the unperturbed Hamiltonian, these quantum numbers usually specify the values of the energy and of the other variables which commute with the Hamiltonian. Consequently, the selection rules can be found by investigating the commutation relations between the perturbation which causes the transition and the variables whose quantum numbers label the stationary states.

The selection rules for electric dipole transitions in which radiation polarized in the x, y or z directions is emitted or absorbed will be found from the commutators of x, y and z with quantities like m_z and θ, the z-component and the square of the angular momentum respectively. The commutation relations for x, y and z with m_z are, from (2.10b) and (4.3),

$$m_z x - x m_z = i\hbar y$$

$$m_z y - y m_z = -i\hbar x$$

$$m_z z - z m_z = 0.$$

From the third of these the rsth element† of the commutator matrix is

$$(m_z z)_{rs} - (z m_z)_{rs} = (m_z)_r z_{rs} - z_{rs}(m_z)_s = 0$$

$$\therefore \quad ((m_z)_r - (m_z)_s) z_{rs} = 0$$

in a representation in which m_z is diagonal, so $z_{rs} = 0$ – and radiation polarized in a plane containing the z-axis cannot be emitted or absorbed in an electric dipole transition between the states labelled by r and s – unless $(m_z)_r = (m_z)_s$. We have thus arrived at a selection rule for transitions associated with radiation with a z-component of polarization:

$$\Delta m_z = 0.$$

† In this section we use r and s rather than m and n to label the initial and final states since m will occur so frequently denoting an angular momentum component.

Corresponding selection rules for dipole transitions associated with radiation having x- or y-components of polarization can be found, with slightly more work. If we eliminate x between the first and second commutation relations above, we get

$$[m_z, [m_z, y]] = m_z(m_z y - y m_z) - (m_z y - y m_z)m_z = \hbar^2 y$$

$$\therefore \quad m_z^2 y - 2 m_z y m_z + y m_z^2 = \hbar^2 y.$$

For the rsth element, then,

$$(m_z)_r^2 y_{rs} - 2(m_z)_r y_{rs}(m_z)_s + y_{rs}(m_z)_s^2 = \hbar^2 y_{rs}$$

and $y_{rs} = 0$ unless

$$((m_z)_r - (m_z)_s)^2 = \hbar^2$$

$$\therefore \quad (m_z)_r - (m_z)_s = \pm \hbar$$

$$\therefore \quad \Delta m_z = \pm \hbar.$$

This is the selection rule for dipole transitions associated with radiation which has a y-component of polarization. Considerations of symmetry – or an exactly similar argument starting with the elimination of y between the first two of the commutation relations above – leads to the same selection rule for radiation with an x-component of polarization.

Again, considerations of symmetry – or similar arguments starting from the commutators of x, y and z with m_x or m_y – lead to the further conclusion that in transitions associated with radiation having a z-component of polarization m_x and m_y must change by $\pm \hbar$. This is not usually a useful statement, open to verification, since if the value of m_z is known, m_x and m_y must in general be indeterminate within the limits allowed by the definition

$$\theta = l(l+1)\hbar^2 = m_x^2 + m_y^2 + m_z^2.$$

But we can see at once from this that for an s-state ($l=0$), for which $\theta = 0$, we can assert positively that $m_x = m_y = m_z = 0$. It follows that a dipole transition cannot occur between states both of which have $l=0$, since none of the components m_x, m_y, m_z can change in that case, whereas the rules we have just found show that *at least one* of these components *must* change in a dipole transition. *Electric dipole transitions symbolized by $\Delta l = 0$ do not occur*, therefore.

The derivation of selection rules in terms of the quantum number l involves more tedious algebra, starting from the commutation relations for x, y and z with θ. Only one of these need be worked out, since, when one is known, the other two can be written down from symmetry. For example, then,

$$[\theta, x] = [m_x^2, x] + [m_y^2, x] + [m_z^2, x]$$
$$= m_x[m_x, x] + [m_x, x]m_x$$
$$+ m_y[m_y, x] + [m_y, x]m_y$$
$$+ m_z[m_z, x] + [m_z, x]m_z.$$

Substituting for these commutators from equations (4.3) and their various permutations, we get

$$[\theta, x] = -i\hbar(m_y z + z m_y) + i\hbar(m_z y + y m_z)$$
$$= -i\hbar(m_y z - z m_y + 2z m_y) + i\hbar(m_z y - y m_z + 2y m_z)$$
$$= -i\hbar(i\hbar x + 2z m_y) + i\hbar(-i\hbar x + 2y m_z)$$
$$= -2i\hbar(z m_y - y m_z + i\hbar x) \tag{i}$$
$$= -2i\hbar(m_y z - y m_z) \tag{ii}$$
$$= -2i\hbar(z m_y - m_z y). \tag{iii}$$

The last three expressions for $[\theta, x]$ have been labelled for reference in the next step. We are going to evaluate $[\theta, [\theta, z]]$ and our aim is to eliminate x, y, m_x and m_y from the expansion of this double commutator. It is expedient to express $[\theta, x]$ in terms of (iii) above, i.e.

$$[\theta, x] = -2i\hbar(z m_y - m_z y),$$

to express $[\theta, y]$ in terms of the appropriate permutation of (ii), i.e.

$$[\theta, y] = -2i\hbar(m_z x - z m_x),$$

and to express $[\theta, z]$ as the appropriate permutation of (i), i.e.

$$[\theta, z] = -2i\hbar(y m_x - x m_y + i\hbar z).$$

Thus

$$[\theta, [\theta, z]] = -2i\hbar[\theta, y m_x - x m_y + i\hbar z]$$
$$= -2i\hbar[\theta, y]m_x + 2i\hbar[\theta, x]m_y + 2\hbar^2[\theta, z]$$
$$= -4\hbar^2(m_z x - z m_x)m_x + 4\hbar^2(z m_y - m_z y)m_y + 2\hbar^2(\theta z - z\theta)$$
$$= -4\hbar^2 m_z(x m_x + y m_y + z m_z) + 4\hbar^2 z(m_x^2 + m_y^2 + m_z^2) + 2\hbar^2(\theta z - z\theta).$$

Now $\quad xm_x + ym_y + zm_z = \mathbf{r} \cdot \mathbf{m} = \mathbf{r} \cdot (\mathbf{r} \wedge \mathbf{p}) \equiv 0$

$\therefore \quad [\theta, [\theta, z]] = 4\hbar^2 z\theta + 2\hbar^2 \theta z - 2\hbar^2 z\theta = 2\hbar^2 (z\theta + \theta z)$

$\therefore \quad \theta(\theta z - z\theta) - (\theta z - z\theta)\theta = 2\hbar^2 (z\theta + \theta z)$

$\therefore \quad \theta^2 z - 2\theta z\theta + z\theta^2 = 2\hbar^2 (z\theta + \theta z).$

Taking the rsth element on each side of this operator equation, and remembering that θ is diagonal and that the appropriate diagonal elements are $\theta_r = l_r(l_r + 1)\hbar^2$ and $\theta_s = l_s(l_s + 1)\hbar^2$, we have

$$\{l_r^2 (l_r + 1)^2 - 2l_r l_s (l_r + 1)(l_s + 1) + l_s^2 (l_s + 1)^2 - 2l_r(l_r + 1) - 2l_s(l_s + 1)\}z_{rs}$$
$$= 0.$$

Evidently $z_{rs} = 0$ unless the expression in brackets vanishes, so the selection rules will be expressed in relations between l_r and l_s which solve the equation

$$l_r^2 (l_r + 1)^2 - 2l_r l_s (l_r + 1)(l_s + 1) + l_s^2 (l_s + 1)^2 - 2l_r(l_r + 1) - 2l_s(l_s + 1) = 0$$

The expression on the left of the equation is symmetrical in l_r and l_s, so we should hope that this expression would factorize into four linear factors. Since both positive and negative signs occur, either two of these factors must contain l_r and l_s in the combination $l_r - l_s$, and two involve $l_r + l_s$, or all four must involve $l_r - l_s$. It is easy to verify, by putting $l_r = -l_s$, that $l_r + l_s$ is itself a factor. Then if the expression above is written with all the bracketed factors multiplied out, the algebraic long division by $l_r + l_s$ can be performed. During that process the various terms are necessarily grouped in a way which – as the reader can verify – shows up the other factors as $(l_r + l_s + 2)$, $(l_r - l_s + 1)$ and $(l_r - l_s - 1)$. Thus we have the selection rules for electric dipole radiation in terms of the quantum number l as

$$l_r + l_s \quad\;\; = 0$$
$$l_r + l_s + 2 = 0$$
$$\left.\begin{array}{l} l_r - l_s + 1 = 0 \\ l_r - l_s - 1 = 0 \end{array}\right\} \quad or \quad \Delta l = \pm 1.$$

The first two of these must be rejected, for the following reasons: Since each of l_r and l_s must obey the condition $l \geqslant 0$, the first of the conditions above can be satisfied only if $l_r = l_s = 0$, a possibility we previously rejected because it would imply $\Delta m_x = \Delta m_y = \Delta m_z = 0$

which is barred by the selection rules for m. The second of the above conditions is incompatible with the rule that l cannot be negative. We are therefore left with the rule $\Delta l = \pm 1$, which is consistent with, and more stringent than, the selection rule for parity.

The emission or absorption of circularly polarized radiation is contingent on the non-vanishing of the matrix elements of such quantities as $(x+iy)$ and $(x-iy)$. The selection rules for this are easily found. From the commutation rules for x and y with m_z it is easily seen that

$$[m_z, x+iy] = i\hbar(y-ix)$$
$$= \hbar(x+iy)$$

$\therefore \qquad m_z(x+iy)-(x+iy)m_z = \hbar(x+iy)$

$\therefore \quad (m_z)_r(x+iy)_{rs}-(x+iy)_{rs}(m_z)_s = \hbar(x+iy)_{rs}$

$\therefore \quad (x+iy)_{rs} = 0 \quad$ unless $\quad (m_z)_r-(m_z)_s = \hbar$

so $(x+iy)_{rs}$ vanishes unless $\Delta m_z = \hbar$.

Similarly, $(x-iy)_{rs}$ vanishes unless $\Delta m_z = -\hbar$.

Reference to the previous section will now show that the following statements can be made:
  (i) Radiation travelling in the positive z-direction and circularly polarized clockwise is absorbed in transitions in which $\Delta m_z = \hbar$, and emitted in transitions in which $\Delta m_z = -\hbar$;
  (ii) Radiation travelling in the positive z-direction and circularly polarized anticlockwise is absorbed in transitions in which $\Delta m_z = -\hbar$, and emitted in transitions in which $\Delta m_z = \hbar$.
These statements imply that angular momentum is transferred between the atom and the circularly polarized radiation field, and that the selection rules are expressions of the conservation of angular momentum in the interaction. Electromagnetic theory does indeed predict, and experiments confirm, that circularly polarized waves exert a torque on matter, and transfer angular momentum to it.

The dipole selection rules derived here find one of their most direct confirmations in the normal Zeeman effect. The σ-components, which are plane-polarized perpendicular to the field-direction (the z-direction) in the transverse Zeeman effect, and circularly polarized in opposite senses in the longitudinal Zeeman effect, result from the transitions for which $\Delta m_z = \pm \hbar$, and the π-component which is plane-polarized parallel to the field in the transverse effect and is not seen in the longitudinal effect results from the transition $\Delta m_z = 0$.

The application of these selection rules to absorption processes is illustrated in optical pumping experiments, in which selected Zeeman sub-levels of an excited state are populated preferentially by placing the absorbing gas or vapour in a magnetic field and illuminating it with light of the appropriate frequency, propagation direction, and state of polarization.

Forbidden transitions

Transitions for which the dipole matrix elements vanish are called 'forbidden transitions'. Such transitions, though 'forbidden', may occur, for the 'forbidden-ness' is predicted from the assumption that the vector potential is constant over the volume of the atom. Suppose we know that the first term in the expansion of $\varepsilon^{i\mathbf{k}.\mathbf{r}}$ in (11.7) vanishes; the next term gives an integral like

$$i \int u_m{}^* \, \mathbf{k} \cdot \mathbf{r} \, \mathrm{grad}_A \, u_n \, d\tau$$

$$= -\frac{1}{\hbar} \int u_m{}^* (\mathbf{k} \cdot \mathbf{r}) \, p_A u_n \, d\tau$$

$$= \frac{\mathbf{A}}{|\mathbf{A}|} \frac{2\pi}{\lambda \hbar} \int u_m{}^* (r_k \cdot p_A) u_n \, d\tau.$$

This depends on both the position and the momentum vectors of the electron, and on their orientation relative to the vectors $\mathbf{A}$ and $\mathbf{k}$ which specify the electromagnetic field; it therefore depends on the orientation and shape of the atom in a more complicated way than the dipole moment. We write

$$r_k \cdot p_A = \tfrac{1}{2}(r_k \cdot p_A - r_A \cdot p_k) + \tfrac{1}{2}(r_k \cdot p_A + r_A \cdot p_k).$$

Since $\mathbf{k}$ and $\mathbf{A}$ are orthogonal we can take their directions as defining the x- and y-axes respectively, so that this becomes

$$r_k \cdot p_A = \tfrac{1}{2}(xp_y - yp_x) + \tfrac{1}{2}(xp_y + yp_x). \tag{11.12}$$

The first bracket here represents the angular momentum about the z-axis, with which there is associated a magnetic dipole moment

$$\frac{\mu_0 e}{2m} \cdot \tfrac{1}{2}(xp_y - yp_x)$$

or, in wave-mechanical form,

$$\frac{\mu_0 e}{4m} \frac{\hbar}{i} \frac{\partial}{\partial \phi}.$$

If the matrix element of this quantity does not vanish we speak of the corresponding transition as a 'magnetic dipole transition'. It results from the interaction between the radiation field and the moving charge through the Lorentz force $e(\mathbf{v} \wedge \mathscr{B})$. In a plane electromagnetic wave $|\mathscr{B}| = |\mathscr{E}|/c$, so the Lorentz force on the electron is smaller than the electrostatic force $e\mathscr{E}$ which appears in the dipole interaction by the factor v/c. It is easy to verify from the Bohr atomic model that $v/c \approx r/\lambda$, where r is the atomic radius (problem 1, p. 261).

The second bracket of (11.12) can be manipulated as follows:

$$\tfrac{1}{2}(r_k \cdot p_A + r_A \cdot p_k)$$

$$= \frac{m}{2}(x\dot{y} + y\dot{x})$$

$$= \frac{m}{2} \frac{d}{dt}(xy) \quad \text{since } x \text{ and } y \text{ commute.}$$

This is the time-derivative of one of a set of six quantities which form the quadrupole moment tensor:

$$e^2 \begin{bmatrix} 3x^2 - r^2 & 3xy & 3xz \\ 3yx & 3y^2 - r^2 & 3yz \\ 3zx & 3zy & 3z^2 - r^2 \end{bmatrix}$$

These quantities are very similar to those which specify the 'ellipsoid of inertia' in the classical dynamics of rigid bodies; they express the non-sphericity of the charge distribution. Transitions for which non-vanishing probabilities exist through these quantities are called 'electric quadrupole transitions'. The intimate link between the magnetic dipole and electric quadrupole transitions suggests that they will tend to have comparable magnitudes. (See however Blatt and Weisskopf, *Theoretical Nuclear Physics*, footnote on p. 592.)

In the emission of γ-rays by excited nuclei magnetic dipole and electric quadrupole transitions are commoner than they are in atomic processes. The charges in the nucleus are all of the same sign, and because of correlations between their motions, they tend to be symmetrically distributed relative to the centre of mass.

Nuclear electric dipole moments are therefore in general rather small, and nuclear electric dipole transitions are not common.

Optical dispersion

Just as the application of a static electric field to an atom produces a static polarization which is responsible for the macroscopic dielectric constant, so the incidence of an alternating electric field in the form of electromagnetic radiation produces an alternating polarization which accounts for the macroscopic refractive index. The variation of the refractive index with frequency is called *dispersion*, and since the time of Maxwell and Sellmeier the study of optical dispersion has generated a series of fruitful speculations about the interaction between atoms or molecules and light-waves.

The Hamiltonian for the interaction is (11.3), viz:

$$H = \frac{p^2}{2m} + V(r) - \frac{e}{m}\mathbf{A} \cdot \mathbf{p}$$

but in place of (11.5) we shall take for $\mathbf{A}$ the simpler form

$$\mathbf{A}(t) = \mathbf{A}_0(\varepsilon^{-i\omega t} + \varepsilon^{i\omega t}).$$

In omitting the factors $\varepsilon^{\pm i\mathbf{k}\cdot\mathbf{r}}$ from the start we are restricting ourselves to the dipole approximation, and the omission of the factors $\varepsilon^{\pm i\alpha}$ implies the choice of a definite phase for the incident radiation. The time-dependent Schrödinger equation now has the form

$$-\frac{\hbar^2}{2m}\nabla^2\psi + V(r)\psi - i\hbar\frac{\partial\psi}{\partial t} = \frac{e}{m}\mathbf{A}_0 \cdot \mathbf{p}(\varepsilon^{-i\omega t} + \varepsilon^{i\omega t})\psi. \tag{11.13}$$

When $\mathbf{A}_0$ is zero this equation has solutions $u_n(\mathbf{r})\,\varepsilon^{-i\omega_n t}$, so we shall attempt to find solutions of the type

$$\psi = u_n(\mathbf{r})\,\varepsilon^{-i\omega_n t} + v(\mathbf{r}, t).$$

In the first-order approximation the amplitude of $v(\mathbf{r}, t)$ will be proportional to A_0. When this ψ is substituted into (11.13) the terms in u_n on the left-hand side vanish, while the terms in v on the right-hand side may be ignored because they are multiplied by A_0 and are therefore of the second order of small quantities. What remains is an inhomogeneous equation for $v(\mathbf{r}, t)$:

$$-\frac{\hbar^2}{2m}\nabla^2 v + Vv - i\hbar\frac{\partial v}{\partial t} = \frac{e}{m}\mathbf{A}_0 \cdot \mathbf{p}(\varepsilon^{-i(\omega_n - \omega)t} + \varepsilon^{-i(\omega_n + \omega)t})u_n$$

which has solutions

$$v(\mathbf{r}, t) = v_+(\mathbf{r})\, \varepsilon^{-i(\omega_n + \omega)t} + v_-(\mathbf{r})\, \varepsilon^{-i(\omega_n - \omega)t}.$$

The $v_\pm(\mathbf{r})$ must satisfy the equations

$$-\frac{\hbar^2}{2m}\nabla^2 v_\pm + V v_\pm - (E_n \pm E)v_\pm = \frac{e}{m}\mathbf{A}_0 \cdot \mathbf{p}\, u_n. \quad (11.14)$$

To solve (11.14), we expand $v_\pm(\mathbf{r})$ and $e/m\, \mathbf{A}_0 \cdot \mathbf{p}\, u_n(\mathbf{r})$ as

$$v_\pm(\mathbf{r}) = \sum_m a_{\pm m} u_m(\mathbf{r}), \quad \frac{e}{m}\mathbf{A}_0 \cdot \mathbf{p}\, u_n(\mathbf{r}) = \sum_m H'_{mn}\, u_m(\mathbf{r})$$

(cf. p. 242) and substitute these expansions in (11.14) to obtain

$$\sum_m a_{\pm m}\left\{ -\frac{\hbar^2}{2m}\nabla^2 u_m + V u_m - (E_n \pm E)u_m \right\} = \sum_m H'_{mn} u_m.$$

But

$$-\frac{\hbar^2}{2m}\nabla^2 u_m + V u_m = E_m u_m,$$

so

$$\sum_m a_{\pm m}\{E_m - (E_n \pm E)\}u_m = \sum_m H'_{mn} u_m.$$

Comparing coefficients we see that

$$a_{\pm m} = \frac{H'_{mn}}{E_n - E_m \pm E}.$$

Hence

$$\psi = u_n \varepsilon^{-i\omega_n t} + \sum_m u_m H'_{mn}\left\{ \frac{\varepsilon^{-i(\omega_n + \omega)t}}{E_n - E_m + \hbar\omega} + \frac{\varepsilon^{-i(\omega_n - \omega)t}}{E_n - E_m - \hbar\omega} \right\}. \quad (11.15)$$

This result will not be valid when $\hbar\omega \approx \pm(E_n - E_m)$, for one of the amplitudes under the summation then becomes so large that the first-order approximation breaks down. In fact, when $\hbar\omega \approx |E_n - E_m|$ the probability of observing the state u_m is controlled by the occurrence of induced transitions between the states u_n and u_m.

From (11.15) we could calculate a charge-probability density $e\psi^* \psi$ which would contain terms representing a forced oscillation of the charge distribution in phase with the applied field. It is of more immediate interest to find the dipole moment of the state represented by ψ. Taking the z-axis to lie along the direction of $\mathbf{A}_0$, and evaluating $e \int \psi^* z\, \psi\, d\tau$, we find that

$$e\langle z\rangle_\psi = e\langle z\rangle_n + e\sum_m \langle z\rangle_{nm} H'_{nm}\left\{\frac{\varepsilon^{-i\omega t}}{E_n-E_m+\hbar\omega}+\frac{\varepsilon^{i\omega t}}{E_n-E_m-\hbar\omega}\right\}$$

(where we have neglected terms in H'^2), and the real part of this is

$$e\langle z\rangle_n + 2e\cos\omega t\sum_m \langle z\rangle_{nm} H'_{nm}\frac{E_n-E_m}{(E_n-E_m)^2-(\hbar\omega)^2}. \quad (11.16)$$

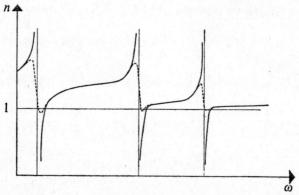

FIG. 11.1. Dispersion curve for a gas. The continuous curve is plotted according to eqn. (11.18); the dotted interpolations show the effect of damping.

Now in the dipole approximation, which is implicit in the expression we adopted for $\mathbf{A}(t)$, the perturbation depends only on the electric vector of the radiation field, so just as in the Stark effect (p. 130) we have

$$H'_{nm} = -e\mathscr{E}z_{nm}.$$

The amplitude of the time-dependent term in (11.16) is therefore

$$2e^2\mathscr{E}\sum_m \frac{|z_{nm}|^2(E_n-E_m)}{(E_n-E_m)^2-(\hbar\omega)^2} = \alpha(\omega)\mathscr{E}. \quad (11.17)$$

This gives the polarization $\alpha(\omega)$ produced by radiation whose frequency is remote from an absorption or emission line in the atomic spectrum. In a dilute material containing N atoms in unit volume the refractive index is

$$n(\omega) = 1 + 4\pi Ne^2\sum_m \frac{|z_{nm}|^2(E_n-E_m)}{(E_n-E_m)^2-(\hbar\omega)^2}$$

$$= 1 + \frac{4\pi Ne^2}{\hbar}\sum_m \frac{|z_{nm}|^2\omega_{nm}}{\omega_{nm}^2-\omega^2}. \quad (11.18)$$

The variation of n with ω is illustrated in Fig. 11.1. The dotted regions of the curve are not consistent with (11.18), but represent the behaviour of n in the regions $\omega \approx |\omega_{nm}|$ to which (11.18) does not apply. (11.18) can be modified to show the correct behaviour in these regions by the addition of 'damping terms' in the denominators; these represent the damping of the oscillating dipoles by their interaction with the total radiation field, including the radiation which they themselves emit.

When the applied electric field is a static one we put $\omega = 0$ in (11.17), and it gives

$$\alpha(0) = 2e^2 \sum_m \frac{|z_{nm}|^2}{E_n - E_m} \tag{11.19}$$

in agreement with (6.11). We see now that the 'oscillator strengths' of chapter 6 are proportional to the spectral transition probabilities calculated in the present chapter, and through the correspondence principle we may visualize the polarization of the atom as the sum of the polarizations of the 'oscillators' which generate the various spectral lines.

Problems

(1) Use the Bohr atomic model to show that

$$\frac{r}{\lambda} \approx \frac{v}{c} \quad \text{(see p. 257)}.$$

(2) Show that the selection rules for magnetic dipole transitions are
$$\Delta l = 0; \ \Delta m = 0, \pm 1.$$

(3) Show that the selection rules for electric quadrupole transitions are $\Delta l = 0, \pm 2; \ \Delta m = 0, \pm 1, \pm 2$.

(4) Calculate and compare the probabilities per second that a hydrogen atom in the state ψ_{310} will decay to the states ψ_{200} or ψ_{100}, given that the state-functions are

$$\psi_{310} = \frac{\sqrt{2}}{81\sqrt{\pi}} \left(\frac{1}{a_0}\right)^{\frac{3}{2}} \left(6 - \frac{r}{a_0}\right) \frac{r}{a_0} \varepsilon^{-r/3a_0} \cos\theta,$$

$$\psi_{200} = \frac{1}{4\sqrt{2\pi}} \left(\frac{1}{a_0}\right)^{\frac{3}{2}} \left(2 - \frac{r}{a_0}\right) \varepsilon^{-r/2a_0},$$

$$\psi_{100} = \frac{1}{\sqrt{\pi}} \left(\frac{1}{a_0}\right)^{\frac{3}{2}} \varepsilon^{-r/a_0}.$$

(5) Show that $\sum_m |z_{mn}|^2 = \langle z^2 \rangle_n$. Use this result along with (11.19)
to estimate the polarizability of a hydrogen atom in its ground
state. The result is: $\alpha/4\pi\varepsilon_0 < 5\cdot3\,a_0^3$. Cf. (6.13) and the last
paragraph of chapter 6.

(6) If $A_{mn} = \int u_m{}^* \operatorname{grad_A} u_n\, d\tau$ show by partial integration that
$-A_{mn} = \int (\operatorname{grad_A} u_m{}^*)\, u_n\, d\tau$ and hence that

$$A_{mn} = \frac{im}{\hbar} \int (S_{mn})_A\, d\tau$$

where

$$S_{mn} = \frac{\hbar}{2im}\{u_m{}^* \operatorname{grad} u_n - (\operatorname{grad} u_m{}^*)\, u_n\}$$

(Cf. (9.16)).

Then use the continuity equation in the form

$$\operatorname{div} S_{mn} + \frac{\partial \rho_{mn}}{\partial t} = \operatorname{div} S_{mn} + i\omega_{mn}\rho_{mn} = 0$$

to show that

$$A_{mn} = \frac{m\omega_{mn}}{\hbar} \langle r_A \rangle_{mn}.$$

(7) Find the eigenvalues, and the character of the corresponding
eigenfunctions, of the operator A defined by the equation

$$A\psi(x) = \psi(-x).$$

Show that this operator A anticommutes with the momentum
operator $p = \frac{\hbar}{i}\frac{\partial}{\partial x}$, i.e. $Ap + pA = 0$. Hence show that eigenfunctions of the momentum operator do not have a definite
parity.

(8) Show that a perturbation of even parity (such that $V'(\mathbf{r}) = V'(-\mathbf{r})$)
can produce transitions only between states of like parity, where-
as a perturbation of odd parity (such that $V'(\mathbf{r}) = -V'(-\mathbf{r})$) can
produce transitions only between states of unlike parity.

(9) At optical wavelengths, say 6,000 Å, an intensity of 0·1 watts/cm^2
in a spectral line whose fractional breadth $\Delta\omega/\omega$ is 10^{-5} is perhaps
obtainable. Estimate the probabilities per atom per second of
spontaneous and induced transitions in an emission line of this
wavelength in an excited gas exposed to such irradiation, assum-
ing that $|r_{mn}|$ might be $0\cdot5 \times 10^{-8}$ cm.

Then carry out the similar calculations for a microwave

transition in gas molecules exposed to an intense microwave beam, assuming a wavelength of 3 cm, an intensity of 100 watts/cm^2, $\Delta\omega/\omega = 10^{-4}$, and a molecular dipole moment corresponding to $|r_{mn}| = 0.8 \times 10^{-8}$ cm.

CHAPTER TWELVE

THE QUANTIZATION OF RADIATION

Although quantum theory originated in attempts to account for phenomena observed when radiation interacts with matter, the greater part of this book has been concerned with the quantization of systems consisting of matter alone. The major exceptions to this have been the discussion of black-body radiation in chapter 8, where the idea that the radiation field could be regarded as an assembly of quanta was used without any preliminary justification; and the discussion of the absorption and emission of radiation by an atom in chapter 11, where the radiation field was described in a quite classical way. The treatment in chapter 11 appears to account satisfactorily for induced emission and absorption, but the subsequent argument about spontaneous emission is not altogether convincing. It is the main task of the present chapter to show that a representation of the field in terms of non-commuting variables leads to a more satisfactory account of the interaction between matter and radiation; this treatment leads directly to a quantization of the field, and enables us to distinguish between situations in which the wave ('classical') or the corpuscular ('quantal') aspects of the field are to the fore.

Hamiltonian representation of the classical electromagnetic field

Since the quantum theory of material systems is based on the Hamiltonian function of classical mechanics, it is convenient to use a similar representation of the radiation field. A pure radiation field can be derived from a vector potential $\mathbf{A}$ which is a function of position and time and satisfies the equations

$$\nabla^2 \mathbf{A} - \frac{1}{c^2}\ddot{\mathbf{A}} = 0 \tag{12.1a}$$

$$\operatorname{div} \mathbf{A} = 0. \tag{12.1b}$$

Then
$$\mathscr{E} = -\dot{\mathbf{A}} \tag{12.2a}$$

and
$$\mathscr{B} = \mu_0 \mathscr{H} = \operatorname{curl} \mathbf{A}. \tag{12.2b}$$

We suppose the radiation to be enclosed in a large cube of side L. If we impose the boundary condition that $\mathbf{A}$ is to be periodic in L, we can represent the general solution of (12.1) as a superposition of orthogonal 'eigenwaves', each of which is separately a solution of (12.1) and satisfies the boundary condition. We have then

$$\mathbf{A} = \sum_\lambda q_\lambda(t)\, \mathbf{A}_\lambda(\mathbf{r}). \tag{12.3}$$

The suffices λ specify the normal modes of the radiation in the cube; the q_λ depend only on time and the $\mathbf{A}_\lambda$ depend only on position. Substituting (12.3) into (12.1), we see that the q_λ must satisfy the differential equation for a simple harmonic oscillator:

$$\ddot{q}_\lambda + \omega_\lambda{}^2\, q_\lambda = 0 \tag{12.4}$$

while the $\mathbf{A}_\lambda$ have to satisfy the equations

$$\nabla^2 \mathbf{A}_\lambda + \frac{\omega_\lambda{}^2}{c^2}\mathbf{A}_\lambda = 0 \tag{12.5a}$$

$$\operatorname{div} \mathbf{A}_\lambda = 0. \tag{12.5b}$$

The solutions of (12.5) which are periodic in L represent a set of orthogonal waves – in fact Fourier components – which can be normalized so that

$$\int_{L^3} \mathbf{A}_\lambda . \mathbf{A}_\mu\, d\tau = \mu_0 c^2 \delta_{\mu\lambda}. \tag{12.6}$$

For instance we may use for the $\mathbf{A}_\lambda$ sin and cos functions like

$$L^{-\frac{3}{2}}(2\mu_0 c^2)^{\frac{1}{2}}\, \mathbf{e}_\lambda \sin \mathbf{k}_\lambda . \mathbf{r} \quad \text{and} \quad L^{-\frac{3}{2}}(2\mu_0 c^2)^{\frac{1}{2}}\, \mathbf{e}_\lambda \cos \mathbf{k}_\lambda . \mathbf{r}.$$

The wave-vectors $\mathbf{k}_\lambda$ specify the wavelengths and directions of propagation, and the $\mathbf{e}_\lambda$ are unit vectors which specify the plane of polarization; from (12.5a) and (12.5b) $\mathbf{k}_\lambda$ and $\mathbf{e}_\lambda$ must be orthogonal. To satisfy the boundary condition on $\mathbf{A}_\lambda$, $\mathbf{k}_\lambda$ must be restricted so that its x-, y- and z-components have only the values

$$k_{\lambda x} = \frac{2\pi}{L} n_{\lambda x}, \quad k_{\lambda y} = \frac{2\pi}{L} n_{\lambda y}, \quad k_{\lambda z} = \frac{2\pi}{L} n_{\lambda z} \tag{12.7}$$

(cf. p. 172) where $n_{\lambda x}$, $n_{\lambda y}$, $n_{\lambda z}$ are positive integers.

The $\mathbf{A}_\lambda$ are completely determined by (12.5) and (12.6), so the state of the field is characterized by the amplitudes $q_\lambda(t)$ associated with its several normal modes. The q_λ satisfy (12.4), and have dimensions $[M^{\frac{1}{2}}L]$. Now the Hamiltonian for a simple harmonic oscillator of unit mass is

$$H_\lambda = \tfrac{1}{2}(p_\lambda^2 + \omega_\lambda^2 q_\lambda^2) \tag{12.8a}$$

and then Hamilton's equations are

$$\frac{\partial H_\lambda}{\partial p_\lambda} = \dot{q}_\lambda = p_\lambda, \qquad \frac{\partial H_\lambda}{\partial q_\lambda} = -\dot{p}_\lambda. \tag{12.8b}$$

These imply (12.4) and define a momentum variable p_λ – with the dimensions $[M^{\frac{1}{2}}LT^{-1}]$ – which is conjugate to q_λ. The total field is described by a set of canonical variables q_λ, p_λ and a total Hamiltonian $H = \sum_\lambda H_\lambda$. The field is thus represented by the set of independent oscillators which are associated with the normal modes of the enclosure and with the independent states of polarization of the radiation.

We shall now verify that the total energy of the radiation field is the sum of the energies of these oscillators, i.e. that

$$U = \tfrac{1}{2}\int_{L^3}(\varepsilon_0\mathscr{E}^2 + \mu_0\mathscr{H}^2)\,d\tau = \sum_\lambda H_\lambda \tag{12.9}$$

– a result which depends in part on the suitable choice of the normalizing constant of (12.6). From (12.2a), (12.3) and (12.8b) we have

$$\mathscr{E} = -\dot{\mathbf{A}} = -\sum_\lambda \dot{q}_\lambda \mathbf{A}_\lambda = -\sum_\lambda p_\lambda \mathbf{A}_\lambda$$

$$\therefore U_e = \frac{\varepsilon_0}{2}\int_{L^3}\mathscr{E}^2 d\tau = \frac{\varepsilon_0}{2}\sum_\lambda\sum_\mu p_\lambda p_\mu \int_{L^3}\mathbf{A}_\lambda \mathbf{A}_\mu\,d\tau.$$

Using (12.6) we then find

$$U_e = \frac{\varepsilon_0\mu_0 c^2}{2}\sum_\lambda p_\lambda^2 = \tfrac{1}{2}\sum_\lambda p_\lambda^2.$$

From (12.2b) and (12.3)

$$\mu_0\mathscr{H} = \operatorname{curl}\mathbf{A} = \sum_\lambda q_\lambda \operatorname{curl}\mathbf{A}_\lambda$$

$$\therefore U_m = \frac{1}{2\mu_0}\int_{L^3}(\mu_0\mathscr{H})^2 d\tau = \frac{1}{2\mu_0}\sum_\lambda\sum_\mu q_\lambda q_\mu \int_{L^3}\operatorname{curl}\mathbf{A}_\lambda \cdot \operatorname{curl}\mathbf{A}_\mu\,d\tau$$

$$= \frac{1}{2\mu_0}\sum_\lambda\sum_\mu q_\lambda q_\mu\left\{\int_{surface}(\mathbf{A}_\lambda \wedge \operatorname{curl}\mathbf{A}_\mu)_n d\sigma + \int_{L^3}\mathbf{A}_\lambda \cdot \operatorname{curl}\operatorname{curl}\mathbf{A}_\mu\,d\tau\right\}.$$

The surface integral vanishes because of the periodicity of $\mathbf{A}$. When the volume integral is manipulated using eqns. (12.5) and the identity

$$\text{curl curl} = \text{grad div} - \nabla^2$$

we get

$$U_m = \frac{1}{2\mu_0} \sum_\lambda \sum_\mu q_\lambda q_\mu \frac{\omega_\mu^2}{c^2} \int_{L^3} \mathbf{A}_\lambda \cdot \mathbf{A}_\mu \, d\tau = \tfrac{1}{2} \sum_\lambda q_\lambda^2 \omega_\lambda^2.$$

Hence

$$U = U_e + U_m = \tfrac{1}{2} \sum_\lambda (p_\lambda^2 + q_\lambda^2 \omega_\lambda^2) = \sum_\lambda H_\lambda,$$

which is the desired result (12.9).

Instead of using sin and cos functions to represent standing-wave solutions of (12.5), we can use complex exponentials to represent travelling-wave solutions. Then we have

$$\mathbf{A} = \sum_\lambda \{ q_\lambda(t) \mathbf{A}_\lambda(\mathbf{r}) + q_\lambda^*(t) \mathbf{A}_\lambda^*(\mathbf{r}) \} \qquad (12.10\text{a})$$

with

$$q_\lambda = |q_\lambda| \, \varepsilon^{-i\omega_\lambda t} \qquad (12.10\text{b})$$

and

$$\mathbf{A}_\lambda = \mathbf{e}_\lambda L^{-\frac{3}{2}} (\mu_0 c^2)^{\frac{1}{2}} \, \varepsilon^{i\mathbf{k}_\lambda \cdot \mathbf{r}}. \qquad (12.10\text{c})$$

The components of the $\mathbf{k}_\lambda$ are the same as those defined in (12.7), except that the n's may now be positive or negative. Waves with opposite directions of travel will be labelled by λ and $-\lambda$. In place of (12.6) we have the normalization condition

$$\int_{L^3} \mathbf{A}_\lambda \cdot \mathbf{A}_\mu^* \, d\tau = \int_{L^3} \mathbf{A}_\lambda \cdot \mathbf{A}_{-\mu} \, d\tau = \mu_0 c^2 \delta_{\mu\lambda}. \qquad (12.11)$$

In this representation the canonical variables are

$$Q_\lambda = q_\lambda + q_\lambda^* \qquad (12.12\text{a})$$

$$P_\lambda = \dot{Q}_\lambda = -i\omega_\lambda (q_\lambda - q_\lambda^*) \qquad (12.12\text{b})$$

and these are real. Then $H_\lambda = \tfrac{1}{2}(P_\lambda^2 + \omega_\lambda^2 Q_\lambda^2)$, (12.13) and (12.9) is still valid.

Hamiltonian representation of a quantized wave field

To take the formalism of the preceding section over into quantum mechanics we shall require the canonical variables P_λ and Q_λ to behave as non-commuting variables or operators, obeying the commutation relations

$$i(P_\lambda Q_\mu - Q_\mu P_\lambda) = \hbar \delta_{\lambda\mu}$$
$$i(P_\lambda P_\mu - P_\mu P_\lambda) = i(Q_\lambda Q_\mu - Q_\mu Q_\lambda) = 0 \qquad (12.14)$$

The possible energies of the oscillator whose Hamiltonian is the H_λ of (12.13) will now be restricted to

$$E_\lambda = (n_\lambda + \tfrac{1}{2})\hbar\,\omega_\lambda \qquad (12.15)$$

where n_λ is a positive integer or zero, and the Q_λ will be represented by Hermitian matrices whose elements are, apart from phase- and time-factors,

$$Q_{n,\,n+1} = \left(\frac{(n_\lambda+1)\hbar}{2\omega_\lambda}\right)^{\!\frac{1}{2}} = (Q_{n+1,\,n})^*. \qquad (12.16)$$

The Q_λ, and hence the P_λ, have non-vanishing matrix elements only for those transitions in which the quantum number of the appropriate radiation oscillator increases or decreases by unity. The non-Hermitian variables q_λ and q_λ^* are, in view of (12.12) and (12.13),

$$q_{n,\,n+1} = \left(\frac{(n_\lambda+1)\hbar}{2\omega_\lambda}\right)^{\!\frac{1}{2}} = q_{n+1,\,n}^* \qquad (12.17)$$

with $q_{n,\,n'} = 0$ unless $n' = n+1$, and $q^*_{n,\,n'} = 0$ unless $n' = n-1$. These also are non-commuting operators, and in terms of them

$$H_\lambda = \omega_\lambda^2 (q_\lambda q_\lambda^* + q_\lambda^* q_\lambda). \qquad (12.18)$$

When, as now, the field variables are defined so as to refer to travelling waves, we can use them to calculate the momentum of the radiation. Classically the momentum of the field is

$$\mathbf{G} = \int_{L^3} \mathscr{D} \wedge \mathscr{B} d\tau = \frac{1}{c^2} \int_{L^3} \mathscr{E} \wedge \mathscr{H} d\tau.$$

Using (12.2) and (12.10) we can write this as

$$\mathbf{G} = -\frac{1}{\mu_0 c^2} \int_{L^3} \dot{\mathbf{A}} \wedge \operatorname{curl} \mathbf{A}\, d\tau$$

$$= -\frac{1}{\mu_0 c^2} \sum_\lambda \sum_\mu \int_{L^3} (\dot{q}_\lambda \mathbf{A}_\lambda + \dot{q}_\lambda^* \mathbf{A}_\lambda^*) \wedge (q_\mu \operatorname{curl} \mathbf{A}_\mu + q_\mu^* \operatorname{curl} \mathbf{A}_\mu^*) d\tau$$

$$= -\frac{1}{\mu_0 c^2} \sum_\lambda \sum_\mu \int_{L^3} (-i\omega_\lambda q_\lambda \mathbf{A}_\lambda + i\omega_\lambda q_\lambda^* \mathbf{A}_\lambda^*) \wedge (q_\mu i\mathbf{k}_\mu \wedge \mathbf{A}_\mu - q_\mu^* i\mathbf{k}_\mu \wedge \mathbf{A}_\mu^*) d\tau.$$

In view of the orthonormality relation (12.11) this reduces to

$$\mathbf{G} = \frac{1}{\mu_0 c^2}\sum_\lambda \omega_\lambda \mathbf{k}_\lambda \{q_\lambda q_\lambda^* \int \mathbf{A}_\lambda . \mathbf{A}_\lambda^* \, d\tau + q_\lambda^* q_\lambda \int \mathbf{A}_\lambda^* . \mathbf{A}_\lambda \, d\tau\}$$

$$= \sum_\lambda \omega_\lambda (q_\lambda q_\lambda^* + q_\lambda^* q_\lambda)\mathbf{k}_\lambda.$$

If we compare this with (12.18) we see that the expression for the momentum can be written

$$\mathbf{G} = \sum_\lambda \frac{H_\lambda}{c}\frac{\mathbf{k}_\lambda}{|\mathbf{k}_\lambda|} = \sum_\lambda \mathbf{G}_\lambda \qquad (12.19a)$$

where $\mathbf{G}_\lambda$ is the momentum associated with the λ-th travelling-wave mode, and has the magnitude

$$|\mathbf{G}_\lambda| = \frac{H_\lambda}{c} = \frac{(n_\lambda + \frac{1}{2})\hbar\omega_\lambda}{c}. \qquad (12.19b)$$

(12.15) and (12.19) state the 'corpuscular' properties of the quantized electromagnetic field. To any normal mode there belongs, in a given state of the field, an energy E_λ and a momentum $\mathbf{G}_\lambda$. These are compatible variables, whose values may be known simultaneously; in free space the ratio of their magnitudes is c. The energy and momentum of this mode can increase or decrease only by discrete amounts $\hbar\omega_\lambda$ and $\hbar\omega_\lambda/c$ respectively, which may be thought of as the energy and momentum of a quantum of radiation of frequency ω_λ travelling in the direction of the vector $\mathbf{k}_\lambda$. Since $E_\lambda = (n_\lambda + \frac{1}{2})\hbar\omega_\lambda$ we say that n_λ is the number of quanta associated with this mode, and that the remaining energy $\frac{1}{2}\hbar\omega_\lambda$ is a *zero-point energy* belonging to this mode. Since each mode has such a zero-point energy, and the number of modes is infinite, the total zero-point energy of the radiation in the cavity appears to be infinite. However, the zero-point energy is unobservable, and may be 'transformed away' by a different choice of canonical variables (see Heitler, *Quantum Theory of Radiation*, 3rd edn., O.U.P., 1956, chapter 2, § 7). We shall therefore take it that the features of the radiation field which are significant in practice are the frequencies ω_λ of the normal modes and the corresponding excitation energies specified by the quantum numbers n_λ.

The conclusion that the radiation in any volume consists of discrete units of energy and momentum does not justify a picture of the field as an assembly of 'real particles'. Except at the instant of the emission or absorption of a quantum by an atom – and the precision of the specification of this event is limited by the uncertainty principle – a quantum cannot be localized. It belongs to one or other of the normal modes of the volume, but the space-function A_λ of that mode has uniform amplitude throughout the volume.† Some aspects of processes like the scattering of light by electrons or the Compton effect are known to be described quite well by a 'photon model' in which the radiation is pictured as consisting of particles which collide with the electrons; in fact the aspects of those processes which can be deduced from such a model are those which involve nothing more than the conservation of total energy and momentum. The analysis of more subtle details of these processes, e.g. the calculation of cross-sections, requires a treatment by quantum electrodynamics, and there it appears that these are 'two-stage processes', in which a quantum is absorbed by a material system and a quantum is subsequently emitted, energy and momentum being conserved between the initial and final states. The localization of these processes – which was assumed possible in the discussion of the 'γ-ray microscope' in chapter 1, for instance – depends on the possibility of localizing emission and absorption processes and does not imply that the position of a quantum can be specified when it is 'in flight'. The term 'photon' is often used in a way which suggests a more definitely corpuscular character than is really possessed by radiation, and this usage is misleading.

Recently it has proved useful in quantum optics to adopt, as basis states for the representation of optical radiation fields, functions of the field variables q_λ and p_λ which are the same kind of superpositions of energy eigenstates as the superpositions used by Schrödinger to provide a description of the macroscopic harmonic oscillator (see pp. 186-187). In quantum optics these superpositions were introduced by Glauber in 1963, and represent states in which the amplitude and phase of the observable part of the electric field are as well-defined as quantum mechanics allows. These are not eigenstates of the energy operator—since they are superpositions of energy eigenstates—but of the non-Hermitian ladder operator q_λ, which, as will be shown in the next section, appears in expressions determining the probability of absorption processes. There are certain formal

† It is of course possible to choose an eigenwave representation of the field in which the amplitudes of the individual eigenwaves are not uniform throughout the volume, but those eigenwaves correspond to modes in which the energy and momentum are not sharp.

difficulties associated with the use of eigenstates of a non-Hermitian operator as basis states—for instance, these states are not necessarily orthogonal; and they form a set which is vastly over-complete so the representation of a given state as a superposition of these basis states may not be unique. However, the advantages accruing from the use of these states make it worth facing the attendant difficulties.

Interaction of radiation with an atom

It was shown in chapter 11 that the Hamiltonian for the non-relativistic motion of an atomic electron in an electromagnetic field is, to first order,

$$\frac{p^2}{2m} + V(r) - \frac{e}{m}\mathbf{A} \cdot \mathbf{p} \quad \text{(eqn. (11.3))}.$$

If we add to this the Hamiltonian of the radiation field and recall (12.10) we get a total Hamiltonian $H = H_0 + H'$ with

$$H_0 = \frac{p^2}{2m} + V(r) + \tfrac{1}{2}\sum_\lambda (P_\lambda{}^2 + \omega_\lambda{}^2 Q_\lambda{}^2) \quad (12.20a)$$

and

$$-H' = L^{-\frac{3}{2}}(\mu_0 c^2)^{\frac{1}{2}}\frac{e}{m}\sum_\lambda (q_\lambda \varepsilon^{i\mathbf{k}\lambda \cdot \mathbf{r}} + q_\lambda^* \varepsilon^{-i\mathbf{k}\lambda \cdot \mathbf{r}})\mathbf{e}_\lambda \cdot \mathbf{p}. \quad (12.20b)$$

The eigenfunctions of H_0 can be written as products of two factors, one representing an unperturbed state of the atomic electron and the other representing an unperturbed state of the radiation field. If $u_n(r)$ represents an eigenstate of the electron with energy E_n, and ϕ_N represents an eigenstate of the radiation field with energy $(N_\lambda + \tfrac{1}{2})\hbar\omega_\lambda$, $u_n \phi_N$ is an eigenfunction of H_0 with energy $E_n + (N_\lambda + \tfrac{1}{2})\hbar\omega_\lambda$. To find the probability that the interaction between the electron and the radiation produces a transition to some other state we must find the matrix element of H' between the initial state $u_n \phi_N$ and that other state, say $u_m \phi_M$. We shall denote this matrix element by $\langle m, M \mid H' \mid n, N \rangle$. Then

$$\langle m, M \mid H' \mid n, N \rangle = -\left(\frac{\mu_0 c^2}{L^3}\right)^{\frac{1}{2}}\frac{e}{m}\Bigg\{\int_{L^3} u_m^* \varepsilon^{i\mathbf{k} \cdot \mathbf{r}} \mathbf{e} \cdot \mathbf{p}\, u_n \, d\tau \times \langle M \mid q \mid N \rangle$$

$$+ \int_{L^3} u_m^* \varepsilon^{-i\mathbf{k} \cdot \mathbf{r}} \mathbf{e} \cdot \mathbf{p}\, u_n \, d\tau \times \langle M \mid q^* \mid N \rangle\Bigg\}.$$

(The suffix λ has been omitted, as we are concerned with only one mode at a time.) From (12.17) the matrix element of q vanishes unless $M = N - 1$, and the matrix element of q^* vanishes unless $M = N + 1$. There are therefore two non-vanishing matrix elements for H':

$$\langle m, N-1 | H' | n, N \rangle = -\left(\frac{N\hbar}{2\omega}\right)^{\frac{1}{2}} \left(\frac{\mu_0 c^2}{L^3}\right)^{\frac{1}{2}} \frac{e}{m} \int_{L^3} u_m^* \varepsilon^{i\mathbf{k} \cdot \mathbf{r}} \mathbf{e} . \mathbf{p} \, u_n \, d\tau$$
(12.21a)

$$\langle m, N+1 | H' | n, N \rangle = -\left(\frac{(N+1)\hbar}{2\omega}\right)^{\frac{1}{2}} \left(\frac{\mu_0 c^2}{L^3}\right)^{\frac{1}{2}} \frac{e}{m} \int_{L^3} u_m^* \varepsilon^{-i\mathbf{k} \cdot \mathbf{r}} \mathbf{e} . \mathbf{p} \, u_n \, d\tau.$$
(12.21b)

The first of these refers to an absorption process, for it represents a transition in which the number of quanta in the field is reduced by one. The probability of this process – which from (10.4) depends on the square of the matrix element – is proportional to N, the number of quanta present, i.e. to the intensity of the incident radiation. This is therefore an *induced absorption*. The second of these matrix elements refers to a process in which the number of quanta is increased by one; this is an emission process. Its probability is proportional to $N+1$. If the intensity of the incident radiation is reduced to zero, so that $N = 0$, there is still a non-zero probability for emission. The part of the emission probability which is independent of N refers to the process of *spontaneous emission*; the other part of the emission probability, which is proportional to N, refers to *induced emission*. It will be noted from (12.21a) and (12.21b) that the probabilities for induced absorption and induced emission between a given pair of atomic states described by state-functions u_m and u_n are the same.

The general discussion of time-dependent perturbations in chapter 10 showed that the only probable transitions are those in which energy is conserved. In the present context that means that $E_m - E_n = \pm \hbar\omega$. The probability of these processes depends on the values of the integrals in (12.21), which are essentially the same as that in (11.7): for $\mathbf{e}$ is a unit vector in the direction of $\mathbf{A}$, so we may replace $\mathbf{e} . \mathbf{p}$ by the operator $(\hbar/i) \, \mathrm{grad}_\mathbf{A}$, and the matrix element for the emission of a quantum becomes

$$\langle m, N+1 | H' | n, N \rangle$$

$$= i\left(\frac{(N+1)\hbar}{2\omega}\right)^{\frac{1}{2}} \left(\frac{\mu_0 c^2}{L^3}\right)^{\frac{1}{2}} \frac{e\hbar}{m} \int_{L^3} u_m^* \varepsilon^{-i\mathbf{k} \cdot \mathbf{r}} \mathrm{grad}_\mathbf{A} \, u_n \, d\tau. \quad (12.22)$$

This integral was discussed in chapter 11, where it was shown that in the dipole approximation its magnitude is

$$\left| \int u_m^* \text{grad}_A \, u_n \, d\tau \right| = \frac{m\omega}{\hbar} \langle r_A \rangle_{mn}. \tag{12.23}$$

(If the volume L^3 over which the state-functions of the radiation field are normalized is large compared with the volume of the atom this integral may without error be evaluated in an infinite volume.) Before we can find a transition probability by substituting these results in (10.4) we require to know the density function $\rho(E_0)$ which occurs there; in the present context this will refer to the density of normal modes of the radiation field in unit energy range around the energy $\hbar\omega$, and when we allow for the two possible states of polarization this is

$$2 . 4\pi \left(\frac{L}{2\pi c} \right)^3 \frac{\omega^2}{\hbar}.$$

The probability of the emission of a quantum is then found by substituting this result, along with (12.22) and (12.23), into (10.4). If at the same time we average over all orientations of the atoms we find that the transition probability for emission is

$$(w_{mn})_{\text{tot}} = (N+1) \frac{\mu_0 e^2 \omega^3}{3\pi\hbar c} \left| r_{mn} \right|^2 \tag{12.24a}$$

and the probability of *spontaneous* emission is extracted from this by putting $N=0$:

$$w_{mn} = \frac{\mu_0 e^2 \omega^3}{3\pi\hbar c} \left| r_{mn} \right|^2. \tag{12.24b}$$

The mean rate of spontaneous radiation is therefore

$$\overline{S} = w_{mn} \hbar\omega = \frac{\mu_0 e^2 \omega^4}{3\pi c} \left| r_{mn} \right|^2. \tag{12.25}$$

(12.24b) and (12.25) are identical with (11.10) and (11.11).

The probabilities for induced emission and absorption are now seen to be both equal to

$$N \frac{\mu_0 e^2 \omega^3}{3\pi\hbar c} \left| r_{mn} \right|^2,$$

in view of (12.24a) and eqns. (12.21). The distinction and the relationship between the probabilities of spontaneous emission and induced emission and absorption thus emerge naturally from the formulation of radiation problems in terms of a quantized field.

The photoelectric effect

If the radiation incident on an atom has a quantum energy greater than the binding energy of an atomic electron, the absorption of a quantum may lead to the ionization of the atom. The difference between the quantum energy and the binding energy of the ejected electron appears in the final state as kinetic energy of the separated electron and ion. The electron is thereby excited from a quantized state of negative energy into one of the continuum of unbound states referred to on p. 106. We wish to calculate the probability of the ejection of an electron from an atom irradiated with light of angular frequency ω. If the process is to occur $\hbar\omega$ must be greater than the ionization energy I of the atom; we shall assume that $\hbar\omega$ is considerably greater than I, but is still small enough for a non-relativistic treatment to be valid. We shall further assume that the resulting positive ion is so massive compared with the electron that in the final state the kinetic energy of the ion may be ignored.

The state-function of an electron in the K-shell of the atom is of the form

$$\psi_n = \left(\frac{1}{\pi a^3}\right)^{\frac{1}{2}} \varepsilon^{-r/a} \quad \text{where} \quad a = \frac{a_0}{Z}.$$

When the kinetic energy of the ejected electron is large compared with the ionization energy its state-function may be assumed to represent a plane wave, i.e.

$$\psi_m = L^{-\frac{3}{2}} \varepsilon^{i\mathbf{k'} \cdot \mathbf{r}}.$$

This function is normalized in a cubical box of side L provided that $\varepsilon^{i\mathbf{k'} \cdot \mathbf{r}}$ is periodic in L, and the density of such states with a given spin orientation – namely, that of the atomic electron – whose energy lies in unit range about $p^2/2m$ and whose momentum vectors lie in a cone of solid angle $d\Omega$ is

$$\rho = \left(\frac{L}{2\pi\hbar}\right)^3 pm\, d\Omega. \qquad \text{(cf. (8.19))}$$

The matrix element for the transition is of the form

$$\langle m, N-1 | H' | n, N \rangle$$
$$= -\left(\frac{N\hbar}{2\omega}\right)^{\frac{1}{2}}\left(\frac{\mu_0 c^2}{L^3}\right)^{\frac{1}{2}}\left(\frac{1}{L^3}\right)^{\frac{1}{2}}\left(\frac{1}{\pi a^3}\right)^{\frac{1}{2}}\frac{e}{m}\int_{L^3} \varepsilon^{-i\mathbf{k'} \cdot \mathbf{r}}\, \mathbf{e} \cdot \mathbf{p}\, \varepsilon^{i\mathbf{k} \cdot \mathbf{r}}\, \varepsilon^{-r/a}\, d\tau.$$

Since $\mathbf{p}$ – the momentum of the ejected electron – is constant it may be taken out of the integral; if we write $\mathbf{K}=\mathbf{k}-\mathbf{k}'$ as the wave-vector associated with the momentum transferred to the electron we have

$$\langle m, N-1\,|\,H'\,|\,n, N\rangle = -\left(\frac{N\hbar}{2\omega}\cdot\frac{\mu_0 c^2}{L^6}\cdot\frac{1}{\pi a^3}\right)^{\frac{1}{2}}\frac{e}{m}\,\mathbf{e}\cdot\mathbf{p}\int_{L^3}\varepsilon^{i\mathbf{K}\cdot\mathbf{r}}\varepsilon^{-r/a}d\tau.$$

A rather tedious integration shows that as long as $a \ll L$

$$\int_{L^3}\varepsilon^{i\mathbf{K}\cdot\mathbf{r}}\varepsilon^{-r/a}d\tau = \frac{8\pi a^{-1}}{(K^2+1/a^2)^2}$$

so

$$\langle m, N-1\,|\,H'\,|\,n, N\rangle = -\left(\frac{N\hbar\mu_0 c^2}{2\pi\omega L^6 a^5}\right)^{\frac{1}{2}}\frac{e}{m}\,p_e\,\frac{8\pi}{(K^2+1/a^2)^2}.$$

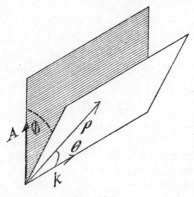

Fig. 12.1.

The transition probability per unit time for the ejection of an electron into the solid angle $d\Omega$ is therefore

$$dw = \frac{2\pi}{\hbar}\frac{L^3 pm}{(2\pi\hbar)^3}\,d\Omega\,\frac{N\hbar}{2\pi\omega}\frac{\mu_0 c^2}{L^6 a^5}\frac{e^2}{m^2}\,p_e^2\,\frac{64\pi^2}{(K^2+1/a^2)^4}$$

$$= \frac{16 N\,p p_e^2\,\mu_0 c^2 e^2}{2\pi\hbar^3\,\omega L^3 m}\cdot\frac{a^3}{(1+a^2 K^2)^4}\,d\Omega.$$

Dividing this differential transition probability by the intensity of the incident radiation, which is Nc/L^3 quanta per sq. cm. per sec., we get the differential cross-section as

$$d\sigma = \frac{16\,p p_e^2\,\mu_0 c e^2}{2\pi\hbar^3\,\omega m}\cdot\frac{a^3}{(1+a^2 K^2)^4}\,d\Omega. \qquad (12.26a)$$

The angular dependence of this expression is implicit, for p_e and $\mathbf{K}$ both depend on angle. Let the angle between $\mathbf{p}$ and $\mathbf{k}$ (the wavevector of the incident light) be θ, and let ϕ be the angle between the plane of polarization and the plane of $\mathbf{p}$ and $\mathbf{k}$ (Fig. 12.1). Then

$$p_e = p \sin\theta\cos\phi$$

and $$K^2 = k^2 + k'^2 - 2kk'\cos\theta.$$

Using the second of these, and remembering that

$$I = \frac{\hbar^2}{2ma^2}, \qquad k' = \frac{p}{\hbar}, \qquad k = \frac{\omega}{c},$$

we find that

$$\frac{1}{(1+a^2K^2)^4} = \frac{1}{\{1+\hbar^2(k^2+k'^2-2kk'\cos\theta)/2mI\}^4}$$

$$= \frac{1}{\left\{1+\dfrac{\hbar^2\omega^2}{2mc^2I}+\dfrac{p^2}{2mI}-\dfrac{\hbar\omega p}{mcI}\cos\theta\right\}^4}.$$

Now by hypothesis $I \ll \hbar\omega \ll mc^2$, and

$$\hbar\omega = \frac{p^2}{2m}+I \approx \frac{p^2}{2m},$$

so the first two terms in the bracket may be neglected in comparison with the third, and we see that

$$\frac{1}{\{1+a^2K^2\}^4} \approx \frac{I^4}{\hbar^4\omega^4\{1-(v/c)\cos\theta\}^4}.$$

Inserting this in (12.26a), and expressing p also in terms of ω, we get

$$d\sigma = \frac{16\mu_0ce^2a_0^2}{\pi Z^2\hbar}\left(\frac{I}{\hbar\omega}\right)^{\frac{7}{2}}\frac{\sin^2\theta\cos^2\phi}{\{1-(v/c)\cos\theta\}^4}\,d\Omega.$$

It is conventional to rewrite this expression in terms of the classical electron radius $r_0 = e^2/4\pi\varepsilon_0 mc^2$ and the dimensionless constant $137 = 4\pi\varepsilon_0\hbar c/e^2$ as

$$d\sigma = 64\frac{(137)^3}{Z^2}r_0^2\left(\frac{I}{\hbar\omega}\right)^{\frac{7}{2}}\frac{\sin^2\theta\cos^2\phi}{\{1-(v/c)\cos\theta\}^4}\,d\Omega. \qquad (12.26b)$$

This shows that there is no photoelectron emission in the plane perpendicular to the plane of polarization, where $\phi = \pi/2$, nor is there any emission along the direction of propagation of the light, where

$\theta = 0$ or π. If v/c is vanishingly small the maximum probability of emission is that for the direction of the electric vector, $\phi = 0$ and $\theta = \pi/2$. However as $\hbar\omega$ – and therefore v/c – increases, the requirement of conservation of momentum, manifesting itself through the variation of the denominator, shifts this maximum towards smaller values of θ, i.e. in the forward direction.

If the second term in the denominator can be ignored the total cross-section is easily shown to be

$$\sigma = 32 \cdot \frac{8\pi r_0^2}{3} \frac{(137)^3}{Z^2} \left(\frac{I}{\hbar\omega} \right)^{\frac{7}{2}}.$$

(The quantity $8\pi r_0^2/3$ is Thomson's classical scattering cross-section for the electron.) σ is the cross-section for the photoelectric effect of a beam of radiation on a single electron in the K-shell. Since the K-shell normally contains two electrons the 'cross-section for the K-shell' is 2σ.

The validity of the classical representation of the electromagnetic field

To conclude, we shall consider briefly two very different situations for which classical electromagnetic theory gives a satisfactory description, in the hope of determining criteria for the validity of the classical treatment. The absorption or emission of signals by a radio aerial is a phenomenon usually discussed in macroscopic terms; looked at microscopically it involves the absorption or emission of very large numbers of quanta by a tuned circuit which contains a very large number of conduction electrons. At the other extreme, the prediction by classical wave-theory of the intensity distribution in an optical interference or diffraction pattern is valid even when, as was remarked in chapter 1, the light intensities are so low that the energy passing through the apparatus at any time corresponds to a single quantum.

(i) The radio aerial

Experiments in microwave spectroscopy, nuclear paramagnetic resonance and the like show that electromagnetic fields in the radio-frequency portion of the spectrum can produce quantum transitions in molecular and atomic systems; these cases involve no new points of principle as compared with, say, the situation in optical and infra-red spectroscopy, where too the transition frequencies are correlated with the structure of individual atoms or molecules. A radio aerial on the other hand is a macroscopic system containing a very large number of electrons – say 10^{25} – which interact strongly with one another, and the well-defined frequency which it radiates is determined not by molecular or atomic constants but by the dimensions of man-made components.

The spectrum of the electronic transitions is virtually a continuum, as is shown by the discussion in chapter 8 of the energy level density in an electron gas. Suppose that the tuning system and the aerial consist of a resonant cavity and a waveguide radiator. The electromagnetic field in the cavity will consist predominantly of a standing wave; we shall suppose that only the fundamental mode of the cavity is excited so that the cavity contains a wave whose angular frequency is known to be close to ω.† The random motions of the electrons in the walls of the cavity generate a 'noise' signal; the power of this signal in the bandwidth $\delta\omega$ when the temperature of the cavity is $T°$ K is $kT\delta\omega/4\pi$, which at room temperature amounts to about $10^{-21} \times \delta\omega$ watts. If the signal in the aerial is to be greater than the thermal noise the rate of energy transfer between aerial and field must be greater than this, so that the number of quanta of angular frequency ω which must be transferred per second is greater than

$$\frac{kT\delta\omega}{4\pi\hbar\omega} \approx 10^{13}\frac{2}{Q}.$$

Here $2\omega/\delta\omega = Q$, the quality factor of the aerial, which may be about 100 for a useful aerial system. Then the number of quanta received per second if the presence of a signal is just detectable must be not less than 10^{11}, and the number radiated per second by a transmitter will be much greater than this. The transmission or reception of radio signals therefore involves the emission or absorption of very large numbers of quanta by a system containing a very large number of electrons.

The number of quanta interacting with the aerial at any instant is the number absorbed in one response time, that is in the time $2\pi Q/\omega$ which can be regarded as the 'lifetime' of a quantum in the cavity. The number of quanta absorbed in this time is $4\pi . 10^{13}/\omega$, which is quite large even at microwave frequencies.

If the number of quanta were not large we should be unable to

---

† It must be remembered that the 'fundamental mode' in the macroscopic sense has a finite bandwidth, say $\delta\omega$, so the spectrum of the radiation will be described by a density function $\rho(\omega)$ which is small except for frequencies in the range $\omega \pm \delta\omega/2$.

retain the concept of a macroscopic field in the cavity, for only when many quanta are present during a single period of the field oscillation can we assign a definite phase to the field. The specification of a precise phase implies the possibility of measuring time intervals δt which are very small compared with the period $2\pi/\omega$ of the field oscillation. If we write $\delta t = 2\pi/n\omega$ where n is a large number, and put this in the uncertainty relation for the conjugate variables E and t:

$$\Delta E \Delta t \geqq \frac{\hbar}{2},$$

we find

$$\Delta E \geqq \frac{n\hbar\omega}{4\pi},$$

so the energy transfer must be very large in relation to the energy of a quantum. Only if this is so can we associate an observable phase with the field.

When the cavity is excited in its fundamental mode the aerial will be both absorbing and emitting energy, the rates of radiation and absorption at any frequency being, from (12.24) and the subsequent discussion,

$$(\overline{S_{mn}})_e = \frac{\mu_0 e^2 \omega_{mn}{}^4}{3\pi c} (N_{mn}+1) \sum_{m,n} W(E_m)|r_{mn}|^2 \qquad (12.27a)$$

and

$$(\overline{S_{mn}})_a = \frac{\mu_0 e^2 \omega_{mn}{}^4}{3\pi c} N_{mn} \sum_{m,n} W(E_n)(r_{mn})^2. \qquad (12.27b)$$

$W(E)$ represents the probability distribution-in-energy of the conduction electrons – a function which depends on the material of the aerial, its temperature, and the way in which power is fed to it by the power supply. The matrix element $e\,r_{mn}$ of the electric dipole moment now involves all the coordinates of the aerial system, and has to be summed over all those pairs of states whose energy differs by $\hbar\omega_{mn}$; N_{mn} is the number of quanta in the cavity with frequency ω_{mn}. Insomuch as the energy levels of the electrons form a continuum, the complete spectrum of the radiation in the cavity will be very extensive, but it is only at one or other of the natural frequencies of the cavity, say ω_r, that the intensity of the field in the cavity will build up strongly, and the rates of absorption and emission are therefore enormously higher at these natural frequencies than at any

QM T

other. The conduction electrons in the metal are thus swung into collective motion by their interaction with the coherent cavity field, and there is a macroscopic field coupled with a macroscopic electric current.

Then in (12.27a) we may ignore 1 compared with N_{mn}, and the net rate of emission of energy is

$$\overline{S}_r = \frac{\mu_0 e^2}{3\pi c} \, \omega_r{}^4 \, N_r \sum_{m,n} \{W(E_m) - W(E_n)\} |r_{mn}|^2. \qquad (12.28)$$

The summation is now over all pairs of states whose energy difference is $\hbar(\omega_r \pm \delta\omega)$, and N_r is the number of quanta present in that energy range. $\overline{S}_r$ may be positive or negative, according as the input of power to the circuits is contrived to make the whole system a transmitter or a receiver.

If we compare (12.28) with (3.17), which is the classical result for the rate of radiation of an oscillating electric dipole, we see that the expressions are formally similar, and that the dipole moment of the aerial system is proportional to

$$N_r \sum_{m,n} \{W(E_m) - W(E_n)\} (r_{mn})^2.$$

The argument of this section shows that radiation or absorption of energy by a radio aerial takes place in a narrow frequency band because it is an induced emission or absorption, controlled by the macroscopic field in the neighbourhood of the aerial. According as the apparatus linked with the aerial is coupled to make the summation in (12.28) negative or positive, the macroscopic field induces a net absorption or emission of energy by the aerial. There will be present also a background of radiation extending over all the frequencies which can cause transitions in the continuum of 'free' levels of the conduction electrons, but this is coupled not to the collective motion of the electrons but to their random motions and so is of a thermal character.

(ii) Classical wave-theory for optical interference experiments

In the previous section we saw that a macroscopic field can be defined if the number of quanta present is large enough so that a definite phase can be associated with the field. But in optical interference experiments this condition may not be satisfied. Why then does classical wave-theory give a satisfactory representation of the results of these experiments?

Let us suppose that a beam of radiation of frequency ω contains n quanta, and that an uncertainty in the energy in the beam is attributed to an uncertainty δn. An uncertainty $\delta \phi$ in the instantaneous value of the phase may be associated with an uncertainty in time δt, through $\omega \delta t = \delta \phi$. Then the relation $\Delta E\, \Delta t \approx \hbar$ is equivalent to

$$\delta n\, \hbar \omega\, \frac{\delta \phi}{\omega} \approx \hbar$$

$$\therefore\ \delta n\, \delta \phi \approx 1.$$

From (2.8) we can conclude that n and ϕ should be represented by non-commuting operators, say N and Φ, for which

$$i(N\Phi - \Phi N) \approx 1.\dagger$$

For either of two beams of radiation we should then write

$$i(N_1\Phi_1 - \Phi_1 N_1) = k \quad \text{where } k \approx 1$$

and

$$i(N_2\Phi_2 - \Phi_2 N_2) = k.$$

On the other hand we must have

$$N_1\Phi_2 - \Phi_2 N_1 = N_2\Phi_1 - \Phi_1 N_2 = 0$$

for an attempt to observe the energy or phase in one beam cannot affect the other beam.

If the two beams are now allowed to overlap, as in an interference experiment, the *total number of quanta* and the *relative phase* are linked by the relation

$$(N_1 + N_2)(\Phi_1 - \Phi_2) - (\Phi_1 - \Phi_2)(N_1 + N_2)$$
$$= (N_1\Phi_1 - \Phi_1 N_1) - (N_2\Phi_2 - \Phi_2 N_2) - (N_1\Phi_2 - \Phi_2 N_1) + (N_2\Phi_1 - \Phi_1 N_2)$$
$$= (-i + i)k$$
$$= 0.$$

This shows that the total energy of the two beams and their relative phase are compatible variables, and may be represented classically.

† This commutation relation may be derived from the properties of the canonical field variables. See e.g. Heitler, *Quantum Theory of Radiation*, 3rd edn., § 7.

For this reason 'the classical wave-theory is sufficient for the discussion of all questions of coherence and interference' (Heisenberg, *The Physical Principles of the Quantum Theory*, p. 88). The experiments of Forrester, Gudmundsen and Johnson (1955) and of Hanbury Brown and Twiss (1956) have provided striking confirmation of this conclusion.

Problems

(1) Since the energy density in a monochromatic electromagnetic wave is $\frac{1}{2}(\varepsilon_0\mathscr{E}^2 + \mu_0\mathscr{H}^2)$, the energy in a volume L^3 in which the wave amplitude is uniform is $(E)_L = \frac{1}{2}(\varepsilon_0\mathscr{E}^2 + \mu_0\mathscr{H}^2)L^3$. Comparing this with the expression given in (3.4) for the energy of a simple harmonic oscillator, viz. $\frac{1}{2}(P^2 + Q^2)$, where P and Q satisfy the commutation relation $i(PQ - QP) = \hbar\omega$, we might expect by analogy that the perpendicular electric and magnetic field vectors $\mathscr{E}$ and $\mathscr{B}$ of the plane wave should satisfy the commutation relation

$$i(\mathscr{E}\mathscr{B} - \mathscr{B}\mathscr{E}) = \hbar\omega\mu_0 c/L^3.$$

Using (12.2), (12.10), and (12.17), deduce the commutation relation between the fields $\mathscr{E}$ and $\mathscr{B}$ associated with a single excited mode in the volume L^3, and show that it is of the expected form.

(2) The smallest volume in which a mode of frequency ω can exist is a cube of side L, where $L = \pi c/\omega$. Verify this, and then, from the commutation relation of problem (1), deduce the uncertainty relation for the perpendicular fields $\mathscr{E}_x$ and $\mathscr{H}_y$ in the volume L:

$$\Delta\mathscr{E}_x\Delta\mathscr{H}_y \geqslant \pi\hbar c^2/L^4.$$

(3) Comparing (11.8) with the term in (12.24a) which represents induced emission, show that

$$N = \frac{\pi^2 c^3}{\hbar\omega^3}\rho(\omega)$$

and hence verify that (the energy per quantum) × (the number of quanta per mode) × (the density-in-*frequency* of modes in the volume L^3) $= \rho(\omega)L^3$

= energy per unit bandwidth in L^3,

provided that N rather than $N + \frac{1}{2}$ is taken as the number of quanta per mode. (This is because the semi-classical treatment, in which the function $\rho(\omega)$ appears, contains no indication of the zero-point energy of the radiation field.)

(4) Comparison of (8.9) and (12.15) suggests that the formula for the black-body radiation distribution given in (8.13) should have added to it a term representing an energy of $\frac{1}{2}h\nu$ or $\frac{1}{2}\hbar\omega$ per degree of freedom. Thus modified, the expression would become

$$u_\nu \delta\nu = \frac{8\pi h\nu^3 \delta\nu}{c^3}\left\{\frac{1}{2}+\frac{1}{\varepsilon^{h\nu/kT}-1}\right\}$$

or

$$\rho(\omega)\Delta\omega = \frac{\hbar\omega^3 \Delta\omega}{\pi^2 c^3}\left\{\frac{1}{2}+\frac{1}{\varepsilon^{\hbar\omega/kT}-1}\right\}.$$

Verify these expressions, and show that the black-body radiation distribution at $0°$ K is (in terms of ω)

$$\rho(\omega)\Delta\omega = \frac{\hbar\omega^3 \Delta\omega}{2\pi^2 c^3}.$$

(5) From (12.26b) estimate what fraction of photoelectrons are emitted in the forward hemisphere (with $0 \leqslant \theta \leqslant \pi/2$) for v^2/c^2 ratios of 10^{-4}, 10^{-3}, 10^{-2} and 10^{-1}.

APPENDIX

THE DENSITY MATRIX

It is often necessary to discuss the behaviour of a system or an ensemble of systems which obeys the laws of quantum mechanics but cannot be represented by a state-function. This need may arise in a number of different ways. For instance, our knowledge about a system or ensemble may not be sufficient to enable us to specify a state-function completely – remember that the state-function, as explained in chapter 1, is a complete specification of the state in the sense that it implies a knowledge of the values of all possible mutually compatible variables, but in practice we may want to make predictions about the behaviour of assemblages consisting of systems about which our knowledge is far from complete. We might want to discuss the behaviour of an assemblage of helium atoms selected so that at a given instant all had the same energy of excitation, but whose angular momenta were randomly distributed. No single state-function could represent such an assemblage. Or again, we might want to eliminate from consideration certain variables which were irrelevant for our purpose, but without the specification of which a state-function could not be specified.

The mathematical apparatus which has proved very effective for such purposes is the technique of the *density matrix*. The density matrix furnishes a description of the states of systems and statistical ensembles of systems which are subject to the laws of quantum mechanics, but for which, either for reasons of expediency or of insufficient knowledge, description by means of a complete state-function is inappropriate. The density matrix method incorporates both the probabilistic aspects of physical theories which are referred to in the last section of chapter 1, the one aspect characteristic of statistical mechanics, and the other characteristic of quantum mechanics, and it has proved an invaluable tool in discussions of the macroscopic behaviour of ensembles of systems – electrons in electron beams, paramagnetic ions in dilute solution in crystals, electromagnetic radiation fields – which obey quantum-mechanical laws.

284

Calculation of expectation values for an ensemble

Suppose that a single quantum-mechanical system is in the state represented by the normalized wave-mechanical state-function Ψ, and that Ψ can be expanded, by the superposition principle, as a linear superposition of a set of orthonormal functions u_k, so that

$$\Psi = \sum_k a_k u_k. \tag{A.1}$$

We shall assume that the functions u_k do not depend explicitly on time, and that for a given function Ψ the coefficients a_k are functions of time only. The time-dependence of Ψ is then contained in the a_k. Now let m be some dynamical variable, represented by the operator M. The expectation value of m for the system in the state Ψ is

$$\langle m \rangle_\Psi = \int \Psi^* M \Psi d\tau \tag{A.2}$$

where the integration is to be carried out over the complete range of all the coordinates on which Ψ depends, but not with respect to time. Then from (A.1)

$$\langle m \rangle_\Psi = \int \sum_r \sum_s \bar{a}_r u_r^* M a_s u_s d\tau$$

$$= \sum_r \sum_s \bar{a}_r a_s \int u_r^* M u_s d\tau$$

$$= \sum_r \sum_s A_{sr} M_{rs}$$

where A_{sr} is an element of a matrix A defined by $A_{sr} = \bar{a}_r a_s$ and M_{rs} is (as usual) the element of the matrix of m coupling the states u_r and u_s. Hence

$$\langle m \rangle_\Psi = \sum_r \sum_s A_{sr} M_{rs} \quad \text{(or } \sum_r \sum_s M_{rs} A_{sr})$$

$$= \sum_s (AM)_{ss} \quad \text{(or } \sum_r (MA)_{rr})$$

$$= \text{Tr}\,(AM) \quad \text{(or Tr}\,(MA))$$

where $\text{Tr}\,(AM) = \text{Tr}\,(MA)$ is the *trace* (i.e. the sum of the diagonal elements) of the product AM or MA.

Now suppose that we have a very large number of identical and non-interacting systems, and that these can be divided into groups, such that a fraction p_i of the systems are in the state represented by the normalized state-function

$$_i\Psi = \sum_k {}_i a_k u_k.$$

Then for this group we should have

$$\langle m \rangle_i = \sum_r \sum_s {}_i\bar{a}_r \cdot {}_ia_s M_{rs} = \sum_r \sum_s {}_iA_{sr} M_{rs}$$

and for the whole ensemble the expectation value of the variable m is

$$\overline{\langle m \rangle} = \sum_i p_i \langle m \rangle_i$$

$$= \sum_i \left(\sum_r \sum_s p_i \cdot {}_i\bar{a}_r \cdot {}_ia_s M_{rs} \right).$$

We define a matrix ρ – the *density matrix* – by

$$\rho_{sr} = \sum_i p_i \cdot {}_i\bar{a}_r \cdot {}_ia_s \tag{A.3}$$

so that we can write

$$\overline{\langle m \rangle} = \sum_r \sum_s \rho_{sr} M_{rs}$$

$$\therefore \quad \overline{\langle m \rangle} = \text{Tr}\,(\rho M) = \text{Tr}\,(M\rho). \tag{A.4}$$

Thus the expectation value of the variable m for the ensemble is the trace of the product of the density matrix and the matrix representing m. The definition of the density matrix through (A.3) shows that it represents the state of the *ensemble* through the statistical weights p_i and the expansion coefficients ${}_ia_k$, and that the time-development of the state, and of the expectation values of variables such as m, is represented through the time-dependence of the density matrix.

Trace relations for the density matrix

Certain algebraic properties of the density matrix follow quickly from (A.3). By inspection it is Hermitian, and its diagonal elements are real. Then, since the ${}_i\Psi$ are normalized to unity, and from the definition of the p_i,

$$\text{Tr}\,(\rho) = \sum_i \left(p_i \sum_r {}_i\bar{a}_r \cdot {}_ia_r \right)$$

$$= \sum_i \left(p_i \sum_r | {}_ia_r |^2 \right)$$

$$= \sum_i p_i = 1$$

$$\therefore \quad \text{Tr}\,(\rho) = 1. \tag{A.5}$$

Further, since the rth diagonal element of ρ is of the form $\sum_i (p_i \mid {}_ia_r \mid^2)$, where p_i and $\mid {}_ia_r \mid^2$ are each real and positive, no ρ_{rr} can be negative, and the result $\mathrm{Tr}\,(\rho) = 1$ shows that no ρ_{rr} can be greater than unity, i.e.,

$$0 \leqq \rho_{rr} \leqq 1 \quad \text{for all } r. \tag{A.6}$$

From the Hermitian property of ρ it follows that ρ can be diagonalized by a unitary transformation; let ρ' be the diagonal form of ρ obtained by the unitary transformation

$$\rho' = T^{-1}\rho T.$$

This corresponds to a different choice of the basis states u_k in (A.1), and such a choice gives a different matrix for the observable m; the matrix M' for m in the transformed representation is related to the matrix M of (A.4) by

$$M' = T^{-1}MT.$$

In the new representation

$$\begin{aligned}
\langle \overline{m} \rangle &= \mathrm{Tr}\,(\rho'M') \\
&= \mathrm{Tr}\,(T^{-1}\rho T T^{-1}MT) \\
&= \mathrm{Tr}\,(T^{-1}\rho MT) \quad (\text{since } T^{-1}T = 1) \\
&= \mathrm{Tr}\,(TT^{-1}\rho M)
\end{aligned}$$

(since the order of the factors can be permuted cyclically)

$$\therefore \quad \langle \overline{m} \rangle = \mathrm{Tr}\,(\rho'M') = \mathrm{Tr}\,(\rho M)$$

– a result which is essential in view of the observable significance of $\langle \overline{m} \rangle$. Similarly it follows that

$$\mathrm{Tr}\,(\rho') = \mathrm{Tr}\,(\rho), \tag{A.7}$$

and in general the trace is invariant under a unitary transformation. Then if we consider a diagonalized density matrix, with elements ρ_r, we have

$$\mathrm{Tr}\,(\rho^2) = \sum_r \rho_r^2 \leqq (\sum_r \rho_r)^2 = (\mathrm{Tr}\,(\rho))^2 = 1$$

$$\therefore \quad \mathrm{Tr}\,(\rho^2) \leqq \mathrm{Tr}\,(\rho). \tag{A.8}$$

The sign of equality, rather than inequality, applies in (A.8) if the density matrix represents a *pure state*. This will now be proved. If, in (A.3), $p_i = 1$ for one particular i (which labels a particular state $_i\Psi$), and all the other p's are zero, (A.3) can be written

$$\rho_{sr} = \bar{a}_r a_s \text{ (where no subscript } i \text{ is needed)}$$

and this defines the density matrix for a pure state Ψ. Then for this pure state

$$(\rho^2)_{sr} = \sum_q \rho_{sq}\rho_{qr}$$

$$= \sum_q \bar{a}_q a_s \bar{a}_r a_q$$

$$= \bar{a}_r a_s \sum_q |a_q|^2$$

$$= \bar{a}_r a_s$$

$$= \rho_{sr}$$

$$\therefore \quad (\rho^2)_{sr} = \rho_{sr}$$

and, for the matrices ρ^2 and ρ,

$$\rho^2 = \rho.$$

Then

$$\text{Tr}(\rho^2) = \text{Tr}(\rho).$$

Equation of motion for the density matrix

The time-dependence of the density matrix, which describes the development in time of the state of the ensemble, is derived from eqns. (2.16) and (A.1). Recalling (2.16) as

$$H\Psi = i\hbar \frac{\partial \Psi}{\partial t}$$

along with the complex conjugate equation

$$H\Psi^* = -i\hbar \frac{\partial \Psi^*}{\partial t}$$

and substituting from (A.1), we have

$$\sum_k a_k H u_k = i\hbar \sum_k \frac{\partial a_k}{\partial t} \cdot u_k$$

and the complex conjugate equation. Multiplying the first of these from the left by u_l^* and integrating so as to make use of the ortho-normality of the functions u_k, we get

$$\sum_k a_k H_{lk} = i\hbar \frac{\partial a_l}{\partial t};$$

and similarly

$$\sum_k \bar{a}_k H_{kl} = -i\hbar \frac{\partial \bar{a}_l}{\partial t} \qquad (\text{since } \bar{H}_{lk} = H_{kl}).$$

Now

$$\frac{\partial \rho_{lm}}{\partial t} = \frac{\partial}{\partial t} \sum_i p_i (_i\bar{a}_m \cdot {}_ia_l)$$

$$= \sum_i p_i \left(\left(\frac{\partial}{\partial t} \, {}_i\bar{a}_m \right) {}_ia_l + {}_i\bar{a}_m \left(\frac{\partial}{\partial t} \, {}_ia_l \right) \right)$$

$$= i\hbar^{-1} \sum_i p_i \left(\sum_k ({}_i\bar{a}_k \cdot H_{km} \cdot {}_ia_l - {}_i\bar{a}_m \cdot {}_ia_k \cdot H_{lk}) \right)$$

$$= i\hbar^{-1} \sum_k (\rho_{lk} H_{km} - H_{lk} \rho_{km})$$

$$= i\hbar^{-1} (\rho H - H\rho)_{lm}$$

whence

$$\frac{\partial \rho}{\partial t} = i\hbar^{-1}(\rho H - H\rho) = \frac{i}{\hbar} [\rho, H]. \tag{A.9}$$

It is important not to confuse this equation with (3.1). Equation (3.1) gives the total time-rate of change of the matrix representing a *dynamical variable*, whereas (A.9) is for the partial derivative with respect to time of the density matrix representing a *state*; in form the equations appear to differ in the sign of the right hand side, but notice that one refers to a total derivative, and the other to a partial derivative.

(A.9) is the quantum mechanical analogue of Liouville's Theorem in classical statistical mechanics, which asserts that when the states of all the systems forming an ensemble are represented by points in the appropriate phase-space, the way these representative points move through the phase space – to represent the temporal develop-ment of the ensemble – keeps the density of representative points in the neighbourhood of each such point constant. If D denotes the density of representative points in a small region of phase space, Liouville's Theorem is contained in the equation

$$\frac{dD}{dt} = \frac{\partial D}{\partial t} + \sum_i \left(\frac{\partial D}{\partial p_i} \cdot \frac{\partial p_i}{\partial t} + \frac{\partial D}{\partial q_i} \cdot \frac{\partial q_i}{\partial t} \right) = 0$$

where the summation is over all degrees of freedom. Using Hamilton's canonical equations,

$$\frac{\partial H}{\partial p_i} = \frac{\partial q_i}{\partial t}, \quad \frac{\partial H}{\partial q_i} = -\frac{\partial p_i}{\partial t},$$

we can re-write Liouville's Theorem as

$$\frac{\partial D}{\partial t} = \sum_i \left(\frac{\partial D}{\partial p_i} \cdot \frac{\partial H}{\partial q_i} - \frac{\partial D}{\partial q_i} \cdot \frac{\partial H}{\partial p_i} \right)$$

$$= \{D, H\}$$

whose quantum mechanical analogue is, according to (2.10b),

$$\frac{\partial D}{\partial t} = \frac{i}{\hbar} [D, H].$$

This is entirely the same as (A.9) if we regard ρ as equivalent to D, and this justifies the name 'density matrix' for ρ.

Time-dependence of the matrix elements of ρ

If H is independent of time, (A.9) can be solved formally for $\rho(t)$ at any time t in terms of $\rho(0)$ at time zero:

$$\rho(t) = \varepsilon^{-iHt/\hbar} \rho(0) \varepsilon^{iHt/\hbar}. \tag{A.10}$$

That this is a solution can be seen by differentiating, and remembering that since H and ρ are operators the order in which they occur must be preserved. We find that

$$\frac{\partial \rho(t)}{\partial t} = -\frac{iH}{\hbar} \varepsilon^{-iHt/\hbar} \rho(0) \varepsilon^{iHt/\hbar} + \varepsilon^{-iHt/\hbar} \rho(0) \frac{iH}{\hbar} \varepsilon^{iHt/\hbar}$$

$$= -\frac{i}{\hbar} (H\rho(t) - \rho(t)H)$$

$$\therefore \quad \frac{\partial \rho(t)}{\partial t} = \frac{i}{\hbar} [\rho(t), H]$$

which agrees with (A.9).

If the functions u_k of (A.1) are eigenfunctions of the Hamiltonian, we can now find the time-dependence of the matrix elements of $\rho(t)$ explicitly by using the form (A.10):

$$\rho_{rs}(t) = \int u_r^* \rho(t) u_s d\tau$$

$$= \int u_r^* \varepsilon^{-iHt/\hbar} \rho(0) \varepsilon^{iHt/\hbar} u_s d\tau$$

$$= \int (\varepsilon^{iHt/\hbar} u_r)^* \rho(0)(\varepsilon^{iHt/\hbar} u_s) d\tau$$

$$= \int \left(\left(1 + \frac{iHt}{\hbar} - \frac{H^2 t^2}{2\hbar^2} - \ldots \right) u_r \right)^* \rho(0) \left(\left(1 + \frac{iHt}{\hbar} - \frac{H^2 t^2}{2\hbar^2} - \ldots \right) u_s \right) d\tau$$

$$= \int \left(\left(1 + \frac{iE_r t}{\hbar} - \frac{E_r^2 t^2}{2\hbar^2} - \ldots \right) u_r \right)^* \rho(0) \left(\left(1 + \frac{iE_s t}{\hbar} - \frac{E_s^2 t^2}{2\hbar^2} - \ldots \right) u_s \right) d\tau$$

$$= \int (\varepsilon^{iE_r t/\hbar} u_r)^* \rho(0)(\varepsilon^{iE_s t/\hbar} u_s) d\tau$$

$$= \varepsilon^{-i(E_r - E_s)t/\hbar} \int u_r^* \rho(0) u_s d\tau$$

$$\therefore \quad \rho_{rs}(t) = \rho_{rs}(0)\varepsilon^{-i(E_r - E_s)t/\hbar}. \tag{A.11}$$

In this representation – the representation in which the matrix of H is diagonal – inspection of (A.9) or (A.11) reveals that the density matrix for an ensemble which is in equilibrium, all of whose properties are independent of time, must be diagonal also.

Entropy, and thermal equilibrium

In classical statistical mechanics, if the probability of finding any member-system of an ensemble in the state labelled i is p_i, the entropy S of the ensemble is defined as

$$S = -k \sum_i p_i \log p_i \tag{A.12}$$

where k is Boltzmann's constant. If all the systems are known to be in a particular state j, then $p_j = 1$, $p_i = 0$ for all $i \neq j$ and then $S = 0$. Thus the entropy is zero when we have this complete knowledge of the state of the ensemble.

But any other configuration or distribution-over-states of the ensemble gives $S > 0$. We may wonder what is the state of *maximum* entropy. This would be found by varying the values of the p_i, subject of course to the normalization condition $\sum_i p_i = 1$. If we vary the p_i, the resulting variation in S is

$$\delta S = -k\delta \sum_i p_i \log p_i = -k \sum_i (1+\log p_i)\delta p_i$$

and the variations in the p_i which maximize S will make

$$\delta S = -k \sum_i (1+\log p_i)\delta p_i = 0.$$

At the same time, because of the normalization condition on the p_i, we must have

$$\sum_i \delta p_i = 0.$$

Using the method of undetermined multipliers as in chapter 8, we multiply the latter equation by an undetermined parameter λ and add it to the previous equation to obtain

$$\sum_i (1+\lambda+\log p_i)\delta p_i = 0.$$

We may now choose λ to make any bracketed set of terms in this summation vanish, say those for $i = 1$, and, since the sum which remains must be zero for arbitrary variations δp_i, we must have for every i

$$\log p_i = -(1+\lambda) = \text{constant},$$

so the p_i are all equal. This specifies the configuration with maximum entropy.

The quantum statistical definition of entropy, analogous to (A.12), is

$$S = -k \, \text{Tr} \, (\rho \log \rho)$$

which slightly resembles (A.12) if the trace is written explicitly as a summation:

$$S = -k \sum_i \sum_j \rho_{ij} (\log \rho)_{ji}$$

and looks even more like (A.12) if ρ is in diagonal form:

$$S = -k \sum_i \rho_i \log \rho_i.$$

For the remainder of this section we shall assume that ρ has been diagonalized.

The condition $\mathrm{Tr}\,(\rho) = 1$ now reads $\sum_i \rho_i = 1$, and if we maximize S subject to this condition we find, precisely as in the classical case already considered, that

$$\log \rho_i = -(1+\lambda) = \text{const.}$$

$$\therefore \quad \rho_i = \varepsilon^{-(1+\lambda)} = \text{const.}$$

On the other hand, if the system is in a pure state we have seen previously that $\mathrm{Tr}\,(\rho^2) = \mathrm{Tr}\,(\rho) = 1$ so, with ρ and therefore ρ^2 both diagonal, we must have

$$\sum_i \rho_i{}^2 = \sum_i \rho_i = 1.$$

Along with the restrictions that $0 \leqq \rho_i \leqq 1$ for all ρ_i, and that all the ρ_i are real, this means that one of the ρ_i is equal to unity, and the rest are all zero, whence

$$-k \sum_i \rho_i \log \rho_i = 0,$$

as in the analogous classical case.

Now let us consider a case in which our knowledge of the system lies between the extremes which make S a maximum or zero. Suppose we know that the ensemble is in thermal equilibrium, and that the average of the energy over all the systems in the ensemble is E. Thus

$$E = \langle \overline{H} \rangle = \mathrm{Tr}\,(\rho H). \tag{A.13}$$

We shall find the form of the diagonal density matrix which maximizes the entropy subject to this constraint. Variation of ρ in such a way as to maximize S while keeping $\mathrm{Tr}\,(\rho)$ and $\mathrm{Tr}\,(\rho H)$ constant gives the three equations

$$\mathrm{Tr}\,(1 + \log \rho)\delta\rho = 0$$

$$\mathrm{Tr}\,(\delta\rho) \qquad = 0$$

$$\mathrm{Tr}\,(H\delta\rho) \qquad = 0.$$

Introducing undetermined multipliers λ and μ, and combining these equations, we get

$$\mathrm{Tr}\,(1 + \lambda + \log \rho + \mu H)\delta\rho = 0$$

from which, in the usual way, we find

$$\log \rho_i = -(1+\lambda+\mu H_i) \quad \text{for all } i$$

$$\therefore \quad \rho_i = \varepsilon^{-(1+\lambda)} \varepsilon^{-\mu H_i} \quad \text{for all } i.$$

Summing on both sides of this equation we get

$$\text{Tr}(\rho) = \varepsilon^{-(1+\lambda)} \text{Tr}(\varepsilon^{-\mu H})$$

and because $\text{Tr}(\rho) = 1$ this gives

$$\varepsilon^{1+\lambda} = \text{Tr}(\varepsilon^{-\mu H})$$

so we have

$$\rho = \varepsilon^{-\mu H} / \text{Tr}(\varepsilon^{-\mu H}) \tag{A.14}$$

or $$\rho_i = \varepsilon^{-\mu H_i} / \sum_j \varepsilon^{-\mu H_j} = \varepsilon^{-\mu H_i} / Z$$

where $Z = \sum_j \varepsilon^{-\mu H_j} = \text{Tr}(\varepsilon^{-\mu H})$ is called the *partition function*.
From the analogy with equation (8.7) we shall assume that μ is $1/kT$ for an ensemble in thermal equilibrium at the temperature T, and it then follows that, in the representation in which H is diagonal, the elements of the density matrix for such an ensemble are simply the normalized Boltzmann factors

$$\rho_i = \varepsilon^{-H_i/kT} / \sum_j \varepsilon^{-H_j/kT}. \tag{A.15}$$

To exemplify the use of this result, let us apply it to calculate the macroscopic magnetization of an ensemble of identical atoms. We suppose there is an ensemble of atoms which do not interact, save in the sense that, given sufficient time, the ensemble will attain thermal equilibrium with its environment at the temperature T. If the (rotational angular momentum)^2 and z-component of magnetic moment of each atom are $l(l+1)\hbar^2$ and $m\mu_B$ respectively, with $-l \leq m \leq l$, the possible values of the energy of the interaction between the atomic magnetic moments and a magnetic field specified by $\mathcal{H}_z = \mathcal{H}$ are the values of $-m\mu_B\mathcal{H}$. These, then, are the elements of the diagonalized Hamiltonian for this interaction, and in the same representation the density matrix of the ensemble is diagonal with elements

$$\rho_m = \varepsilon^{m\mu_B\mathcal{H}/kT} \left/ \sum_{m=-l}^{+l} \varepsilon^{m\mu_B\mathcal{H}/kT} \right.$$

The expectation value of the z-component of the atomic magnetic moment averaged over the ensemble is then

$$\overline{\langle m\mu_B \rangle} = \mathrm{Tr}\,(m\mu_B \cdot \rho)$$

$$= \sum_{m=-l}^{+l} m\mu_B \varepsilon^{m\mu_B \mathscr{H}/kT} \Bigg/ \sum_{m=-l}^{+l} \varepsilon^{m\mu_B \mathscr{H}/kT}$$

and the macroscopic magnetic moment of the material is this expectation value multiplied by the number of atoms in the ensemble. For an ensemble of unit volume, this is called the intensity of magnetization, and the intensity of magnetization produced by a field of unit intensity is called the magnetic susceptibility, χ. Thus we can write

$$\chi = n\mu_B \overline{\langle m \rangle} \,/\, \mathscr{H} = n\mu_B \sum_{m=-l}^{+l} m\varepsilon^{m\mu_B \mathscr{H}/kT} \Bigg/ \sum_{m=-l}^{+l} \varepsilon^{m\mu_B \mathscr{H}/kT}.$$

For fields weak enough and temperatures high enough that $kT \gg \mu_B \mathscr{H}$ the summation in the numerator simplifies:

$$\sum_{m=-l}^{+l} m\varepsilon^{m\mu_B \mathscr{H}/kT} = \sum_{m=-l}^{+l} (m + m^2 \mu_B \mathscr{H} \,/\, kT);$$

now

$$\sum_{m=-l}^{+l} m = 0 \quad \text{and} \quad \sum_{m=-l}^{+l} m^2 = \tfrac{1}{3}l(l+1)(2l+1),$$

so

$$n\mu_B \sum_{m=-l}^{+l} m\varepsilon^{m\mu_B \mathscr{H}/kT} \to \frac{n\mu_B^2 \mathscr{H}}{3kT} \cdot l(l+1)(2l+1)$$

in this limit. In the same limit, the sum in the denominator is

$$\sum_{m=-l}^{+l} (1 + m\mu_B \mathscr{H} \,/\, kT) = 2l+1.$$

Hence

$$\chi = n \cdot l(l+1)\mu_B^2 \,/\, 3kT$$

which is the well-known *Curie-Weiss Law of Paramagnetism*.

At the limit of strong fields and low temperatures, when $\mu_B \mathscr{H} \gg kT$, the expression for χ becomes simply

$$\chi = n \cdot l\mu_B$$

and this defines the saturation magnetization of the material.

QM U

As a further example of the application of (A.14) we shall consider a cavity containing radiation in thermal equilibrium with the walls of the cavity at the temperature T. The mean excitation energy of a mode of the radiation field whose frequency is ω is $\overline{E_\omega} = \bar{n}\hbar\omega$, $\bar{n}$ being the average number of quanta present in that mode. The Hamiltonian for the excitation of this mode will be assumed to be diagonalized, so that we can represent it by a diagonal matrix with elements $H_n = n\hbar\omega$ where n ranges upwards in integral steps from zero. (Notice that we are dealing here with only the excitation energy, and we therefore omit the zero-point energy $\hbar\omega/2$.) Then from (A.13) and (A.15)

$$\langle\overline{E_\omega}\rangle = \langle\bar{n}\rangle\hbar\omega = \hbar\omega \sum_{n=0}^{\infty} n\varepsilon^{-n\hbar\omega/kT} \left/ \sum_{n=0}^{\infty} \varepsilon^{-n\hbar\omega/kT}\right..$$

If we put $x = \varepsilon^{\hbar\omega/kT}$, this gives us

$$\langle\bar{n}\rangle = \sum_{n=0}^{\infty} nx^{-n} \left/ \sum_{n=0}^{\infty} x^{-n} = 1/(x-1)\right.$$

whence

$$\langle\overline{E_\omega}\rangle = \frac{\hbar\omega}{\varepsilon^{\hbar\omega/kT}-1}.$$

This is consistent with our previous result (8.12), and if we multiply by the number of modes in the frequency range ω to $\omega+\delta\omega$ in unit volume of the cavity in both states of polarization, which is $\omega^2\delta\omega/\pi^2c^3$, we get Planck's formula for the spectral energy density of black-body radiation in the form which appears in chapter 11:

$$\rho(\omega)\delta\omega = \frac{\hbar\omega^3\delta\omega}{\pi^2c^3} \frac{1}{\varepsilon^{\hbar\omega/kT}-1}$$

(in which expression $\rho(\omega)$ of course represented the spectral energy density and *not* the density matrix!).

Polarization of electron beams

A beam of slow (non-relativistic) electrons may be regarded as an ensemble of electron spins. Since the spin-state of each electron may be represented by a linear superposition of two spin-functions representing pure states of oppositely directed spin, the density matrix for the ensemble will be a 2×2 matrix. Thus, if for the ith electron we write

$$_i\Psi = {}_ia.\alpha + {}_ib.\beta$$

we have for an ensemble containing N electrons

$$\rho = N^{-1} \begin{bmatrix} \sum_i {}_i a \cdot {}_i \bar{a} & \sum_i {}_i a \cdot {}_i \bar{b} \\ \sum_i {}_i b \cdot {}_i \bar{a} & \sum_i {}_i b \cdot {}_i \bar{b} \end{bmatrix} \qquad \text{(A.16)}$$

Experimenters find it convenient to describe the amount and direction of spin-alignment in the beam by a *polarization vector* which has the magnitude and direction of the ensemble-average of the individual electron spin vectors,

$$\mathbf{P} = \overline{\langle \boldsymbol{\sigma} \rangle} = \mathrm{Tr}\,(\rho \boldsymbol{\sigma})$$

where $\boldsymbol{\sigma}$ denotes the operator whose components are

$$\sigma_x = \begin{bmatrix} 0 & 1 \\ 1 & 0 \end{bmatrix}, \quad \sigma_y = \begin{bmatrix} 0 & -i \\ i & 0 \end{bmatrix}, \quad \sigma_z = \begin{bmatrix} 1 & 0 \\ 0 & -1 \end{bmatrix}.$$

These matrices satisfy the relations

$$\left. \begin{array}{l} \sigma_x \sigma_y = i\sigma_z = -\sigma_y \sigma_x \\ \sigma_y \sigma_z = i\sigma_x = -\sigma_z \sigma_y \\ \sigma_z \sigma_x = i\sigma_y = -\sigma_x \sigma_z \end{array} \right\} \quad \therefore \quad \left\{ \begin{array}{l} [\sigma_x, \sigma_y] = 2i\sigma_z \\ [\sigma_y, \sigma_z] = 2i\sigma_x \\ [\sigma_z, \sigma_x] = 2i\sigma_y \end{array} \right. \quad \text{(A.17)}$$

$$\sigma_x{}^2 = \sigma_y{}^2 = \sigma_z{}^2 = \mathbf{1}$$

and

$$\begin{array}{l} \mathrm{Tr}\,(\sigma_x) = \mathrm{Tr}\,(\sigma_y) = \mathrm{Tr}\,(\sigma_z) = 0 \\ \mathrm{Tr}\,(\sigma_x{}^2) = \mathrm{Tr}\,(\sigma_y{}^2) = \mathrm{Tr}\,(\sigma_z{}^2) = 2 \\ \mathrm{Tr}\,(\sigma_x \sigma_y) = \mathrm{Tr}\,(\sigma_y \sigma_z) = \mathrm{Tr}\,(\sigma_z \sigma_x) = 0. \end{array} \qquad \text{(A.18)}$$

Since the specification of any 2×2 Hermitian matrix (such as ρ) requires the determination of four real numbers, it is possible to represent any such matrix as a linear combination of four linearly independent matrices, and the three Pauli spin matrices along with the unit matrix form a suitable set of matrices for this purpose. So we write

$$\rho = a_0 \mathbf{1} + a_x \sigma_x + a_y \sigma_y + a_z \sigma_z \qquad \text{(A.19)}$$

where the a_0, a_x, a_y, a_z are to be determined.

Since $\mathrm{Tr}\,(\rho) = 1$, we see from (A.18) along with the obvious result $\mathrm{Tr}\,(\mathbf{1}) = 2$ that $a_0 = \frac{1}{2}$, so

$$\rho = \begin{bmatrix} \frac{1}{2}+a_z & a_x-ia_y \\ a_x+ia_y & \frac{1}{2}-a_z \end{bmatrix}.$$

Since $\mathbf{P} = \mathrm{Tr}\,(\rho\boldsymbol{\sigma})$, we have
$$P_x = \mathrm{Tr}\,(\rho\sigma_x)$$
$$P_y = \mathrm{Tr}\,(\rho\sigma_y)$$
$$P_z = \mathrm{Tr}\,(\rho\sigma_z)$$

and $\qquad \rho\sigma_x = \begin{bmatrix} a_x-ia_y & \frac{1}{2}+a_z \\ \frac{1}{2}-a_z & a_x+ia_y \end{bmatrix} \qquad \therefore \; P_x = 2a_x$

and by the corresponding steps $P_y = 2a_y$, $P_z = 2a_z$, whence

$$\rho = \frac{1}{2}\begin{bmatrix} 1+P_z & P_x-iP_y \\ P_x+iP_y & 1-P_z \end{bmatrix} \qquad (A.20)$$

and (A.19) can be written as

$$\rho = a_0\mathbf{1}+\mathbf{a}.\boldsymbol{\sigma} = \frac{1}{2}(\mathbf{1}+\mathbf{P}.\boldsymbol{\sigma}). \qquad (A.21)$$

We arranged that $\mathrm{Tr}(\rho) = 1$ by our choice of a_0, and it is easy to verify that

$$\mathrm{Tr}\,(\rho^2) = \frac{1}{2}(1+P_x{}^2+P_y{}^2+P_z{}^2) = \frac{1}{2}(1+|\mathbf{P}|^2).$$

Now a pure state with definite spin orientation has $|\mathbf{P}| = 1$ (for instance, (A.16) shows that the pure states α and β have density matrices

$$\rho_\alpha = \begin{bmatrix} 1 & 0 \\ 0 & 0 \end{bmatrix}, \quad \rho_\beta = \begin{bmatrix} 0 & 0 \\ 0 & 1 \end{bmatrix}$$

in which cases $P_z = \pm1$ respectively and $P_x = P_y = 0$) so for a completely polarized beam with $P = 1$ we have $\mathrm{Tr}\,(\rho^2) = 1$; for a completely unpolarized beam with $P = 0$, $\mathrm{Tr}\,(\rho^2) = \frac{1}{2}$, and this is the distribution with maximum entropy.

An ideal polarization detector would be a device which responded with efficiency unity to electrons whose spins were aligned in a specified direction, and did not respond at all to oppositely aligned electrons. The response of the detector could therefore be regarded as an observable, represented by an operator, say D, whose eigenstates would be vectors characterizing the directions of maximum and minimum response. If these (normalized) eigen-vectors are $\mathbf{d}^+$ and $\mathbf{d}^-$ we could write

$$D.\mathbf{d}^+ = 1.\mathbf{d}^+ \quad \text{and} \quad D.\mathbf{d}^- = 0.\mathbf{d}^-$$

where the efficiencies of response appear as the eigenvalues 1 and 0 belonging to the eigenvectors $\mathbf{d}^+$ and $\mathbf{d}^-$. The probability that this detector will respond to an electron whose spin vector is $\boldsymbol{\sigma}$ must depend on the scalar product $\mathbf{d}^+.\boldsymbol{\sigma}$. If we write

$$D = \tfrac{1}{2}(\mathbf{1}+\mathbf{d}^+.\boldsymbol{\sigma}), \quad \text{or in full,}$$

$$D = \tfrac{1}{2}\begin{bmatrix} 1+d_z{}^+ & d_x{}^+ - id_y{}^+ \\ d_x{}^+ + id_y{}^+ & 1-d_z{}^+ \end{bmatrix}$$

it is easy to verify that this has the eigenvalues 1 and 0. Further, with this form for the detector operator the value of the response of the detector to a beam whose polarization is described by the vector $\mathbf{P}$ can be found from the relation $\langle \overline{D} \rangle = \mathrm{Tr}\,(\rho D)$ as

$$\mathrm{Tr}\,(\rho D) = \tfrac{1}{4}[(1+d_z{}^+)(1+P_z)+(d_x{}^+ - id_y{}^+)(P_x+iP_y)+$$
$$+(d_x{}^+ + id_y{}^+)(P_x - iP_y)+(1-d_z{}^+)(1-P_z)]$$

$$= \tfrac{1}{4}(2+2d_x{}^+P_x+2d_y{}^+P_y+2d_z{}^+P_z)$$

$$= \tfrac{1}{2}(1+\mathbf{d}^+.\mathbf{P})$$

$$= \tfrac{1}{2}(1+P\cos(\mathbf{d}^+,\mathbf{P}))$$

which ranges between 1 and 0 when $|\mathbf{P}| = 1$, depending on the orientation of $\mathbf{P}$ relative to $\mathbf{d}^+$, and reduces to $\tfrac{1}{2}$ for unpolarized radiation when $P = 0$.

Larmor precession of the electron polarization

If the magnetic moment associated with the electron spin is $\gamma.\tfrac{1}{2}\hbar\boldsymbol{\sigma}$ where γ is the gyromagnetic ratio, the Hamiltonian for the interaction between the spin-magnetic-moment and a magnetic field $\mathscr{H}$ is $H = -\tfrac{1}{2}\gamma\hbar\boldsymbol{\sigma}.\mathscr{H}$. When an ensemble of electron spins interacts with a magnetic field, then the change in the density matrix is related to the change in the polarization by

$$\frac{\partial\rho}{\partial t} = \tfrac{1}{2}\frac{\partial}{\partial t}(1+\mathbf{P}.\boldsymbol{\sigma}) \quad \text{(on differentiating (A.21))}$$

$$= \tfrac{1}{2}\frac{\partial\mathbf{P}}{\partial t}.\boldsymbol{\sigma}$$

since σ does not depend explicitly on time. But

$$\frac{\partial \rho}{\partial t} = i\hbar^{-1}[\rho, H] \qquad\qquad\qquad \text{(see (A.9))}$$

$$= -i\hbar^{-1}((1+\mathbf{P}.\boldsymbol\sigma)\mathscr{H}.\boldsymbol\sigma - \mathscr{H}.\boldsymbol\sigma(1+\mathbf{P}.\boldsymbol\sigma))\gamma\hbar/4$$

$$= -\frac{i\gamma}{4}((P_x\sigma_x + P_y\sigma_y + P_z\sigma_z)(\mathscr{H}_x\sigma_x + \mathscr{H}_y\sigma_y + \mathscr{H}_z\sigma_z) -$$
$$- (\mathscr{H}_x\sigma_x + \mathscr{H}_y\sigma_y + \mathscr{H}_z\sigma_z)(P_x\sigma_x + P_y\sigma_y + P_z\sigma_z))$$

$$= -\frac{i\gamma}{2}(i(P_x\mathscr{H}_y - \mathscr{H}_x P_y)\sigma_z + i(P_y\mathscr{H}_z - \mathscr{H}_y P_z)\sigma_x +$$
$$+ i(P_z\mathscr{H}_x - \mathscr{H}_z P_x)\sigma_y) \qquad \text{(using (A.17))}$$

$$= \frac{\gamma}{2}(\mathbf{P} \wedge \mathscr{H}).\boldsymbol\sigma$$

$$\therefore \quad \tfrac{1}{2}\frac{\partial \mathbf{P}}{\partial t}.\boldsymbol\sigma = -\frac{\gamma}{2}(\mathscr{H} \wedge \mathbf{P}).\boldsymbol\sigma$$

whence

$$\frac{\partial \mathbf{P}}{\partial t} = -\gamma\mathscr{H} \wedge \mathbf{P} = -\boldsymbol\omega \wedge \mathbf{P} \qquad (A.22)$$

where $\boldsymbol\omega = \gamma\mathscr{H}$; the frequency ω is the Larmor frequency, and equation (A.22), which is identical with the classical equation of motion for a spinning magnet in a magnetic field, represents a precession of the polarization vector about the field direction with angular velocity $-\gamma\mathscr{H}$. We can see this in the following way. Take the z-axis in the direction of $\mathscr{H}$, so that $\mathscr{H}$ has components $(0, 0, \mathscr{H})$. Then (A.22) becomes

$$\frac{\partial P_z}{\partial t} = \gamma(P_x\mathscr{H}_y - \mathscr{H}_x P_y) = 0 \qquad \therefore \quad P_z = \text{constant.}$$

$$\frac{\partial P_x}{\partial t} = \gamma(P_y\mathscr{H}_z - \mathscr{H}_y P_z) = \gamma P_y\mathscr{H},$$

$$\frac{\partial P_y}{\partial t} = \gamma(P_z\mathscr{H}_x - \mathscr{H}_z P_x) = -\gamma P_x\mathscr{H},$$

so $\quad \dfrac{\partial^2 P_x}{\partial t^2} = -(\gamma\mathscr{H})^2 P_x, \quad \dfrac{\partial^2 P_y}{\partial t^2} = -(\gamma\mathscr{H})^2 P_y.$

A solution of these equations is $P_x = P_1 \cos \omega t$, $P_y = -P_1 \sin \omega t$, and $P_z = P_0$, with $\omega = \gamma \mathscr{H}$; and this represents a precession with angular velocity ω of a polarization vector whose length is $P = (P_0{}^2 + P_1{}^2)^{\frac{1}{2}}$. The density matrix is

$$\rho = \tfrac{1}{2} \begin{bmatrix} 1+P_0 & P_1 \varepsilon^{i\omega t} \\ P_1 \varepsilon^{-i\omega t} & 1-P_0 \end{bmatrix}$$

with $\mathrm{Tr}\,(\rho) = 1$, $\mathrm{Tr}\,(\rho^2) = \tfrac{1}{2}(1+P^2)$.

We may notice again that if there is no polarization, i.e., $P_0 = P_1 = 0$,

$$\rho = \tfrac{1}{2} \begin{bmatrix} 1 & 0 \\ 0 & 1 \end{bmatrix}$$

so that $\mathrm{Tr}\,(\rho^2) = \tfrac{1}{2}$, while if the ensemble is in either of the pure states α or β we have $\mathrm{Tr}\,(\rho^2) = 1$; and $\mathrm{Tr}\,(\rho^2)$ is still unity if we have a pure state which is not an eigenstate of σ_z, such as a state for which $P_0 = 0$, $P_1 = 1$. For such a state the density matrix is

$$\rho = \tfrac{1}{2} \begin{bmatrix} 1 & \varepsilon^{i\omega t} \\ \varepsilon^{-i\omega t} & 1 \end{bmatrix}$$

where it is easy to verify that

$$\overline{\langle \sigma_z \rangle} = 0$$

$$\overline{\langle \sigma_x \rangle} = \tfrac{1}{2} \mathrm{Tr} \begin{bmatrix} 0 & 1 \\ 1 & 0 \end{bmatrix} \begin{bmatrix} 1 & \varepsilon^{i\omega t} \\ \varepsilon^{-i\omega t} & 1 \end{bmatrix} = \cos \omega t$$

$$\overline{\langle \sigma_y \rangle} = \tfrac{1}{2} \mathrm{Tr} \begin{bmatrix} 0 & -i \\ i & 0 \end{bmatrix} \begin{bmatrix} 1 & \varepsilon^{i\omega t} \\ \varepsilon^{-i\omega t} & 1 \end{bmatrix} = -\sin \omega t.$$

These results should be compared with those obtained in chapter 4, in the discussion of the equivalent problem for a single electron in a pure state (see pp. 71-75).

Polarization of ensembles of systems other than electrons

If the systems in an ensemble are particles for which the largest value of angular momentum is j, the density matrix is a $(2j+1) \times (2j+1)$ matrix. In general an $n \times n$ density matrix is specified by $n^2 - 1$ parameters – one less than the number required to specify a general $n \times n$ Hermitian matrix, since the relation $\mathrm{Tr}\,(\rho) = 1$ reduces the number of independent parameters by 1. A $(2j+1) \times (2j+1)$ density matrix therefore requires $4j(j+1)$ parameters for its specification – 3 if $j = \frac{1}{2}$, 8 if $j = 1$, 15 if $j = \frac{3}{2}$, etc. The polarization vector provides only 3 parameters, sufficient only when $j = \frac{1}{2}$. In the case of larger j-values the components of **P** are called the components of the *dipole polarization* vector, and the additional parameters are called the components of the quadrupole polarization tensor (which number 5), the octupole polarization tensor (7 components), etc.

The polarization of a light-beam, on the other hand, can be described in a way which is formally identical with the description of electron spin. It was pointed out in chapter 1 that the polarization-state of a photon can be represented by a 2-component state-function. From this a 2×2 density matrix can be constructed, and like any 2×2 Hermitian matrix this can be decomposed into an expansion in terms of the unit matrix and a set of Pauli matrices σ, according to equation (A.19). This leads to equations corresponding to (A.20 and 21), with **P** now the polarization vector of the light-beam – though as we shall soon see it is not a vector in real physical space.

In classical optics, if the electric field $\mathscr{E}$ of the light wave is decomposed into components along x- and y-axes perpendicular to the direction of propagation, so that

$$\mathscr{E} = (\mathscr{E})_x \mathbf{i} + (\mathscr{E})_y \mathbf{j} \quad \text{(where } (\mathscr{E})_x, (\mathscr{E})_y \text{ may be complex)}$$

or $\qquad \mathscr{E} = \mathscr{E} \cos \theta \mathbf{i} + \mathscr{E} \sin \theta \mathbf{j}$

a *coherency* matrix is defined as

$$C = \begin{bmatrix} \langle (\mathscr{E})_x^* (\mathscr{E})_x \rangle & \langle (\mathscr{E})_x^* (\mathscr{E})_y \rangle \\ \langle (\mathscr{E})_y^* (\mathscr{E})_x \rangle & \langle (\mathscr{E})_y^* (\mathscr{E})_y \rangle \end{bmatrix} = |\mathscr{E}|^2 \begin{bmatrix} \langle \cos^2 \theta \rangle & \langle \cos \theta \sin \theta \varepsilon^{i\delta} \rangle \\ \langle \sin \theta \cos \theta \varepsilon^{-i\delta} \rangle & \langle \sin^2 \theta \rangle \end{bmatrix}$$

In what follows we shall omit the factor $|\mathscr{E}|^2$.

Five special cases may be noted at once:

(i) If the light beam is plane polarized in the x-direction, $\sin \theta = 0$, $\cos \theta = 1$, $\delta = 0$, so

$$C_x = \begin{bmatrix} 1 & 0 \\ 0 & 0 \end{bmatrix}.$$

(ii) For plane polarization in the y-direction, $\sin \theta = 1$, $\cos \theta = 0$, $\delta = 0$, so

$$C_y = \begin{bmatrix} 0 & 0 \\ 0 & 1 \end{bmatrix}.$$

(iii) For plane polarization with $\theta = \pm 45°$ and $\delta = 0$,

$$C_{\pm 45} = \tfrac{1}{2} \begin{bmatrix} 1 & \pm 1 \\ \pm 1 & 1 \end{bmatrix}.$$

(iv) For circular polarization in one or other sense $\delta = \pm \pi/2$, $\cos \theta = \sin \theta = 1/\sqrt{2}$, so

$$C_{\pm} = \tfrac{1}{2} \begin{bmatrix} 1 & \pm i \\ \mp i & 1 \end{bmatrix}.$$

(v) For completely unpolarized radiation θ and δ are random variables so $\langle \cos^2 \theta \rangle = \langle \sin^2 \theta \rangle = \tfrac{1}{2}$, $\langle \cos \theta \sin \theta \varepsilon^{\pm i\delta} \rangle = 0$, and

$$C_0 = \tfrac{1}{2} \begin{bmatrix} 1 & 0 \\ 0 & 1 \end{bmatrix}.$$

These matrices are all Hermitian, and have trace unity; we note also that

$$\mathrm{Tr}\,(C_x{}^2) = \mathrm{Tr}\,(C_y{}^2) = \mathrm{Tr}\,(C_{\pm 45}^2) = \mathrm{Tr}\,(C_{\pm}^2) = 1; \; \mathrm{Tr}\,(C_0{}^2) = \tfrac{1}{2}.$$

The discussion of the representation of photon polarization in chapter 1 shows how similar the description of photon states can be made to that used here, and the resulting density matrices for variously polarized light beams are just those we have found here. The fact that C_0 can be formed by a superposition of *either* C_x and C_y or C_+ and C_- is consistent with the assertion that an unpolarized light beam in an isotropic medium may be regarded as either an incoherent superposition of orthogonally plane-polarized beams, or of oppositely circularly polarized beams. Finally, the fact that $\mathrm{Tr}\,(C_0{}^2) < 1$ is consistent with the view that an unpolarized beam is not in a pure state.

If we write the density matrix for the light beam as

$$\rho = \tfrac{1}{2} \begin{bmatrix} 1 + P_\zeta & P_\xi - iP_\eta \\ P_\xi + iP_\eta & 1 - P_\zeta \end{bmatrix}, \qquad \text{(cf. (A.20))}$$

we see that $P_\zeta = 1$, $P_\xi = P_\eta = 0$ makes $\rho \equiv C_x$, so $P_\zeta = 1$ specifies a plane-polarized beam with a particular direction of polarization; $P_\zeta = -1$, $P_\xi = P_\eta = 0$ makes $\rho \equiv C_y$, so this represents plane polarization at right angles to the last. $P_\xi = \pm 1$, $P_\eta = P_\zeta = 0$ makes $\rho \equiv C_{\pm 45}$, which is the matrix for plane-polarization in one or other of the planes inclined at 45° to the previous two. $P_\eta = \pm 1$, $P_\xi = P_\zeta = 0$ makes $\rho \equiv C_{\pm}$, which shows that this represents circular polarization.

In all these cases the vector $(P_\xi, P_\eta, P_\zeta) = \mathbf{P}$ does not represent the polarization direction in real space, as it did for the electron polarization, but in the symbolic space of the Poincaré sphere of classical optics. The values of P_ξ, P_η and P_ζ, and hence the density matrix elements, may be found by measuring the intensities of the light transmitted through suitably oriented polarization analysers; found in this way, these quantities and the total intensity are equivalent to the Stokes parameters of the light beam. The expression of the density matrix in the form

$$\rho = \tfrac{1}{2}(1 + \mathbf{P} \cdot \boldsymbol{\omega}), \qquad \text{(cf. (A.21))}$$

where $\boldsymbol{\omega}$ is the set of Pauli matrices $(\omega_\xi, \omega_\eta, \omega_\zeta)$ which relate to the ξ, η and ζ directions in the space of the Poincaré sphere, thus exhibits at once the *degrees* of polarization P_ξ, P_η, P_ζ associated with the three *types* of polarization labelled by $\omega_\xi, \omega_\eta, \omega_\zeta$ respectively.

Scattering of light

When a light-wave falls on an assemblage of atoms, say in the form of a gas, an oscillatory polarization is produced, which can be regarded as the source of the scattered light. If the frequency ω of the incident light-wave is very much closer to one of the excitation frequencies of the atoms, say ω_{12}, than to any other, the atoms may to first approximation be regarded as 2-level systems, since in the perturbation theoretical expression for the polarization (11.17) the term in ω_{12} will predominate over all the others. We shall therefore adopt this simplification here. But now we shall consider, not the perturbation of a single atom by the incident radiation, but the representation of the material polarization with the aid of the density matrix in the presence of the oscillatory radiation field.

For the (effectively) two-level system the density matrix ρ and the electric dipole matrix μ are both 2×2 matrices:

$$\rho = \begin{bmatrix} \rho_{11} & \rho_{12} \\ \rho_{21} & \rho_{22} \end{bmatrix}$$

(which we shall assume to be normalized so that ρ_{11} and ρ_{22} are the actual population densities in the states 1 and 2, i.e. the populations in unit volume)

and $\qquad \mu = \begin{bmatrix} 0 & \mu_{12} \\ \mu_{21} & 0 \end{bmatrix} = e \begin{bmatrix} 0 & z_{12} \\ z_{21} & 0 \end{bmatrix}$

The polarization of the ensemble is then

$$P = \text{Tr}\,(\mu\rho) = \mu_{12}\rho_{21} + \mu_{21}\rho_{12} = 2\,\text{Re}\,(\mu_{21}\rho_{12})$$

and depends only on the off-diagonal elements of the density matrix.

We write the Hamiltonian for the single electron (in each atom) with which we suppose the incident electromagnetic field to interact as $H = H_0 + H'$, where H_0 is the Hamiltonian in the absence of the light wave, and H' represents the interaction between the electron and the light wave, thus:

$$H' = -\frac{e}{m}\,\mathbf{A}\cdot\mathbf{p}.$$

For $\mathbf{A}(t)$ we put $\mathbf{A}_0\,(\varepsilon^{i\omega t} + \varepsilon^{-i\omega t}) = 2\mathbf{A}_0\cos\omega t$, where for simplicity we ignore the spatial variation of the electromagnetic field; this will have the consequence that our results will be strictly applicable only to a volume of scatterer which is small compared with the optical wavelength. Then

$$H'_{mn} = -\frac{e}{m}\,(\mathbf{A}\cdot\mathbf{p})_{mn} = -\frac{e}{m}\,A_0(p_\mathbf{A})_{mn}(\varepsilon^{i\omega t} + \varepsilon^{-i\omega t})$$

$$= -ie\omega_{mn}z_{mn}A_0(\varepsilon^{i\omega t} + \varepsilon^{-i\omega t}),$$

if the z-direction is chosen to be the direction of the polarization vector of the light wave.

The equation of motion of the density matrix is

$$\frac{\partial\rho}{\partial t} = \frac{i}{\hbar}\,[\rho, H] = \frac{i}{\hbar}\,[\rho, H_0] + \frac{i}{\hbar}\,[\rho, H']$$

$$\therefore\quad \frac{\partial\rho_{mn}}{\partial t} = \frac{i}{\hbar}\,(\rho_{mn}E_n - E_m\rho_{mn}) + \frac{i}{\hbar}\sum_k (\rho_{mk}H'_{kn} - H'_{mk}\rho_{kn}).$$

For our two-level system the matrix of H' (or z) has non-vanishing elements H'_{12} and H'_{21} (or z_{12} and z_{21}) only, so for the rate of change of ρ_{12} we get

$$\left(\frac{\partial}{\partial t} + i\omega_{12}\right)\rho_{12} = \frac{i}{\hbar}\,(\rho_{11} - \rho_{22})H'_{12}$$

$$= \frac{eA_0}{\hbar}\,(\varepsilon^{i\omega t} + \varepsilon^{-i\omega t})(\rho_{11} - \rho_{22})\omega_{12}z_{12} \quad\text{(A.23)}$$

and there is a similar equation, containing no further information, for ρ_{21}; the rates of change of ρ_{11} and ρ_{22} – which are equal and opposite since Tr (ρ) is constant – are:

$$\frac{\partial \rho_{11}}{\partial t} = \frac{i}{\hbar} \, (\rho_{12} H'_{21} - H'_{12} \rho_{21}) = -\frac{\partial \rho_{22}}{\partial t}.$$

We shall not solve these equations completely however, being content to find a steady-state solution for ρ_{12}. But before we can pursue even this more limited objective we must modify equation (A.23) to allow for an effect we have not considered so far, and will consider only in a rather general and descriptive way now.

Before the light-wave first falls on the ensemble, ρ_{11} and ρ_{22} will be assumed to have the values appropriate to thermal equilibrium, in which case our assumption that ω_{12} is close to an optical frequency implies that ρ_{11}/ρ_{22} must be very large. For the moment we assume that the incident radiation does not produce a rapid change in ρ_{11} and ρ_{22}; we shall comment on this assumption later. Even a slow change in ρ_{11} and ρ_{22} might in time lead to a substantial change in the populations of the states 1 and 2, but any deviation from the equilibrium values is opposed by whatever *relaxation mechanisms* are involved in the establishment of thermal equilibrium. We shall allow for this effect simply – perhaps too simply! – by including on the left-hand side of (A.23) a term containing a 'phenomenological relaxation time' τ whose origin we do not attempt to explain beyond saying that interatomic collisions, collisions of atoms with the walls of the containing vessel, and natural radiative decay – all processes whose characteristic times are 10^{-10} s or longer – may contribute to it.

With the differential equation thus modified, we shall seek a solution which represents the steady-state value of ρ_{12} in the form

$$\rho_{12} = \lambda^{+} \varepsilon^{i\omega t} + \lambda^{-} \varepsilon^{-i\omega t}.$$

With the relaxation term included, insertion of the trial solution for ρ_{12} into (A.23) gives

$$\left(\frac{\partial}{\partial t} + i\omega_{12} + \frac{1}{\tau} \right) (\lambda^{+} \varepsilon^{i\omega t} + \lambda^{-} \varepsilon^{-i\omega t}) =$$

$$= e A_0 \hbar^{-1} (\rho_{11} - \rho_{22}) \omega_{12} z_{12} (\varepsilon^{i\omega t} + \varepsilon^{-i\omega t}).$$

Collecting the coefficients of terms containing $\varepsilon^{i\omega t}$, we have

$$\lambda^+(i\omega + i\omega_{12} + \tau^{-1}) = eA_0\hbar^{-1}(\rho_{11} - \rho_{22})\omega_{12}z_{12}$$

$$\therefore \quad \lambda^+ = \frac{eA_0(\rho_{11} - \rho_{22})\omega_{12}z_{12}}{i\hbar(\omega + \omega_{12} - i/\tau)}$$

$$= \frac{ieA_0(\rho_{11} - \rho_{22})\omega_{12}z_{12}}{\hbar(\omega_{21} - \omega + i/\tau)}$$

$$\text{since } \omega_{21} = -\omega_{12}$$

and similarly

$$\lambda^- = \frac{ieA_0(\rho_{11} - \rho_{22})\omega_{12}z_{12}}{\hbar(\omega_{21} + \omega + i/\tau)}.$$

We note that, since the expression for λ^+ has a resonance denominator, λ^+ would become infinite for $\omega = \omega_{21}$ if the relaxation term were not included.

ρ_{12} and ρ_{21} are thus determined, and the macroscopic polarization is now found to be

$$P = 2\,\text{Re}\,(\mu_{21}\rho_{12})$$

$$= 2\,\text{Re}\,\{ez_{21}(\lambda^+\varepsilon^{i\omega t} + \lambda^-\varepsilon^{-i\omega t})\}$$

$$= 2e^2A_0\omega_{12}\,|z_{12}|^2(\rho_{11} - \rho_{22})\,\text{Re}\left\{\frac{i\varepsilon^{i\omega t}}{\hbar(\omega_{21} - \omega + i/\tau)} + \frac{i\varepsilon^{-i\omega t}}{\hbar(\omega_{21} + \omega + i/\tau)}\right\}$$

Since ω and ω_{21} are both of the order of $10^{15}\,\text{s}^{-1}$ while $1/\tau$ is of order $10^{10}\,\text{s}^{-1}$ or less, two particularly interesting special cases can very quickly be extracted from this general result. At resonance, that is when $\omega \approx \omega_{21}$, only the first term needs to be considered and we get

$$P_{\text{res}} = -2e^2A_0\omega_{21}\,|z_{12}|^2(\rho_{11} - \rho_{22})\hbar^{-1}\tau\cos\omega_{21}t.$$

Since the electric intensity is $\mathscr{E} = -\dot{A} = -2A_0\omega\sin\omega t$ we see at once that the polarization is $\pi/2$ out of phase with the incident electric field, and that the magnitude of the macroscopic polarizability at resonance is

$$\alpha_{\text{res}} = \frac{|P|_{\text{res}}}{|\mathscr{E}|_{\text{res}}} = e^2\,|z_{12}|^2(\rho_{11} - \rho_{22})\tau/\hbar.$$

Far from resonance, on the other hand, the relative magnitudes of ω, ω_{21} and $1/\tau$ ensure that the terms in $1/\tau$ may be omitted from each denominator, and the real quantity in braces then becomes

$$\left\{ \frac{-\sin \omega t}{\hbar(\omega_{21}-\omega)} + \frac{\sin \omega t}{\hbar(\omega_{21}+\omega)} \right\} = -\frac{2\hbar\omega \sin \omega t}{\hbar^2(\omega^2_{21}-\omega^2)}.$$

Putting this in the expression for P, and replacing $-2A_0\omega \sin \omega t$ by $\mathscr{E}$, we find that

$$P = -2e^2 \left| z_{12} \right|^2 (\rho_{11}-\rho_{22}) \frac{\hbar\omega_{21}}{\hbar^2(\omega^2_{21}-\omega^2)} \cdot \mathscr{E}$$

which should be compared with the expression in equation (11.17) for the polarization of a single atom at frequencies far from any absorption line.

Since the macroscopic dipole moment per unit volume is P, the rate of radiation is proportional to $\ddot{P}^2$, so the intensity of scattered (or reradiated) light is proportional to $(\rho_{11}-\rho_{22})^2$; when, as we have thought it reasonable to assume here, $\rho_{11} \gg \rho_{22}$, this means that the intensity is proportional to the square of the number of scatterers, and this means that the scattering is coherent – only if the amplitudes of the waves scattered by different atoms add coherently can the intensity be proportional to the square of the number of scatterers. We must remember, though, that we omitted space-dependent factors from the representation of the incident field, thereby limiting the validity of our conclusions to the case of a scattering volume whose linear dimensions are small compared with λ.

There remains for further consideration one other initial assumption – that the value of $\rho_{11}-\rho_{22}$ is not much changed by the inter-action with the radiation. This point could be investigated rigour-ously by solving the simultaneous differential equations for the elements of the density matrix, not for the steady state but quite generally for all times subsequent to the 'switching on' of the incident radiation. We shall not do this here, but rather exploit our physical understanding of the meaning of the diagonal elements to decide under what conditions of illumination the steady-state values of ρ_{11} and ρ_{22} will not differ much from their values in thermal equilibrium.

Suppose a very intense illumination is incident from a gas laser, say 10m W/mm^2 at a frequency of 10^{15} radians per second and with a bandwidth of 10^5 radians per second. Then if $|z_{12}|$ is 10^{-10} m the probability per atom per second of an absorptive transition is, from (11.8), 10^{12}(!). It is better to regard the reciprocal of this as a characteristic time for the process of radiative excitation; this is then 10^{-12} s, which is less by at least two orders of magnitude than the relaxation time we assumed above for non-radiative de-excitation processes. Excitation therefore proceeds much more quickly than non-radiative de-excitation: consequently ρ_{22} increases and ρ_{11} decreases correspondingly, and the process which limits this change is the increased frequency of stimulated emission as the number of atoms in the excited state increases. The result is that ρ_{22} increases to a value only slightly less than ρ_{11} (if spontaneous decay and the non-radiative relaxation processes did not occur ρ_{22} would become exactly equal to ρ_{11}), and the transition is then said to be 'saturated'; the macroscopic polarization being proportional to $\rho_{11} - \rho_{22}$ is thus reduced to a very small value. However, a shift of only τ^{-1} radians per second in the frequency of the exciting radiation (or say $\Delta\lambda \approx \cdot05$ Å) reduces the effectiveness of the radiative interaction to a quarter of its value at resonance, and a shift of more than $\cdot5$ Å makes the characteristic time for radiative excitation comparable with the relaxation time for nonradiative de-excitation. For frequency deviations (between the resonant frequency and the incident radiation frequency) greater than this the relaxation mechanism will prevent any substantial net transfer of population from the lower to the higher state.

If a 'thermal' light source – say a gas discharge lamp with characteristics similar to those of the source described in problem 9 of page 262 – is used, the characteristic time for radiative excitation is 10^{-6} s, which is much longer than the relaxation time. In these circumstances the value of ρ_{11} is not significantly affected by the radiation, even at the resonant frequency.

In the results obtained above ρ_{11} and ρ_{22} can therefore be set equal to their thermal equilibrium values, for non-laser illumination without restriction on frequency, and for laser illuminants with wavelengths more than about 1 Å away from the atomic absorption lines.

BACKGROUND READING AND
FURTHER STUDY

Some familiarity with atomic physics, or at least a willingness to look elsewhere for information about the historical and experimental background of quantum physics, is assumed throughout this book. Born's *Atomic Physics* (Blackie, 1962), Slater's *Modern Physics* (McGraw-Hill, 1955) and Garbuny's *Optical Physics* (Academic Press, 1965) are excellent sources for this material. *The Foundations of Physics* by Lindsay and Margenau (Dover reprint, 1957) is a comprehensive survey of the development and scope of theoretical physics, with chapters on classical mechanics, statistical mechanics, and quantum theory.

The early development of quantum mechanics is conveniently epitomized in a number of compilations and translations, e.g., *Selected papers on wave mechanics* by de Broglie and Brillouin (Blackie, 1928), *Collected papers on wave mechanics* by Schrödinger (Blackie, 1928), Sommerfeld's *Wave Mechanics* (Methuen, 1930) and Heisenberg's *The physical principles of the quantum theory* (University of Chicago Press, 1930, reprinted by Dover Publications). Two very useful early text-books are Pauling and Wilson's *Introduction to Quantum Mechanics* (McGraw-Hill, 1935) and Rojansky's *Introductory Quantum Mechanics* (Blackie, 1939).

Among recent advanced texts, Landau and Lifshitz's non-relativistic *Quantum Mechanics* (Pergamon, 1958), Messiah's two volume *Quantum Mechanics* (North Holland Publishing Company, 1961 and 1962) and Roman's *Advanced Quantum Theory* (Addison Wesley, 1965) are outstanding, while Dirac's *Principles of Quantum Mechanics* (O.U.P., 1958) is a classic exposition of the formal approach to the subject. A comprehensive account of quantum electrodynamics is to be found in Heitler's *The Quantum Theory of Radiation* (O.U.P., 1954).

The necessary mathematical techniques are excellently treated in the appropriate sections of Margenau and Murphy's *The Mathematics of Physics and Chemistry* (Van Nostrand, 1956) and in Morse and Feshbach's two volume treatise *The Methods of Theoretical Physics* (McGraw-Hill, 1953).

INDEX

Adjoint operator, 13, 24
Angular momentum, 58
  addition of, 77ff, 79ff
  commutation relations, 59ff
  eigenfunctions for, 89ff
  eigenvalues of, 61ff
  electron spin (*see* Spin, Spin
    function)
  in non-central field, 132, 134, 155f
  matrix treatment, 61, 91
  uncertainty relations, 91
  vector model, 73
  wave-mechanical treatment, 86ff
Anomalous Zeeman effect, 123ff
Anti-symmetry (*see* Symmetry)

Band, electron energy, in metals, 208
Batho, H. F. (*see* Dempster and Batho)
Bernoulli, D., 9
Black-body radiation, 171ff, 245ff,
  283, 296
Blatt, J. M. and Weisskopf, V. F., 257
Bloch eigenfunctions, 208
Bohm, D., 203, 238
Bohr, N., 1, 56, 105, 261
Bohr frequency condition, 42, 242
Bohr magneton, 69, 76, 123, 126, 194
Bohr radius, 104
Boltzmann factors, 294
Boltzmann statistics, 168ff
Born, M., 222, 226, 229
Born approximation, 229ff, 238, 239
Bose-Einstein statistics, 170, 182
  of black-body radiation, 171ff
  of gas in equilibrium, 173ff
Boundary conditions, 20, 35
Brillouin, L., 198
de Broglie relation (wavelength), 174,
  175, 185
Brown, R. Hanbury, and Twiss,
  R. Q., 282

Canonical (Hamilton's) equations,
  30, 39, 266, 290
Canonical variables, 31
  for electromagnetic field, 266, 267
Central field, 59
  angular momentum in, 58ff
  degeneracy in, 97, 100, 104, 113
  motion in, 27
  radial motion in, 40, 93ff

Centrifugal potential, 93, 115, 164
Clebsch-Gordan coefficients, 86
Coherency matrix, 302
Coherent state, 187
Collision theory, 222ff
  Born approximation, 229ff, 238, 239
  classical limit, 230
  partial-wave method, 233ff
  (*see also* Rutherford scattering,
    Scattering cross-section)
Commutation relations,
  and Poisson brackets, 29ff
  and uncertainty relations, 27ff
  for angular momentum, 59ff, 91, 92
  for electromagnetic field, 268, 281,
    282
Commutator, 27, 29ff
Commuting operators, 17ff, 60, 124
Compatible variables, 6f, 16f
Compton effect, 220, 270
Condon, E. U. and Shortley, G., 86
Coulomb field,
  energy levels of electron in, 101ff
  scattering in, 226ff, 233
  (*see also* Degeneracy)
Critchfield, C. L. (*see* Gamow and
  Critchfield)
Crystal lattice, periodic potential in,
  204f
Curie-Weiss law, 295

Dancoff, S. and Inglis, D. R., 80
Degeneracy, 14
  for 2-dimensional oscillator, 114
  for 3-dimensional oscillator, 53f, 100
  in 3-dimensional potential well, 97,
    106, 113
  in central field, 97
  in Coulomb field, 104
  of electronic states in metal, 206,
    208
  of cavity radiation, 173
  (*see also* Bose-Einstein statistics,
    Fermi-Dirac statistics,
    Perturbation method)
Delta function, 20
Dempster, A. J. and Batho, H. F., 2
Density matrix, 12, 284ff
Deuteron, binding energy of, 113f,
  115
  radius of, 115

Diamagnetism, and Zeeman effect, 129
Dipole (*see* Electric dipole, Magnetic dipole)
Dirac, P.A.M., 20, 34, 56, 67
Dispersion, optical, 258ff
 curve for electrons, 211, 212, 216
Düker, H. (*see* Möllenstedt and Düker)
Dulong and Petit, 180

Effective mass of electron, 208ff, 212ff
Ehrenfest, P., 187, 217
Ehrenfest, P. and Oppenheimer, J.R., 167
Ehrenfest's theorem, 187ff, 201
Eigendifferential, 22
Eigenvalues,
 continuously distributed, 20
 of linear operator, 13
 representing results of measurements, 15
Eigenvectors,
 of linear operator, 13
 of Hermitian operator, orthogonality of, 14
 representing states, 13
 linear independence of, 12, 15
 when eigenvalues form a continuum, 20f
Electric dipole moment, 57, 134, 245, 247ff, 249ff, 259, 279f
 of ensemble, 304ff
Electric dipole transition (*see* Radiation)
Electric quadrupole moment, 257
 (*see also* Radiation)
Electromagnetic field,
 classical behaviour in the limit, 277ff
 commutation relations, 268, 282
 corpuscular properties of, 269f
 Hamiltonian for, 266
 interaction of atomic electron with, 240ff, 271ff
 polarization of material by, 304ff
 quantization of, 264ff
 uncertainty relation, 282
 (*see also* Black-body radiation, Radiation, Radiation field)
Entropy of ensemble, 291ff
Ensemble, representation of state of, 284, 286
Equation of motion, 37, 42, 47f, 216, 288f
Exchange forces, 150
Exchange integral, 145
Exclusion (Pauli's) principle, 150ff, 208
 and periodic system, 156ff
 and quantum statistics, 167, 176

Expectation value, 16, 21, 50ff
 classical behaviour of, 187
 for an ensemble, 285f
 of velocity for wave-packet, 189ff

f-sum rule, 135
Fabrikant, V., 3, 10
Feshbach, H. (*see* Morse and Feshbach)
Fermi, E., 159, 180
Fermi-Dirac statistics, 175ff, 182
 of electrons in metal, 178ff
 (*see also* Thomas-Fermi atom model)
Fermi function, 177f, 180
Fine-structure constant ($=137$), 276
Fock, V., 161
Forbidden transitions, 256ff
Forrester, A.T., Gudmundsen, R.A. and Johnson, P.O., 282

g-factor, 126
Gamow, G. and Critchfield, C.L., 203
Gaussian wave-function and wave-packet, 39, 187, 216
Gerlach, W. (*see* Stern and Gerlach)
Glauber, R.J., 187, 270
Green, H.S., 11
Group velocity, 189ff, 202
Gudmundsen, A.T. (*see* Forrester, Gudmundsen and Johnson)
Gyromagnetic ratio, 126, 299

Harmonic oscillator (*see* Simple harmonic oscillator)
Hartree, D.R., 159ff, 180
Heisenberg, W., 34, 56, 282
Heitler, W., 269, 281
Heitler, W. and London, F., 161, 163
Helium atom,
 perturbation treatment of, 143ff
 space functions for, 146
 spin functions for, 153, 164
 variation treatment of, 148ff
Homopolar bond, 161
Hydrogen atom, 101ff
 energy levels of, 104
 solution of radial wave equation, 101ff, 115
 (*see also* Polarizability, Stark effect, Second-order Zeeman effect)
Hydrogen molecule, 161ff, 164
Hydrogen negative ion, 164f
Hylleraas, E.A., 150

Identical particles, 151, 166
Incompatible variables, 5, 16ff, 29
Indeterminacy, 10, 16, 23, 27, 77
 (*see also* Uncertainty)

Indistinguishability, 166f, 170, 176
Induced emission, 245, 262, 272f, 280, 309
Inglis, D. R. (see Dancoff and Inglis)
Interference,
    in electron optics, 3, 10
    in light optics, 2f, 5, 280ff
    of probabilities, 150f

Janossy, L. and Naray, Zs., 2
Jeans, Sir James, 1
Jenkins, F. A. and Segré, E., 130
Johnson, P. O. (see Forrester, Gudmundsen and Johnson)

Kemble, E. C., 198
Kennard, E. H., 175
Kramers, H. A., 198

Laguerre polynomials, associated, 101
Landau, L. D. and Lifschitz, E. M., 11
Langevin, P., 1
Larmor frequency, 123, 299f
Laser, 154, 247, 308f
Lattice, periodic potential in, 204f, 208
Leech, J. W., 29
van Leeuwen, Miss, 1
Legendre's equation, 88
Legendre polynomials, associated, 89
Lifshitz, E. M. (see Landau and Lifshitz)
Liouville's theorem, 289f
London, F. (see Heitler and London)
L-S coupling, 79ff, 92, 123ff

Magnetic dipole moment of atomic state, 123, 192ff, 256f
    and paramagnetism, 294f
    (see also Bohr magneton)
Magnetic dipole transition (see Radiation)
Magneton (see Bohr magneton)
Many-electron atoms,
    and exclusion principle, 156ff
    by self-consistent field method, 159ff
    by variation method, 159ff
    by Thomas-Fermi model, 180ff, 183
    energy levels in, 154ff
Margenau, H. and Murphy, G. M., 89, 105
Maser, 247
Maxwell, J. C., 258
Measurement, meaning of, 11
Metal, theory of electrons in, 178ff, 203ff
Möllenstedt, G. and Düker, H., 10
Morse, P. M. and Feshbach, H., 101

Morse potential, 164
Mott, N. F. and Sneddon, I. N., 141
Murphy, G. M. (see Margenau and Murphy)

Naray, Zs. (see Janossy and Naray)
von Neumann, J., 56
Neutron-proton force, approximation to, 113, 115, 238
Neutron-proton scattering, 238f
Normalization, 21f
    of perturbed eigenfunctions, 120

Operator,
    choice of, 34ff
    eigenvalues of, 13
    eigenvectors of, 13
    functions of, 34
    Hermitian, 13f
    linear, 13
Oppenheimer, J. R. (see Ehrenfest and Oppenheimer)
Optical pumping, 256
Orthogonality,
    of eigendifferentials, 22
    of eigenvectors of Hermitian operator, 14
    of perturbed state-functions, 118, 120, 122, 134
    of wave-functions, 21
Oscillating wave-packet, 186f
Oscillator (see Simple harmonic oscillator)
Oscillator strength, 134f, 261

Panofsky, W. K. H. and Phillips, M., 80
Paramagnetism, 295
Parity, 249f, 262
Partial waves, method of, 233ff, 238
Paschen-Back effect, 127, 128, 142
Pauli, W., 56, 67, 154, 180
Pauli matrices,
    for electron spin, 67ff, 77, 91
    for light beam, 304
Pauli exclusion principle, 150ff, 156ff, 167, 176, 208
Pauling, L. and Wilson, E. B., 89, 105, 129, 152
Periodic potential, state-functions in, 203ff
Periodic system of elements, 156ff
Perturbation method in quantum dynamics, 218ff
    and conservation of energy, 222
    for collision problems, 222f
    for radiation problems, 240ff, 271ff
    parity considerations, 262

314 INDEX

Perturbation method in quantum
  statics, 116ff
  for degenerate states, 121f
  for electrons in a metal, 205ff
  for helium atom, 143ff
  for hydrogen molecule, 161ff
  for oscillator, 141
  for rotator, 142
  for screened Coulomb field, 154ff
  for Stark effect, 130ff, 142
  for Zeeman effect, 122ff, 142
Phase,
  condition of stationary, 190, 202
  of state functions, 12, 70, 120
  specification of in radiation field,
    270, 279ff
Phillips, M. (see Panofsky and
  Phillips)
Photoelectric effect, 2, 274ff, 283
Planck, M., 170
Planck's constant, 4f, 22, 29, 31
Planck's radiation law (see Black-body
  radiation)
Poisson bracket, 29ff, 32f, 39, 40
  of angular momentum variables,
    59ff, 92
Polarizability of atom,
  and optical dispersion, 260f
  by perturbation method, 134ff, 262
  by variation method, 138ff
Polarizability of rigid rotator, 142
Polarization,
  of electron spins, 296ff
  of light, 6ff, 302ff
  of material by light-wave, 304ff
Potential barriers,
  and WKB method, 202f
  penetration of, 194ff, 202f, 216f
Precession,
  of electron polarization, 299ff
  of electron spin, 71ff
  Thomas, 80
Probabilities, interference of, 150f
Probability and quantum theory, 22f,
  284
  (see also Superposition principle)
Probability current density, 66, 192ff,
  196, 215
Probability distribution, 5f, 11, 23
Probability flux (see Probability
  current density)

Quantal aspects of electromagnetic
  field, 269f
Quantum conditions, general statement of, 31

Radiation:
  absorption, 242f, 244, 255, 272, 279
  and off-diagonal matrix elements, 54

Radiation—contd:
  black-body, 171ff, 245ff, 283, 296
  electric dipole transitions, 244ff,
    247ff, 249ff
  electric quadrupole transitions, 257
  from radio aerial, 277ff
  from simple harmonic oscillator, 55
  induced and spontaneous transi-
    tions, 245f, 247, 262f, 273, 280,
    309
  magnetic dipole transitions, 257
  selection rules, 248, 249ff, 256ff, 261
  transition probability, 54, 218, 222,
    244, 261, 273, 275
Radiation field:
  classical behaviour of, 277ff
  corpuscular properties of, 269f
  Hamiltonian representation of
    classical, 264ff
  Hamiltonian representation of
    quantized, 267ff
  interacting with atom, 240ff, 271ff
  interacting with radio aerial, 277ff
  polarization of atom by, 260f
  polarization of material by, 304ff
  representation by classical vector
    potential, 241, 258, 305
Radio aerial, interaction of radiation
  with, 277ff
Raman effect, 220
Rayleigh, Lord, 190
Rectangular potential well,
  approximation to neutron-proton
    force, 113, 115, 238
  bound states in, 106ff, 115
  scattering by, 228f, 233, 236ff, 238
Reduced mass, 101, 114
Ritz, W., 136
Rutherford, Lord, 226
Rutherford scattering, 226ff

Scattering cross-section, 222ff
  energy-dependence of, 239
  for Coulomb field, 227, 228
  for Gaussian potential, 239
  for neutron-proton scattering, 238f
  for screened Coulomb field, 227,
    228, 239
  for spherical potential well, 228,
    237, 238, 239
  Thomson's, for electron, 277
  (see also Collision theory)
Scattering,
  of α-particles, 227f, 233
  of electrons, 233
  of light, 304ff
  neutron-proton, 238f
Schrödinger, E., 22, 34, 35, 56, 58, 66,
  186, 240, 270

Schrödinger's equation, 35, 49, 192, 194, 203, 218
Screened Coulomb field,
  bound states in, 154ff
  scattering by, 226ff, 239
Segré, E. (*see* Jenkins and Segré)
Selection rules, 58, 142, 249ff, 261
Self-consistent field, 159f, 204
Sellmeier, W., 258
Shortley, G. (*see* Condon and Shortley)
Simple harmonic oscillator:
  and oscillating wave-packet, 186f, 270
  by variation method, 138, 142
  energy eigenvalues for, 45, 53, 100
  equation of motion for, 47f
  in one dimension, 36, 42ff
  in two dimensions, 114
  in three dimensions, 53f, 98ff
  perturbation of, 141
  state functions, 49f, 57, 101
  uncertainty relations for, 52
Single-valuedness, requirement of, 66, 91f
Slater, J.C., 152, 161
Sneddon, I.N. (*see* Mott and Sneddon)
Sommerfeld, A., 56, 180, 194, 203, 205
Spherical potential well (*see* Rectangular potential well)
Spin, 67ff
  in 2-electron system, 77ff, 153ff, 164
  Pauli matrices, 67, 77, 91, 304
  polarization of, 206ff
  precession, 72ff, 299ff
Spin functions,
  for single electron, 68, 70, 75
  for helium atom, 153ff, 164
Spin-orbit coupling, 79ff, 92, 123ff
Spontaneous emission, 245ff, 262, 272f
Stark effect,
  first order, 130ff, 142, 260
  second order, 134ff
State of an ensemble, 284, 286
State of a system, 5f, 9ff, 12ff
State vector, 12, 117f
Stationary phase, condition of, 190, 202
Statistical interpretation of ψ-function, 22
Statistics:
  Boltzmann, 168ff
  Bose-Einstein, 170ff
  Fermi-Dirac, 175ff
Stern, O. and Gerlach, W., 67
Stern-Gerlach experiment, 11, 75ff, 92
Stimulated emission (*see* Induced emission)
Sugiura, Y., 162

Superposition, principle of, 6ff
Symmetry,
  and quantum statistics, 167
  conservation of, 151
  of state-functions, 150ff

Taylor, G.I., 2
Thomas-Fermi atom model, 159, 180ff, 183, 227
Thomas precession, 80
Thomson, G. P., 3
Trace, of density matrix, 286ff
  of matrix products, 285f
Transition probabilities, 222
  for harmonic oscillator, 54
  for radiative transitions, 244ff, 257, 261, 262f, 273
  (*see also* Radiation)
Tunnel effect, 197, 205
Twiss, R.Q. (*see* Brown and Twiss)

Uncertainty (definition of), 26
Uncertainty principle, 29, 32
Uncertainty product, minimum, 38f
Uncertainty relation,
  for angular momentum, 91
  for electromagnetic field variables, 282
  for energy and time, 222, 279
  for phase and number of quanta, 281
  for position and momentum, 32
  for wave-packet, 186

Variation method, 136ff
  and self-consistent field method, 159f
  for atomic polarizability, 138ff
  for electron in metal, 209ff
  for helium atom, 148ff
  for hydrogen molecule, 162f, 164
  for hydrogen negative ion, 164f
  for simple harmonic oscillator, 138, 142
Vector model for angular momentum, 72f, 85
Virial theorem, 57, 105

Wave equation, time dependent, 37
  time independent, 35
Wave mechanics, 19ff
Wave packet:
  expectation velocity and group velocity of, 189ff
  in WKB method, 201f
  motion of, in field of force, 187ff, 212f
  oscillating, 186f
  representation of particle by, 184ff, 234
  spreading of, 185f, 217

Weisskopf, V. F. (*see* Blatt and Weisskopf)
Wenzel, G., 198, 226
Wilson, E. B. (*see* Pauling and Wilson)
WKB method, 190ff

Zeeman effect, 134, 142, 248, 255f
    anomalous, first order, 123ff
    normal, first order, 122f
    second order, 128ff
Zero-point energy of electromagnetic field, 269